# SCIENCE *of*

UNDERSTAND THE ANATOMY AND PHYSIOLOGY TO PERFECT YOUR PRACTICE

# PILATES

# SCIENCE *of*

UNDERSTAND THE ANATOMY AND PHYSIOLOGY TO PERFECT YOUR PRACTICE

# PILATES

**TRACY WARD**

# CONTENTS

# INTRODUCTION

**Dating back to the early 20th century**, Pilates is a fitness trend that has never slowed down and has become a globally renowned exercise method. Pilates was initially created as a physical practice, but it was always rooted in a holistic approach. From correcting posture, strengthening the core, reducing pain, and focussing the mind, the benefits of Pilates are endless, and needed now more than ever.

Recent times have shown an enduring mindset shift that has reframed how we view exercise and how we honour what our bodies need. More people are seeking an exercise method that is as much about gaining enjoyment and making a mindfulness connection, as it is about physical health.

Pilates offers strong, lean muscles with full body mobility and has the flexibility to vary intensity and adapt to the fitness level and ability of the participant. Its popularity continues to grow, as the diversity of the method offers inclusivity and empowerment, and cumulatively creates a successful impact across many of life's challenges.

I first discovered Pilates during my undergraduate years when I was searching for an exercise class to complement my regular gym sessions. I didn't realize it at the time, but Pilates was exactly what my body needed. Muscular aches from sitting studying for long hours and sporting injuries all resolved after I started attending classes. More recently, I found a whole new meaning to Pilates, as I feel I owe my two very positive pregnancies and straightforward births to my consistent Pilates practice. I know this may have merely been luck – birth is so unpredictable – but even the Pilates breathing and mindset alone completely empowered my labours.

I now practise Pilates regularly for my physical fitness, but also for the mental clarity the mind-body connection brings. I use it extensively in my clinical role as a physiotherapist and witness every day the benefits it brings to my patients, from the athlete and the postpartum mum, to those with acute back pain or hypermobility, and everything in between.

## WHY THIS BOOK?

In every aspect of my work I receive inquisitive questions, from teaching on courses and in classes, in clinic, or via my online platforms. This has led to me writing this book – a serendipitous opportunity to provide the ultimate combination of my passion for Pilates, my scientific background, and my clinical experience. *Science of Pilates* is a comprehensive

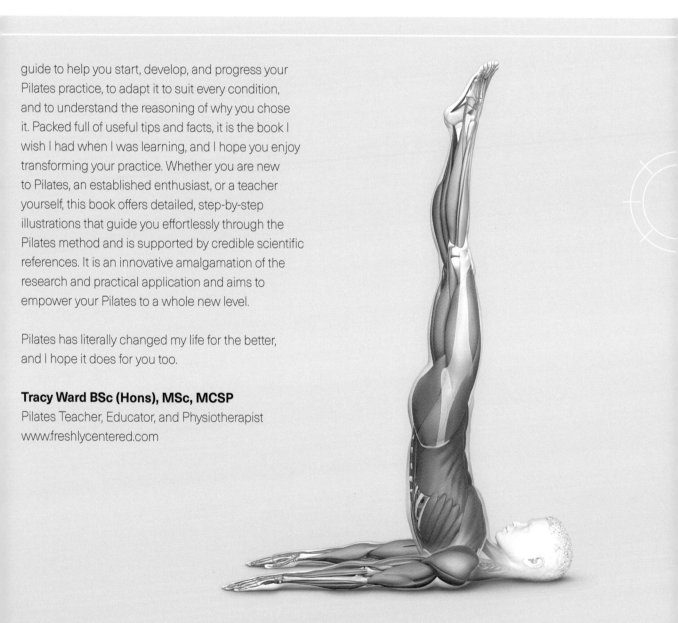

> **Pilates** *is a **full-body*** strength *and* mobility *workout that **can improve health**, fitness, and* **mindset***, and is inclusive for all.*

guide to help you start, develop, and progress your Pilates practice, to adapt it to suit every condition, and to understand the reasoning of why you chose it. Packed full of useful tips and facts, it is the book I wish I had when I was learning, and I hope you enjoy transforming your practice. Whether you are new to Pilates, an established enthusiast, or a teacher yourself, this book offers detailed, step-by-step illustrations that guide you effortlessly through the Pilates method and is supported by credible scientific references. It is an innovative amalgamation of the research and practical application and aims to empower your Pilates to a whole new level.

Pilates has literally changed my life for the better, and I hope it does for you too.

**Tracy Ward BSc (Hons), MSc, MCSP**
Pilates Teacher, Educator, and Physiotherapist
www.freshlycentered.com

# HISTORY AND PRINCIPLES OF PILATES

**The concept of Pilates** was created by German-born Joseph Pilates during World War I. Pilates was originally a body-builder and gymnast, then while interned on the Isle of Man, he created his revolutionary approach to exercise as a way to train both the body and mind to their full potential. This unique approach was originally called "Contrology", but later became known as Pilates.

## WHERE PILATES CAME FROM

Joseph Pilates was born in 1883 and his list of childhood illnesses – including asthma, rickets, and rheumatic fever – fuelled his determination to excel in health and fitness to heal and strengthen his body. He trained in yoga, martial arts, meditation, gymnastics, self-defence, and skiing and this led to him moving to England in 1912 to work as a gymnast, boxer, and self-defence teacher.

As an "enemy national" during World War I, Joseph was interned in hospitals as an orderly. Appalled at the condition of the patients in their beds, he devised an exercise regime that saw them recover faster. Joseph relocated back to Germany after the war where his exercise method became popular in the dance world and in 1926 he emigrated to the USA. He met his wife Clara and together they opened The Pilates Studio in New York. Dancers from the New York Ballet practised Pilates to treat their injuries, and his reputation expanded with studios opening across the country to share the unique exercise routine.

### THEORY AND EVOLUTION OF THE METHOD

Joseph was visionary in his beliefs of self-discipline, self-care, and commitment to a healthy lifestyle, and his method was rooted in principles of routine, flexibility, and core strength. He believed that the development of whole-body physical fitness, combined with mental control, would relieve the body of illness, balance the mind, body, and spirit, and foster self-confidence. The Pilates holistic approach was deeply embedded.

The original Pilates regime was developed for the mat, but when working in the hospitals Joseph had explored the use of springs on the beds to apply resistance and progressive overload to strengthen the body. As the demand grew for his method in New York, he later created pieces of studio equipment including the Cadillac, Reformer, Wunda Chair, and Arc Barrel. Using these would facilitate better movement, strength, and flexibility beyond the mat. Joseph died in 1967, but his legacy continues to expand, passed down through his students who later learned how to teach Pilates to others.

> *Contrology develops the body ...corrects **postures**, restores **physical vitality,** and invigorates the mind...*
> – Joseph Pilates

# PRINCIPLES OF **PILATES**

Pilates exercises are based around strict breathing patterns and breathing is the original and fundamental principle of the discipline. The remaining five principles account for the unique Pilates technique, and their integration with each other provides the mind and body connection, leading to the true effectiveness of a Pilates programme. These principles can also be applied in your everyday life off the mat.

**CENTRING**
This refers both to the engagement of your central core muscles, and on finding mental and physical focus during your practice.

**CONCENTRATION**
This is the specific attention to detail within each movement, including how you perform it and how it feels when you do it. The theory is that with practice you will perform the exercises subconsciously by developing body awareness and mindfulness.

**BREATHING**
The breathing pattern should complement the movements – a full, lateral breath (see p.36) is encouraged for optimal physical and mental value.

**FLOW**
Exercises should be completed with grace and ease and transition from one to the next smoothly. The energy used in one exercise should integrate the whole body.

**PRECISION**
This refers to the conscious awareness of every single movement within the exercises including the execution, placement, and alignment of each body region.

**CONTROL**
Each exercise is completed with control through your specific muscle movements and your breathing. It also refers to you being mentally in control and using mindfulness to direct the movements accordingly.

# **ADVANCES** IN RESEARCH

**The original aim of Pilates was to rehabilitate** the ill in the World War I hospitals; the method was later developed for the elite, and influenced by the dancers' world. At the turn of the century, the need for more mindful exercise methods emerged and this method was adapted based on research and the need for rehabilitation-based exercises.

## EVOLUTION OF **PILATES**

Pilates previously placed a large emphasis on bracing the core and activating the global musculature to provide rigidity and support to complete the different movements.

This is evident during exercises such as Scissors (see p.78) and Control Balance (see p.156), where the legs do the moving but the spine must remain still to support the body. Many of the Pilates exercises demanded an already good level of flexibility in the muscles and joints to achieve the long leg levers, end range positions, and large spinal movements. These physical demands also required a good sense of body awareness to control the body into the correct positions.

### ADAPTATIONS

Contemporary adaptations focus on mastering the localized core system first to provide the spinal stability, before progressing to global activation. While some exercises may require flexibility, these are often prescribed in a series of progressions to allow the participant to perform a lower level exercise and to gradually work up to the more demanding exercises as they improve. This method is deemed as a safer approach for the average person than the original one designed by Pilates. It also introduces variation to allow for both the students' level of ability and also to relate their exercises to their own movements and their specific functional needs. These could vary from wanting increased flexibilty and better balance, to addressing ailments such as lower back pain.

### Overview of the methods

| TRADITIONAL | CONTEMPORARY |
|---|---|
| **Based on the exercises** taught by Joseph Pilates in the set order that he taught them. | **Modernized version** of the traditional exercises with new variations included. |
| **Each exercise** in sequence builds on the previous one. | **No set sequence** but selected based on needs. |
| **Strict repetition dosage** set prescribed for each exercise. | **Dosage selected** for specific need. |
| **Starts lying down** where gravity assists in activation of the core connection and progresses to more vertical positions. | **Often starts lying down**, where gravity assists the core connection, and can progress to various positions. |
| **Pelvis** usually in posterior tilt with a flattened back. | **Pelvis** set in neutral. |
| **Lever length** is long for arms and/or legs. | **Lever length** often shorter with flexed legs initially. |

# TECHNIQUE **PROGRESSION**

There are four key areas where the technique of Pilates has evolved and research has led to changes in the execution of the method aside from the actual exercise performed.

### FLAT vs NEUTRAL SPINE

Traditionally, the spine was instructed to be flat to the mat, called imprinting. A flat spine position has been shown to have no shock-absorbing properties and is equally less functional than exercising in the neutral spine. The neutral spine position also provides the most isolated activation of the core muscles for optimal results, compared to having the pelvis tilted forwards or backwards.

### MAXIMUM vs LOW ABDOMINAL CONTRACTION

Belly button to spine, which activates the global abdominal muscles with maximal exertion and effort, was previously the cue for abdominal activation. This can cause overactivity and early fatigue, whereas the low-level engagement isolates the transversus abdominis first and allows for stabilization of the spine and control.

### FLEXED vs NEUTRAL NECK

Holding the neck in a flexed position can cause unwanted stress to the muscles of the cervical spine, and tension elsewhere in the upper body. Placing the neck in a neutral position minimizes this stress and aligns the neck correctly, promoting a more comfortable, beneficial, and natural posture.

### SPECIFIC BREATHING vs VARIED PATTERN

Joseph instructed specific breathing cues to match his movements. Now, exhalation is often performed on exertion in Pilates exercises, as this gives a more effective activation of the transversus abdominis core muscle.

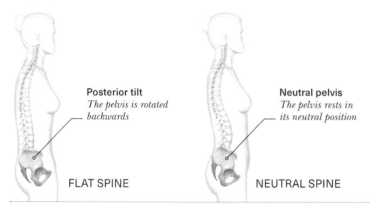

**Posterior tilt**
*The pelvis is rotated backwards*

**FLAT SPINE**

**Neutral pelvis**
*The pelvis rests in its neutral position*

**NEUTRAL SPINE**

# PRESCRIPTION **PROGRESSION**

There are several distinct differences in the prescription of Pilates exercises between the original criteria in Joseph's teachings and the way in which they have been modified over the years. Here we compare some of the key differences.

**Strict order vs movement selection**
The traditional method has a strict order of 34 movements. Contemporary teachings base their movement selection on clinical or individual reasoning with the view that one form of delivery does not fit everyone.

**One level vs many**
The original exercises were designed as a single stand-alone exercise, whereas contemporary schools generally have multiple levels and/or variations of each exercise to ensure that Pilates can be beneficial to all.

**Set reps vs dosage**
Traditional exercises had a strict exercise dosage and students were instructed not to perform any more or less that what was prescribed. By contrast, modern dosage is based on exercise principles, individual ability, and fatigue levels.

**Ballistic vs control**
Many of the original exercises have a ballistic element with pulses incorporated. Modern variations often remove this, as well as focussing on neutral control over increased range of movement.

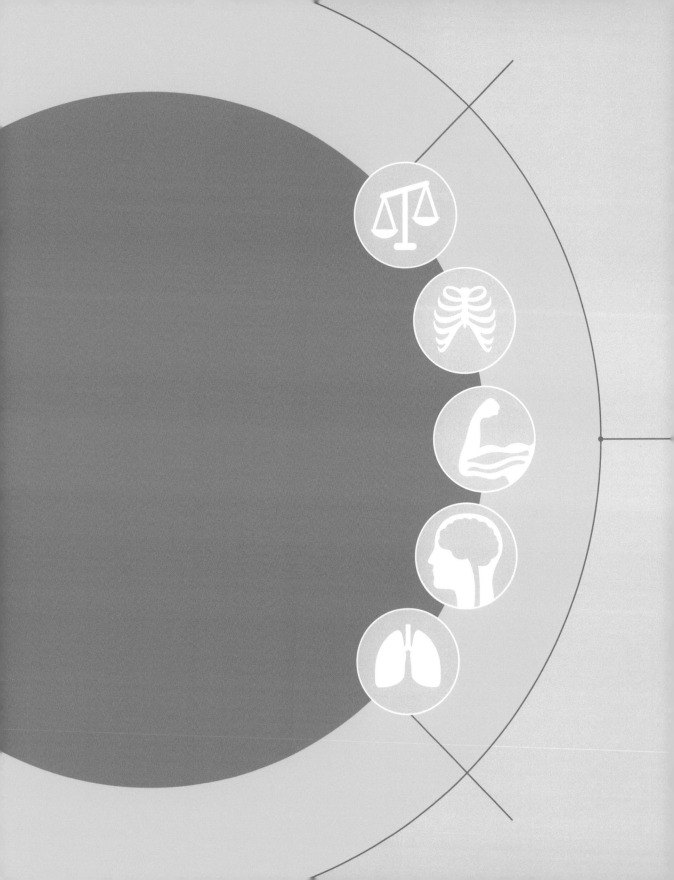

# PHYSIOLOGY OF **PILATES**

**Pilates teaches movement from your core** to create strong, lean muscles and an efficient movement system. Understanding the anatomy and physiology of how the musculoskeletal system works, the effects of posture and breathing, and the influence these collectively have on pain and psychological wellbeing will transform your thinking in Pilates. The application of this knowledge will optimize your Pilates technique and exercise selection, and spark intention within workouts.

# MUSCULAR
## ANATOMY

**Our musculature system supports posture** and allows the body to move. Skeletal muscles are attached to bones at either end via tendons, and pull on these bones to create movement.

## SKELETAL MUSCLE

Muscles rarely work in isolation. The primary mover is called the agonist, and there may be several assisting muscles involved. The antagonist is the muscle that works in opposition to slow the movement and provide joint stability. Performing Pilates strengthens the body through muscle slings, the system that links the soft tissues to transmit forces (see p.18).

*A zoomed-in view shows myofibrils lined up with one another*

**Elbow flexors**
*Biceps brachii*
*Brachialis (deep)*
*Brachioradialis*

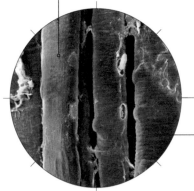

*Visible stripes (striations) reflect the arrangement of muscle proteins*

### Skeletal muscle fibres
Skeletal muscle fibres consist of thousands of myofibrils arranged in parallel bundles. These contain the contractile proteins that make the muscle contract.

**Pectorals**
*Pectoralis major*
*Pectoralis minor*

*Intercostal muscles*

*Brachialis*

**Abdominals**
*Rectus abdominis*
*External abdominal obliq*
*Internal abdominal obliq*
*(deep, not shown)*
*Transversus abdominis*

**Hip flexors**
*Iliopsoas (ilia*
*and psoas me*
*Rectus femor*
*(see quadrice*
*Sartorius*
*Adductors*
*(see below)*

**Adductors**
*Adductor longus*
*Adductor brevis*
*Adductor magnus*
*Pectineus*
*Gracilis*

**Quadriceps**
*Rectus femoris*
*Vastus medialis*
*Vastus lateralis*
*Vastus intermedius*
*(deep, not shown)*

**Ankle dorsiflexors**
*Tibialis anterior*
*Extensor digitorum longus*
*Extensor hallucis longus*

**SUPERFICIAL**　　　　**DEEP**

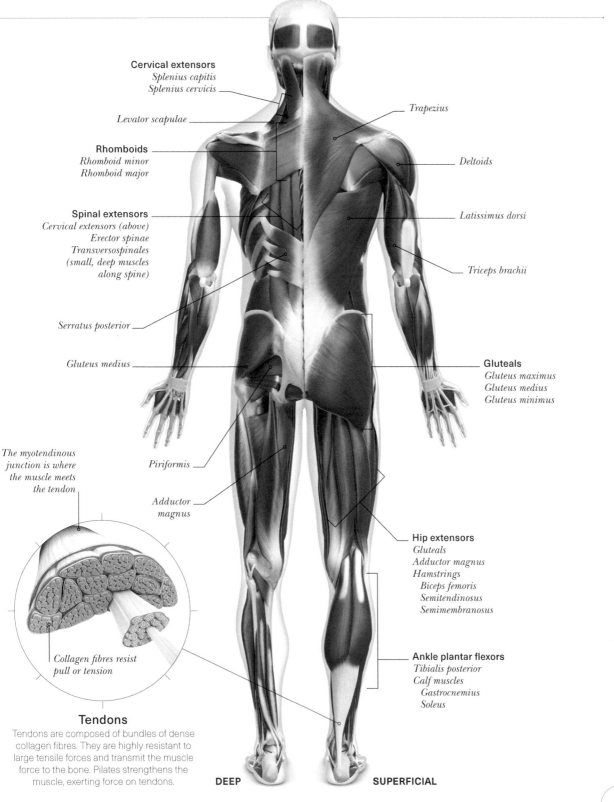

**Cervical extensors**
*Splenius capitis*
*Splenius cervicis*

*Levator scapulae*

**Rhomboids**
*Rhomboid minor*
*Rhomboid major*

**Spinal extensors**
*Cervical extensors (above)*
*Erector spinae*
*Transversospinales*
*(small, deep muscles*
*along spine)*

*Serratus posterior*

*Gluteus medius*

*Piriformis*

*Adductor*
*magnus*

*Trapezius*

*Deltoids*

*Latissimus dorsi*

*Triceps brachii*

**Gluteals**
*Gluteus maximus*
*Gluteus medius*
*Gluteus minimus*

**Hip extensors**
*Gluteals*
*Adductor magnus*
*Hamstrings*
*Biceps femoris*
*Semitendinosus*
*Semimembranosus*

**Ankle plantar flexors**
*Tibialis posterior*
*Calf muscles*
*Gastrocnemius*
*Soleus*

*The myotendinous*
*junction is where*
*the muscle meets*
*the tendon*

*Collagen fibres resist*
*pull or tension*

### Tendons

Tendons are composed of bundles of dense
collagen fibres. They are highly resistant to
large tensile forces and transmit the muscle
force to the bone. Pilates strengthens the
muscle, exerting force on tendons.

**DEEP**

**SUPERFICIAL**

# UNDERSTANDING **LOCAL** AND **GLOBAL** MUSCLES

**Our bodies produce movement and support via muscle activation** and their contractions. There are two different muscular systems that allow our bodies to distribute these forces efficiently. These are classified based on their location as well as numerous other different properties.

## TWO **SYSTEMS**

The coordination of the local and global muscle systems is the essence of the Pilates method. They should be thought of as the following: the local muscles as the inner core, the global muscles as the outer core, and the addition of the extremity muscles as the movement system.

### LOCAL MUSCLES

Local muscles are situated within close proximity to the joint and are directly attached to the spine. They increase joint stiffness to limit compression, shearing (tearing), and rotational forces on the spine. They also provide stability and support between the vertebrae during movement by increasing intra-abdominal pressure. Your local muscles consist of the transversus abdominis, multifidus, pelvic floor, and diaphragm.

### GLOBAL MUSCLES

Global muscles are more superficial than local muscles and attach from the pelvis to the spine. Their role is predominantly for movement and they transfer load between the upper and lower body extremities through the core. They also provide stabilization and eccentric (lengthening) control to the core during these movements. Global muscles consist of the quadratus lumborum, psoas major, external obliques, internal obliques, rectus abdominis, gluteus medius, and all of the hip adductor muscles including adductor magnus, longus and brevis, gracilis, and pectineus.

### MOVEMENT SYSTEM

The activation of both the local and global muscle systems, plus the addition of the movement system, is required for best performance. This system consists of muscles that attach the spine and/or the pelvis to the upper or lower extremities. It generates force at speed and is responsible for producing much larger movements. The movement system produces concentric force and eccentric deceleration control. Muscles include the latissimus dorsi, hip flexors, hamstrings, and quadriceps. We can understand the combined approach of all through the muscle slings (see p.18).

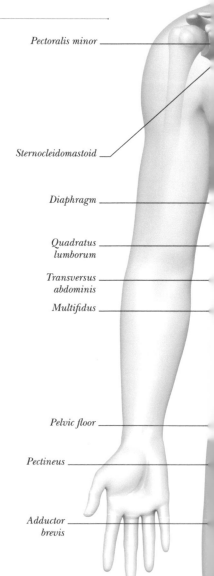

Pectoralis minor

Sternocleidomastoid

Diaphragm

Quadratus lumborum

Transversus abdominis

Multifidus

Pelvic floor

Pectineus

Adductor brevis

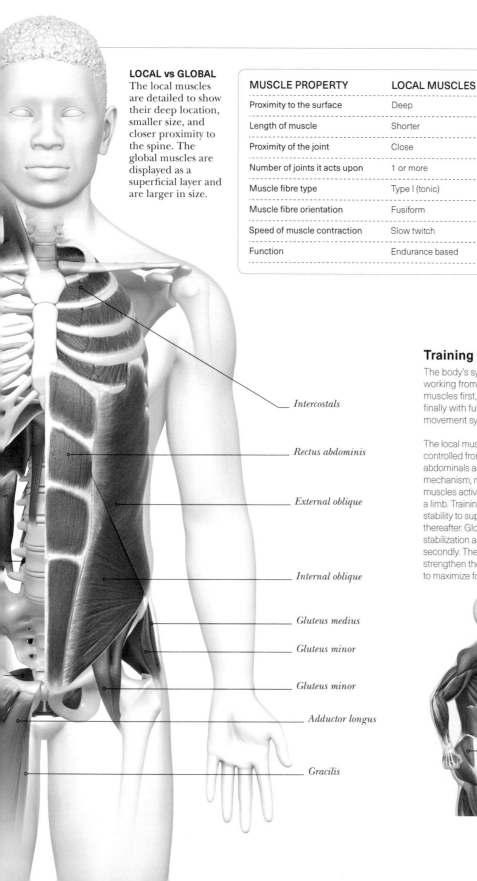

## LOCAL vs GLOBAL
The local muscles are detailed to show their deep location, smaller size, and closer proximity to the spine. The global muscles are displayed as a superficial layer and are larger in size.

| MUSCLE PROPERTY | LOCAL MUSCLES | GLOBAL MUSCLES |
| --- | --- | --- |
| Proximity to the surface | Deep | Superficial |
| Length of muscle | Shorter | Longer |
| Proximity of the joint | Close | Further away |
| Number of joints it acts upon | 1 or more | 2 or more |
| Muscle fibre type | Type I (tonic) | Type II (phasic) |
| Muscle fibre orientation | Fusiform | Aponeurotic |
| Speed of muscle contraction | Slow twitch | Fast twitch |
| Function | Endurance based | Short burst effort |

*Intercostals*

*Rectus abdominis*

*External oblique*

*Internal oblique*

*Gluteus medius*

*Gluteus minor*

*Gluteus minor*

*Adductor longus*

*Gracilis*

## Training for function
The body's systems should be trained by working from the inside out with the local muscles first, global muscles second, and finally with full integration to the movement system.

The local muscles are independently controlled from the more global abdominals and have a feedforward mechanism, meaning that the core muscles activate prior to the movement of a limb. Training them first ensures spinal stability to support any additional load thereafter. Global muscles lack this specific stabilization and therefore are included secondly. The final step would be to strengthen the power-producing muscles to maximize force production at speed.

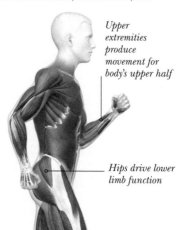

*Upper extremities produce movement for body's upper half*

*Hips drive lower limb function*

# UNDERSTANDING
## MUSCLE SLINGS

**Muscles transmit their forces** onto the bones to which they are attached, and produce movement through the joint motion. Muscle slings link muscle, fascia (connective tissue), and ligaments (tissue attaching bone to bone) via the fascia to transmit forces from one body part to another. They provide increased stability and support during movement, and allow force production to be transmitted beyond the muscle that is contracting.

## TYPES OF **MUSCLE SLINGS**

When the forces between muscle slings are balanced, optimal alignment is achieved. When there is a weak component within the musculature, the tension in the sling is altered. This then alters the force transmission through the sling and an imbalance can cause malalignment or dysfunction.

### ANTERIOR OBLIQUE SLING

This stabilizes the pelvis and provides force closure at the pubic symphysis joint at its base. It also stabilizes the body on the standing leg in gait, and controls rotation of the pelvis when moving forwards. As the body's speed increases from walking to running, the demand on the anterior (front) oblique sling increases and it plays a significant role within sports for accelerating, decelerating, and rotating.

Dysfunction in this sling results in shearing forces across the pelvis and can cause abdominal or groin muscle injuries.

### POSTERIOR OBLIQUE SLING

This sling stabilizes the pelvis from the posterior (back) and provides force closure at the sacroiliac joint. It powers the propulsive phase of gait as the gluteus maximus is responsible for driving the leg

forwards – a process that becomes more prominent when running. The latissimus dorsi assists in the coordination of the propelling leg and pulling back of the opposite arm to facilitate the running motion.

Weakness in either muscle can result in excess hamstring loading and cause a muscle strain. Additionally, weak posterior pelvis stability can result in sacroiliac joint pain from shearing motions.

### DEEP LONGITUDINAL SLING

This sling is responsible for both spinal and pelvic stability through its multifidus activation. It also produces spinal and hip extension-based movement through its more superficial muscles – the erector spinae and biceps femoris. It is largely involved in posture and keeping the body upright, as well as supporting the trunk through flexion-based activities such as

bending forwards and returning back upright again.

A weakness in this sling can manifest as lower back pain due to less stability or muscular support at the lumbar spine and pelvis. For example, if you are bending forwards you may struggle to return back upright again or you may experience pain when you try to flex your body too far forwards.

### LATERAL SLING

This sling allows movement in the coronal plane, which divides the body vertically into front and back. It keeps the pelvis level in single-leg activities such as walking, climbing stairs and lunge-style movements. Dysfunction may show a positive Trendelenburg sign (see diagram on the right) pronation of the foot, and medial knee alignment. Pilates exercise examples are: Clam, Side Kick, and Leg Lift and Lower.

## ANTERIOR OBLIQUE SLING

**Muscles involved:** internal and external obliques and the contralateral adductors, connected by the adductor-abdominal fascia.

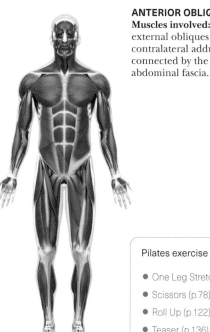

Pilates exercise examples:

- One Leg Stretch (p.60)
- Scissors (p.78)
- Roll Up (p.122)
- Teaser (p.136)

## POSTERIOR OBLIQUE SLING

**Muscles involved:** latissimus dorsi and contralateral gluteus maximus, connected by the thoracolumbar fascia.

Pilates exercise examples:

- One Leg Kick (p.74)
- Shoulder Bridge (p.84)
- Swimming (p.88)
- Rocking (p.152)

## DEEP LONGITUDINAL SLING

**Muscles involved:** erector spinae, multifidus, sacro-tuberous ligament, and biceps femoris, connected by the thoracolumbar fascia.

Pilates exercise examples:

- Swan Dive (p.70)
- One Leg Kick (p.74)
- Shoulder Bridge (p.84)
- Rocking (p.152)

## LATERAL SLING

**Muscles involved:** gluteus medius, gluteus minimus, tensor fasciae latae, and the contralateral adductors.

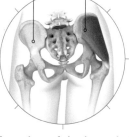

*The left side of the pelvis will drop downwards*

*Weakness in right gluteals causes the right side to hitch upwards*

### Dysfunction of the lateral sling

A weakness in the hip abductors, mainly gluteus medius and minimus, will cause the pelvis to tilt downwards on the non weight-bearing leg, causing a person to lean away from the affected hip. This is called the Trendelenburg sign.

# HOW MUSCLES WORK

**Muscles contract in different ways** to facilitate and control movement. The way in which they contract is dependent upon the level of the muscle's contractile force and the external force acting upon it.

## MUSCLE STRUCTURE

Skeletal muscles consist of an intricate organization of muscle cells, blood cells, and nerve fibres. Bundles of muscle fibres are called fascicles. Within each muscle fibre are myofibrils, which house the contractile protein filaments that produce muscle contractions.

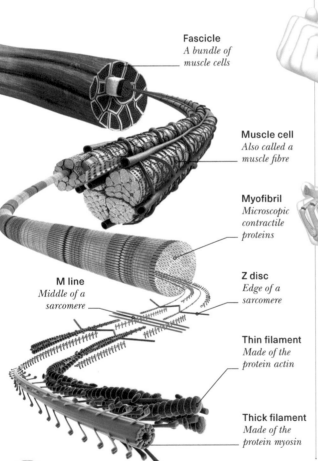

**Fascicle**
*A bundle of muscle cells*

**Muscle cell**
*Also called a muscle fibre*

**Myofibril**
*Microscopic contractile proteins*

**M line**
*Middle of a sarcomere*

**Z disc**
*Edge of a sarcomere*

**Thin filament**
*Made of the protein actin*

**Thick filament**
*Made of the protein myosin*

**Antagonist**
*The biceps brachii is the antagonist as it lengthens with tension*

**Extension**
*Angle of joint increases*

**Agonist**
*The triceps brachii is the agonist as it concentrically contracts to extend the elbow*

### ECCENTRIC CONTRACTION

An eccentric contraction occurs when the muscle is lengthening while still under tension. The biceps work eccentrically here to control the downward arm movement and in Pilates this would be evident in your gluteals in Shoulder Bridge as you extend your leg vertically (see p.84).

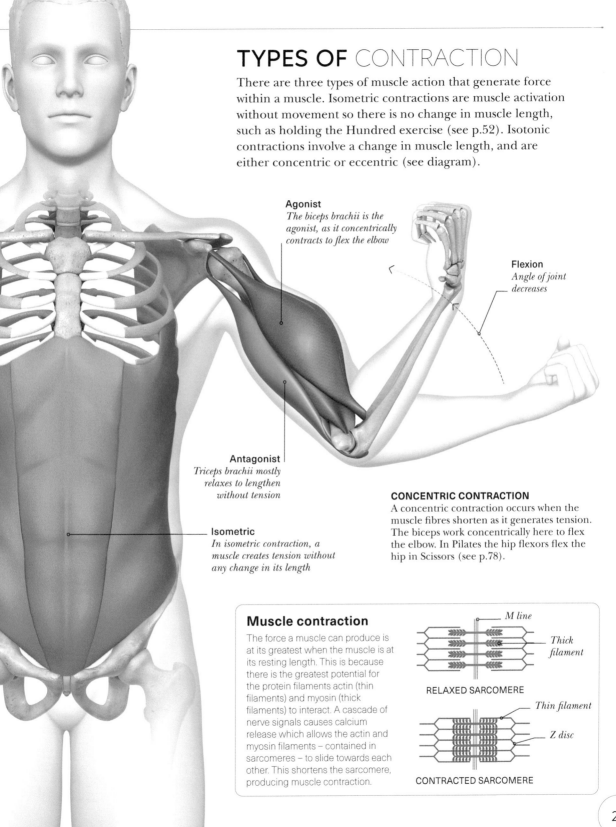

# TYPES OF CONTRACTION

There are three types of muscle action that generate force within a muscle. Isometric contractions are muscle activation without movement so there is no change in muscle length, such as holding the Hundred exercise (see p.52). Isotonic contractions involve a change in muscle length, and are either concentric or eccentric (see diagram).

**Agonist**
*The biceps brachii is the agonist, as it concentrically contracts to flex the elbow*

**Flexion**
*Angle of joint decreases*

**Antagonist**
*Triceps brachii mostly relaxes to lengthen without tension*

**Isometric**
*In isometric contraction, a muscle creates tension without any change in its length*

**CONCENTRIC CONTRACTION**
A concentric contraction occurs when the muscle fibres shorten as it generates tension. The biceps work concentrically here to flex the elbow. In Pilates the hip flexors flex the hip in Scissors (see p.78).

## Muscle contraction

The force a muscle can produce is at its greatest when the muscle is at its resting length. This is because there is the greatest potential for the protein filaments actin (thin filaments) and myosin (thick filaments) to interact. A cascade of nerve signals causes calcium release which allows the actin and myosin filaments – contained in sarcomeres – to slide towards each other. This shortens the sarcomere, producing muscle contraction.

*M line*

*Thick filament*

**RELAXED SARCOMERE**

*Thin filament*

*Z disc*

**CONTRACTED SARCOMERE**

# SKELETAL
## SYSTEM

**The body's vital framework** is made up of bones and cartilage and connected together via ligaments. It provides structure and protection to your body and allows movement through the bony levers.

## SYSTEM OVERVIEW

Bone is a living organ and a form of hard connective tissue made of collagen. It stores calcium, which is needed for bone strength and body functions, and the bone marrow within is a continuous supply of new blood cells. Bones connect together at joints and are supported by ligaments. Pilates exercises can be performed in weight bearing positions to support your bone health.

**"**

**Hormones**, *nutrition, and **physical activity** all influence* bone growth *and* development.

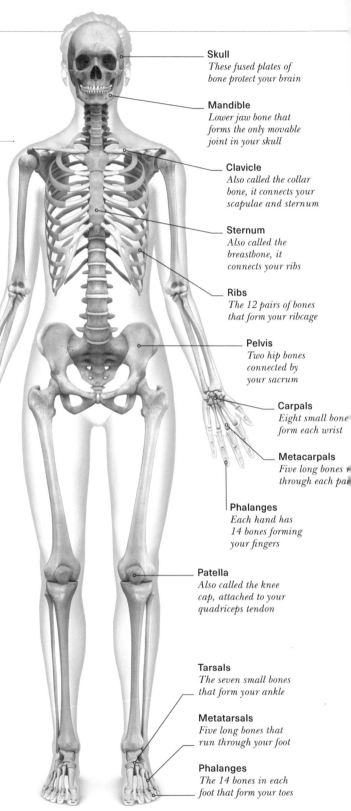

**Skull**
*These fused plates of bone protect your brain*

**Mandible**
*Lower jaw bone that forms the only movable joint in your skull*

**Clavicle**
*Also called the collar bone, it connects your scapulae and sternum*

**Sternum**
*Also called the breastbone, it connects your ribs*

**Ribs**
*The 12 pairs of bones that form your ribcage*

**Pelvis**
*Two hip bones connected by your sacrum*

**Carpals**
*Eight small bone form each wrist*

**Metacarpals**
*Five long bones r through each pa*

**Phalanges**
*Each hand has 14 bones forming your fingers*

**Patella**
*Also called the knee cap, attached to your quadriceps tendon*

**Tarsals**
*The seven small bones that form your ankle*

**Metatarsals**
*Five long bones that run through your foot*

**Phalanges**
*The 14 bones in each foot that form your toes*

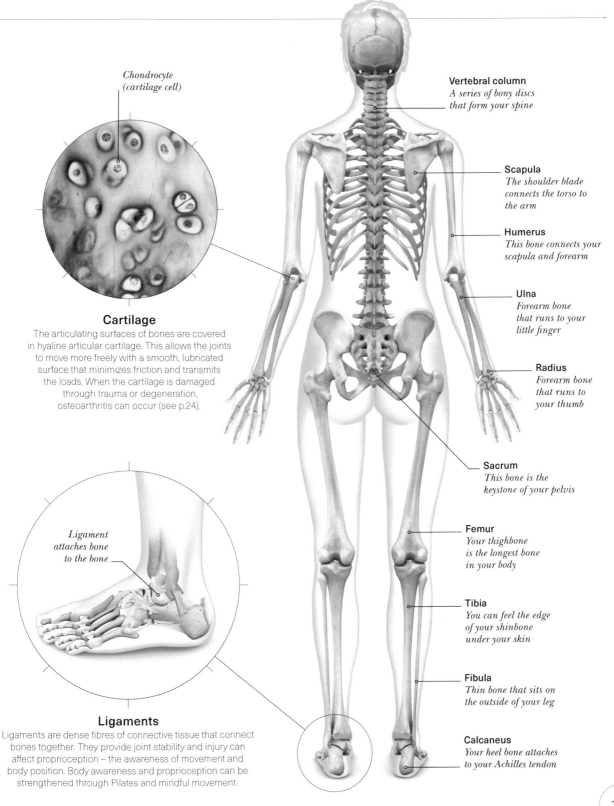

*Chondrocyte
(cartilage cell)*

## Cartilage

The articulating surfaces of bones are covered in hyaline articular cartilage. This allows the joints to move more freely with a smooth, lubricated surface that minimizes friction and transmits the loads. When the cartilage is damaged through trauma or degeneration, osteoarthritis can occur (see p.24).

*Ligament
attaches bone
to the bone*

## Ligaments

Ligaments are dense fibres of connective tissue that connect bones together. They provide joint stability and injury can affect proprioception – the awareness of movement and body position. Body awareness and proprioception can be strengthened through Pilates and mindful movement.

**Vertebral column**
*A series of bony discs
that form your spine*

**Scapula**
*The shoulder blade
connects the torso to
the arm*

**Humerus**
*This bone connects your
scapula and forearm*

**Ulna**
*Forearm bone
that runs to your
little finger*

**Radius**
*Forearm bone
that runs to
your thumb*

**Sacrum**
*This bone is the
keystone of your pelvis*

**Femur**
*Your thighbone
is the longest bone
in your body*

**Tibia**
*You can feel the edge
of your shinbone
under your skin*

**Fibula**
*Thin bone that sits on
the outside of your leg*

**Calcaneus**
*Your heel bone attaches
to your Achilles tendon*

# BONE STRENGTH
## AND JOINTS

**Our bones and their joints provide the framework** that supports our bodies, the lever systems to facilitate movement, and the underlying structure for body strength. Bone is a highly specialized living tissue that adapts to mechanical stress. Regular Pilates practice can support our bones and joints.

## BONE GROWTH

Ossification is the process of bone formation. New bone is laid down by cells called osteoblasts, and old bone is removed by cells called osteoclasts to maintain bone thickness. The outer connective tissue provides toughness and elasticity to the bone while the mineral salts provide rigidity. Calcium is one important mineral for maintaining bone strength.

Rapid bone growth occurs throughout childhood as osteoblast production is elevated to develop the skeletal system. Skeletal maturity peaks at age 16–18 years but bone density can continue to improve until age 20–30. Regular strength training will maximize and maintain bone density, as from the age of 35 bone density declines.

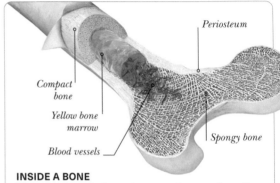

*Periosteum*

*Compact bone*

*Yellow bone marrow*

*Blood vessels*

*Spongy bone*

**INSIDE A BONE**
The outer layer is the periosteum. Compact bone lies underneath and surrounds the deep spongy bone. The internal architecture has arrays of trabeculae, a honeycomb-like arrangement organized to resist mechanical stress.

**Arthritis**
Osteoarthritis, which is the degeneration of the articular cartilage, is the most common joint pathology. It causes pain as a result of a loss of the articular surfaces and lubrication of the joints. Completing eight weeks of Pilates has shown reductions in pain and improvements in general function in those with osteoarthritis.

**PROGRESSION**
Cartilage is degraded through wear and tear or as a result of trauma. As it wears the joint space narrows, and the synovial membrane can become inflamed and painful. Spurs (bumps) and cysts can also form in the bone.

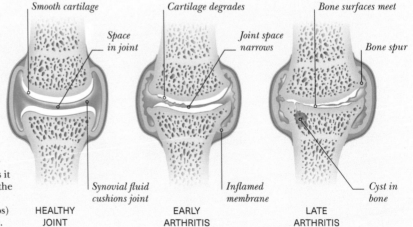

*Smooth cartilage*

*Space in joint*

*Synovial fluid cushions joint*

HEALTHY JOINT

*Cartilage degrades*

*Joint space narrows*

*Inflamed membrane*

EARLY ARTHRITIS

*Bone surfaces meet*

*Bone spur*

*Cyst in bone*

LATE ARTHRITIS

# JOINTS

Bones unite at joints and joints articulate about each other to allow movement. There are three different types of joint: fibrous, cartilaginous, and synovial, and the amount of mobility gradually increases from fibrous to synovial. Synovial joints are the most mobile and those that are mobilized within Pilates movements.

## JOINT ACTIONS

Synovial joints are freely mobile and their movement is restricted by the supporting muscles, ligaments, and the enclosing fibrous joint capsule. Hinge joints only permit flexion and extension, e.g. your elbow and knee. Ball and socket joints permit multi-directional movements and are found in larger mobile joints like your shoulder and hip.

### TYPES OF MOVEMENT

| | |
|---|---|
| Flexion | Angle at joint generally gets smaller |
| Extension | Angle at joint generally gets larger |
| Abduction | A limb moves away from the body |
| Adduction | A limb moves closer towards the body |
| External rotation | A limb rotates outwards |
| Internal rotation | A limb rotates inwards |
| Axial rotation | The spine twists on its axis |
| Plantarflexion | Pointing the feet |
| Dorsiflexion | Flexing the feet |

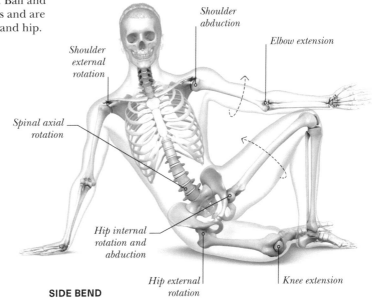

*Shoulder external rotation*
*Shoulder abduction*
*Elbow extension*
*Spinal axial rotation*
*Hip internal rotation and abduction*
*Hip external rotation*
*Knee extension*

**SIDE BEND**

## Inside a joint

The joint capsule is lined by the synovial membrane. This secretes lubricating synovial fluid into the joint cavity, a process that responds to pressure upon the joints. Greater activity and load to the joints can increase the viscosity of the synovial fluid and aids in joint protection. Loaded Pilates positions such as standing or four point kneeling can enhance this.

### SYNOVIAL JOINT

Synovial joints are typical of almost all limb joints. They contain synovial fluid which nourishes the articular cartilage and lubricates the joint to allow movement without friction.

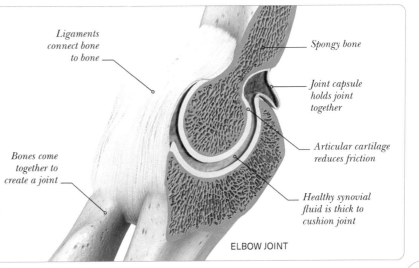

*Ligaments connect bone to bone*
*Spongy bone*
*Joint capsule holds joint together*
*Bones come together to create a joint*
*Articular cartilage reduces friction*
*Healthy synovial fluid is thick to cushion joint*

ELBOW JOINT

# CORE MUSCLES

**Your core is made up of four muscle groups** that form a three-dimensional support unit around your trunk region. Together they coordinate trunk movement, and provide the link between the upper and lower body. They also control respiration and continence.

## IMPORTANCE OF STABILITY

Increased core stability allows the spine to move through its vertebral segments without injury. Lack of core stability can place extra strain on the vertebrae during simple movements such as bending or reaching out away from the body.

### Breathing: Your pelvic floor and diaphragm

Your pelvic floor and diaphragm work together to allow the natural biomechanics of your ribcage and to reduce any resistance in contracting the core muscles. If you inhale on exertion, your abdominal cavity will fill with air and make the movement more difficult. Pilates exercises encourage a more natural breathing pattern that allows ribcage expansion with inhaling to the base of the lungs, and exhaling to relax the ribcage.

The pelvic floor contracts and moves upwards as you exhale and it relaxes and descends when you inhale. With practice, you will learn how to control this pelvic floor activation and coordinate it with your breathing and abdominal muscles for an efficient core system.

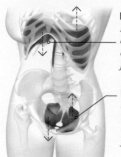

**Inhale**
*Respiratory diaphragm and pelvic floor descend*

**Exhale**
*Respiratory diaphragm and pelvic floor ascend*

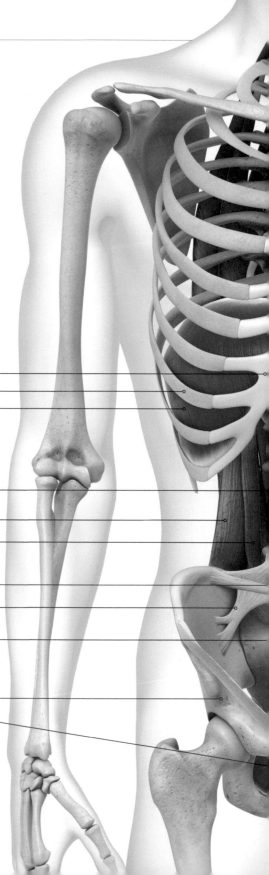

Intercostal cartilage

Ribcage

Respiratory diaphragm
*The diaphragm contracts when you inhale, and relaxes when you exhale*

Multifidus
*This back muscle stabilizes the spine locally*

Quadratus lumborum

Spinal extensors
*Long muscles that move the spine into extension*

Spine

Iliolumbar ligament

Anterior longitudinal ligament
*Stabilizes the vertebrae and prevents anterior movement*

Pelvis

Pelvic floor
*A group of muscles that support the bladder, bowel, and uterus*

**ANTERIOR–LATERAL VIEW**

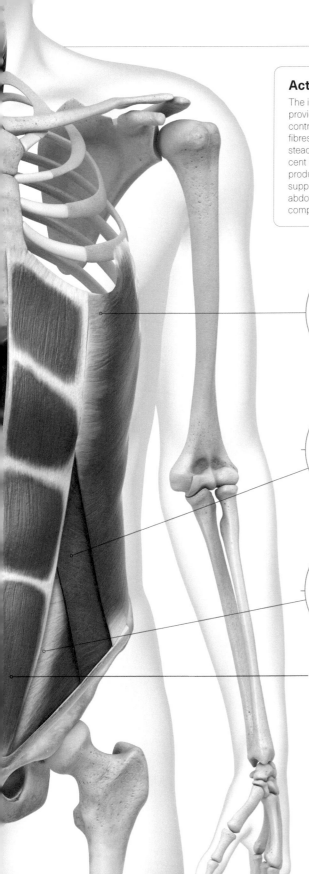

## Activating your core

The ideal activation needed for the core muscles to contract efficiently and provide the best level of stability to your spine is 30 per cent. Exhaling as you contract your core muscles allows better recruitment of the type 1 muscle fibres – slow-twitch muscle fibres that generate activation at a slow and steady pace and are designed for endurance. Activating greater than 30 per cent brings the type 2 muscle fibres into play, which are designed for producing power quickly, but they also fatigue quickly and will not provide support for any length of time. Watch out for breath-holding, bracing the abdominals, or squeezing the buttocks when you engage your core. These compensatory mechanisms will make core activation far less efficient.

### External Oblique

The largest and most superficial abdominal muscle has fibres covering both sides and the front of the trunk that join anteriorly at the rectus sheath. When both sides are contracted, the trunk will flex. When one side is contracted, it will produce side flexion to the same side, and rotation to the opposite side.

### Internal Oblique

This broad muscle sits underneath the external oblique with muscle fibres running at right angles to those of the external oblique. It works with the external oblique to produce trunk flexion; contraction on one side will flex and rotate to the same side.

### Transversus Abdominis

This deepest set of core muscles wraps around the trunk, with its fibres running horizontally. It is activated prior to movement to provide spinal stability and can be influenced by your breathing pattern. We exhale as we execute a movement as this will give the best muscle activation and support for the joints, discs, and muscles.

### Rectus abdominis

*This vertical abdominal muscle consists of a long, broad muscle split into three tendinous intersections. The rectus abdominis is joined centrally by the linea alba*

### LAYERS OF CORE MUSCLES

The core muscles are multi-layered. The muscles that stabilize the trunk are situated deeply, while the muscles that create movement are closer to the surface.

27

# NEUTRAL
## SPINE ANATOMY

**Our upright posture is possible** due to the spine and its fascinating anatomy. We move our bodies via the spinal curves, and the relationship the spine has with the pelvis. While variability exists in every individual, deviations have a consequential effect on the rest of the spine and the way in which it works.

## ROLE OF THE SPINE

The spinal column supports our upright posture, allows movement of the spine, and protects the spinal cord and other neural structures. Each section has unique features for its position.

The spine consists of 24 vertebrae: 7 cervical, 12 thoracic, and 5 lumbar. There are also 5 fused vertebrae that form the sacrum (the triangular bone at the base of the lumbar vertebrae), and 4 fused vertebrae that form the coccyx (tailbone). The vertebral bodies – the thick, oval-shaped parts – are located at the front, and are for weight-bearing and shock absorption. The back of the spine has spinous (in the middle) and transverse (to either side) processes, which are for muscles and ligaments to attach to.

The "S"-shaped curve of the spine allows the transmission and distribution of forces through it while protecting the spinal cord and intervertebral discs. These discs allow motion of the spine as they move tiny amounts to allow the spine to bend, twist, and rotate. If the spine was in a straight line, the forces would transmit directly through the intervertebral discs and no movement would occur.

The cervical spine is the most mobile region and primarily functions to control our line of vision. The neck also stabilizes and holds the weight of the head. Problems with the neck can cause you to overuse the upper trapezius and scapular muscles, as they try to assist the head and neck.

The thoracic spine is the least mobile region and, along with the ribcage, it protects our heart and lungs. The thoracic curve affects the mobility of the neck above it, as well as the shoulder girdle, and that of the lumbar spine below it. This makes the thoracic spine an important aspect of postural and mobility-based Pilates exercises.

The lumbar spine has the largest vertebrae and these, along with its natural lordotic (inward) curve, protect the spine from compressive forces. Deviations of the lumbar spine curve can be influenced by the abdominal and gluteal musculature and can lead to lower back pain.

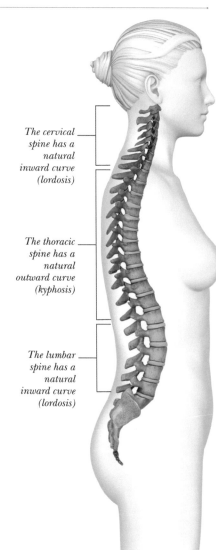

*The cervical spine has a natural inward curve (lordosis)*

*The thoracic spine has a natural outward curve (kyphosis)*

*The lumbar spine has a natural inward curve (lordosis)*

# WHY NEUTRAL MATTERS

Having the spine and pelvis in their neutral position optimizes the function of the spine and its curves. It aligns the body in a way to evenly distribute the weight of the body with the least amount of stress on the joints and soft tissue. The position of the pelvis will affect the lumbar, thoracic, and cervical spine above, so there is a knock-on effect.

The neutral spine and pelvis position is functional: it is how we walk and move about. If we perform our Pilates exercises in a flat back position, there is no shock absorption and there is a risk of discomfort or strain to the lumbar and sacral vertebrae as they are pulled away from their natural position.

The core muscles, primarily the transversus abdominis, are crucial to provide localized support and stabilization of the spine. The best activation of this muscle occurs when the pelvis is in neutral, compared to when it is either anteriorly or posteriorly tilted.

Pelvic tilt is controlled by the surrounding muscles; maintaining a neutral pelvis balances these muscles. An anterior (forward-

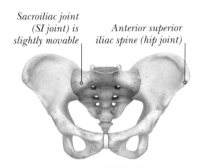

*Sacroiliac joint (SI joint) is slightly movable*    *Anterior superior iliac spine (hip joint)*

**FEMALE PELVIS**

facing) tilt occurs with weak abdominals, gluteals, and hamstrings and results in the person leaning forwards to shift their centre of gravity. A posterior (backward-facing) tilt can be caused by poor postural habits such as slouching, or lack of regular exercise. It occurs with tightness in the abdominals and hamstrings.

## Neutral pelvis and its variations

Neutral pelvis is the ideal position if the pelvis and spine all aligned exactly as they should. In reality there will be variability in finding this in each individual and neutral pelvis should be thought of as a zone between the two extremes of anterior and posterior pelvic tilt.

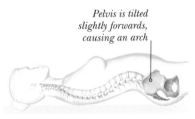

*Pelvis is tilted slightly forwards, causing an arch*

**ANTERIOR TILT**
This occurs when the pelvis is tilted forwards and the lumbar lordosis is increased so that the spine arches away from the mat.

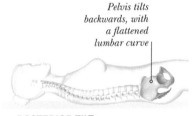

*Pelvis tilts backwards, with a flattened lumbar curve*

**POSTERIOR TILT**
This occurs when the pelvis is tilted backwards and the spine flattens to the floor so there is no curve under the back.

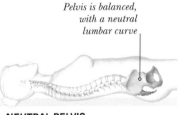

*Pelvis is balanced, with a neutral lumbar curve*

**NEUTRAL PELVIS**
This occurs when the pelvis is not tilting forwards or backwards. It is "ideal" when the anterior superior iliac spines (front hip bones) are level at the front.

---

## Spinal relationships

### Neutral pelvis and the ribcage
An anteriorly tilted pelvis increases the lumbar lordosis posteriorly and will elongate the abdominal region anteriorly, which causes a lengthening of the abdominal muscles and an elevation of the lower ribcage. This results in loss of the abdominal and core muscle connection, as the core muscles cannot engage correctly while stretching away from neutral. The diaphragm is also housed within the ribcage region and is part of the core muscle group, therefore ribcage deviation will also affect diaphragm function, impacting the overall stability of the spine and trunk. Each Pilates exercise should begin with setting

the pelvis in neutral and relaxing the ribcage down. Engaging your core will maintain this relationship and ensure your spine remains stable for the duration of the exercise.

### Ribcage and the shoulder girdle
The scapula is a central point for transferring energy from the lower limbs and the core to the upper limbs, and it connects the clavicle to the humerus. It is the base for all movements of the shoulder girdle (the shoulder blades and collar bones). The stabilizing muscles of the scapula include the upper and lower fibres of the trapezius, and the serratus anterior muscles.

# UNDERSTANDING POSTURE

**Posture is the position and alignment of the body** at any one given time. We fluctuate through many different postures over a 24-hour period, and subtle changes in each of these alter our joint position and muscle activity. It is normal to deviate from ideal posture when moving, but there are key points to note.

## DOES POSTURE ACTUALLY MATTER?

We rarely consider posture – it is an automatic and subconscious activity and is simply how we hold ourselves. It is our response to gravity and the environment that surrounds us, and can be static or dynamic.

A static posture is the position we adopt when we are still; a dynamic posture is how we hold our body through movements. Posture is then maintained and adapted by muscle contractions and controlled by the nervous system and its response to input from a range of sources including the joints, ligaments, muscles, eyes, and ears.

The joints in the upper cervical spine are particularly important for your posture as they have additional receptors to receive posture input, and any alteration t o the head and neck position can influence the posture of the rest of the body.

Adequate posture is required for balance and the ability to resist gravity, as well as for higher functions such as transitioning through static and dynamic Pilates positions. While some people may hold positions without any difficulty, others may experience the result of tight muscles, stiff joints, and over time, weakening of muscles. As the body adapts to these, there may be disturbances in function.

### WHAT IS BAD POSTURE?

A bad posture is unstable, places excess stress on the muscles and joints, and increases work for the body. This may not be an issue if the position is transient or only adopted for a short duration, however exposure to bad posture over longer periods of time may result in soft tissue or joint dysfunctions, restricted movement, or pain within these structures.

### IDEAL POSTURE

While there is no one "normal" posture, there is an "ideal" posture. This is the position that places the lowest level of stress on the body and keeps it aligned so that weight is distributed evenly through the joints and muscles for their specific use. Ideal posture also maintains the natural curves in the spine to allow maximum function of the internal organs and allow the body to support upper and lower limb function efficiently. Try to align the points on the diagram when standing upright.

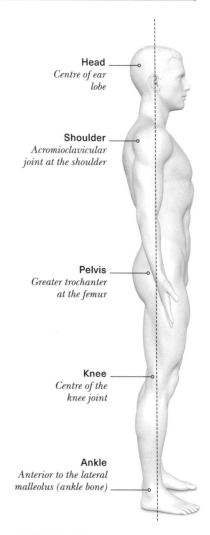

**Head**
*Centre of ear lobe*

**Shoulder**
*Acromioclavicular joint at the shoulder*

**Pelvis**
*Greater trochanter at the femur*

**Knee**
*Centre of the knee joint*

**Ankle**
*Anterior to the lateral malleolus (ankle bone)*

**ALIGNING POSTURE**
The plumb line reference points show alignment of ideal standing posture. Both the right side and left side should be symmetrical with these points.

# POSTURE **TYPES**

Different posture types are classified based on the curves of the spine and their adaptations. These can be genetic, inherent from childhood, or can occur over time as a result of constant stress on the body through life and responses to activities such as working positions or hobbies.

## SWAY BACK

This posture presents with the hips forward from your plumb line giving an increased lordosis, an increased posterior pelvic tilt, and a thoracic kyphosis (outward curve).

This is the result of weak abdominals and hip flexors, and tight gluteus maximus and hamstrings, which allow the pelvis to shift and tilt. The pectoral muscles are tight and pull the head forwards, with weakening of the neck extensors, scapular muscles, and spinal extensors.

## FLAT BACK

Flat back posture is when there is a reduction in the curve at the lumbar spine and the pelvis tilts posteriorly, causing slight flexion in the hips and knees and forcing the head to come forwards. The hip extensors are tight as they rotate the pelvis backwards and the hip flexors are weak. The pectorals are tight and the scapular muscles are weak. The abdominals are usually strong, however, as the person is continually using them to stand up straight rather than flex forwards.

## LORDOSIS

This posture type presents with an inward curve of the lumbar spine and a normal curve in the cervical and thoracic spine. An increased lordosis can occur with weak abdominals, gluteals, and hamstrings and tight hip flexors and spinal extensors.

## KYPHOSIS

Kyphosis is an outward curve of the thoracic spine but with a normal shape in the lumbar and sacral spine. An increased kyphosis can present with weak neck flexors and scapular muscles, and tight neck extensors and pectoral muscles. Exercises should focus on strengthening the deep neck flexors and upper back extensors and stretching the chest.

## KYPHO-LORDOTIC

This posture is the combination of an exagerrated thoracic kyphosis and lumbar lordosis and shares the presentation of both of these individual postures. Correcting one and restoring balance can often result in further deviation of the other, so the two will need to be treated together.

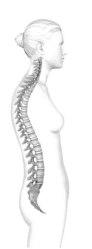

**SWAY BACK**

**FLAT BACK**

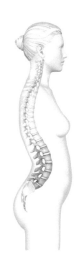

**LORDOSIS**

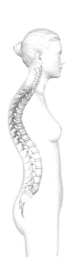

**KYPHOSIS**

### Effect of sitting postures on the spine

Sitting supported as close to normal (neutral) posture is the best practice. Prolonged sitting has been shown to significantly increase muscle stiffness and the longer the duration of sitting, the increase in the likelihood of adopting a slumped sitting posture, which has been related to lower back pain. Regular breaks from sitting are recommended to avoid slumping.

Sitting with postures that involve the head and neck forwards (protruded or flexed) or the trunk flexed (slumped posture) causes an increase in loading of these joints as the joints are not aligned optimally.

# THE NATURE OF
# MECHANICAL PAIN

**Pain can occur in a variety of different structures** and can be local or referred. The way we experience pain differs based on individual circumstances and is associated with altered mechanics. The full experience of these alterations, and the physical and emotional response, contributes to the severity of pain felt. Pilates can assist with both mechanical and psychological needs to reduce pain.

## WHAT IS PAIN?

The International Association for the Study of Pain defines it as "an unpleasant sensory and emotional experience associated with, or resembling that associated with, actual or potential tissue damage". This considers pain to be both a physical and a psychological response by an individual.

Perception of pain is influenced by three main factors: biological, psychological, and social. These different aspects mean that a response to pain will not be perceived the same by everyone, therefore a Pilates programme for pain will also require an individual prescription, influenced by both their physical response and psychological state.

### SENSORY OR EMOTIONAL

The sensory dimension of pain refers to the intensity and characteristics of the pain and is usually related to tissue damage. The emotional response to pain reflects how unpleasant the sensation is to a person, as well as the motivation to react to the pain with a protective mechanism. The reality will be the product of both, complicated further by the duration of the pain and the many other influencing factors.

**INFLUENCING FACTORS**

Pain responses have been shown to differ between the sexes. Women have a greater response to pain and also report pain more than men do. As we age our brain deteriorates and the connections from the body to the brain degrade. This may be responsible for the increase in pain threshold in older persons. Anxiety, depression, and distress are also associated with feeling pain more.

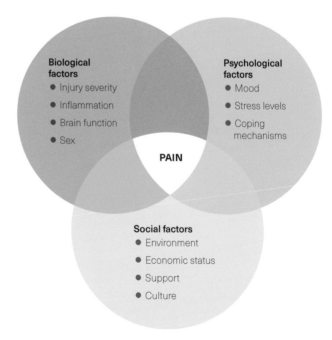

**Biological factors**
- Injury severity
- Inflammation
- Brain function
- Sex

**Psychological factors**
- Mood
- Stress levels
- Coping mechanisms

**PAIN**

**Social factors**
- Environment
- Economic status
- Support
- Culture

# TYPES OF PAIN

Pain is multifaceted and often presents from more than one structure. Nociceptive pain is the pain felt when there is damage to one or more tissues such as a muscle, joint, or nerve.

All of these structures are highly innervated with nociceptive nerve endings and therefore susceptible to producing pain. This may be the result of direct trauma; indirectly via chemical reactions such as inflammation; or mechanically due to a restriction in the movement, for example nerve or muscle tension.

Radicular pain is pain associated with nerve root compression and is accompanied with referred pain away from the injury site within the path of the nerve called the dermatome. This is why people with sciatica may feel pain down their leg, but the source of pain originates in the lumbar spine.

It is important to monitor patterns of movement and compensations during pain, as this can prevent it from worsening.

> *Pilates can be **effective** at treating all types of **pain**, with **physical** benefits and calming mindful effects.*

# WHAT HAPPENS WHEN YOU HAVE PAIN?

Painful sensations are detected by receptors, called nociceptors, at the site of injury, whether this is within muscle, tendon, ligament, bone, fascia, or nerve structures. These receptors send messages to the brain to process and elicit a response.

Messages prompt a cascade of chemical reactions to trigger processes such as inflammation, swelling, and a strong sense of pain as a protective mechanism to prevent further damage occurring. This is where you may find yourself non-weight bearing or fearful to move the injured area because the pain levels are so extreme, or the fear of further injury prevents you.

The longer the injury persists, the more likely you are to adopt abnormal movement patterns to compensate. The nociceptive nerve endings within the injury site can also become increasingly sensitive and require less input for them to fire nerve impulses to the brain, so the brain produces a larger response and the pain perception is heightened.

Under normal circumstances, your core muscles anticipate movement and will activate prior to this movement to provide the stability you require. When there is a painful response however, this mechanism is delayed or even inhibited and therefore no local muscle stabilization occurs. A single episode of back pain can cause inhibition of the multifidus muscle and a decrease in the muscle's size within the first 24 hours of the pain sensation. Pilates exercises work to restore this muscle activation and can be completed at a low level so as not to aggravate pain.

### Muscle inhibition secondary to pain

Soft tissue damage can affect how our muscles function. An injured muscle may result in neuromuscular inhibition, where the nerves that tell the muscle how to function don't fire efficiently, and the muscle has a reduced response rate and force. This can lead to joint instability secondary to a reduction in muscle support, which in turn contributes to the pain response. A vicious cycle of pain/instability/continuing pain forms.

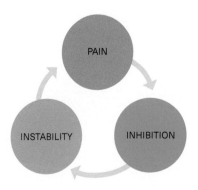

# PILATES AND PAIN RELIEF

**The principles of Pilates can be successfully applied to all kinds of pain.**
Pilates exercises have been proven to significantly improve certain types of
pain, as well as physical impairment, and physical function. They also have a
positive psychological effect on those with lower back and neck pain.

## WHY PILATES CAN HELP WITH PAIN

Pilates offers versatility to accommodate each individual's needs.
Carefully selected Pilates exercises are safe and effective to promote
movement and reduce the fear of moving – a fear that can cause
abnormal movement patterns for those who suffer pain.

After only 24 hours, episodes of
pain can reduce the efficiency of
the local muscles multifidus and
transversus abdominis in the core.
Engaging these muscles effectively
in a Pilates practice can positively
improve muscle support. Global
muscle activation is then included
for a successful system to restore

normal movement patterns.
Breathing control encourages
muscle activation and dampens
down anxiety and emotional
distress. The mindfulness aspect
of integrating breath with
movement focusses the mind
and provides a psychological
shift in perspective.

**PANJABI'S STABILITY MODEL**
Orthopaedic professor Manohar
Panjabi created the Stability
Model. It shows how the joints
(articular system), muscles
(muscular system), and nerves
(neural system) within the body
all coordinate together to provide
stability and control your spine's
movement. Any disruption to one
system will affect the other systems
and impair overall function.

The joints and ligaments
provide passive support, called
form closure. Muscles provide
active support to the joints as
their contractions cause force
closure (external tightness).
The nerves control the signals
to the muscles and adapt the
level of stability required. Reduced
force closure can result in joint
instability, and excess movement
can cause pain. Pilates incorporates
each of these elements by
providing joint stability, muscular
strength, and neural activation,
and therefore is well placed as
a pain relief intervention.

**Neural system:**
nerves and reflexes

**INTEGRATED
STABILITY
SYSTEMS**

**Articular system:**
joints and ligaments

**Muscular system:**
local and global muscles

# PRESCRIPTION OF
## PILATES FOR PAIN

Pain produces a different emotional response in each individual, and their ability to cope or adapt to the pain experience will also differ. There are five key areas that can be modified to tailor Pilates for pain.

### LEVER LENGTH
Having the arms and legs flexed provides a shorter lever length and less stress on the body to manage. Extending one limb would lightly increase the demand and once this is manageable, subsequent limbs could be extended. The duration the limbs are extended for can be modified to increase or reduce the challenge of the exercise you are performing.

### LIMB LOAD
The load (amount of effort) should begin at a lower level and gradually be progressed as the increased demands can be achieved. This can be managed by starting with the arms and legs lower down, such as on the mat, and maintaining this mat contact (closed-chain). To progress this, one limb can be raised off the mat initially (open-chain), and subsequently lifted more to raise the load further. Moving the limbs further away from the trunk will add additional load, and holding the positions for longer durations or adding weight will increase it more.

### CUEING STRATEGY
The exercises should be cued (communicated) by the Pilates instructor in a way that relates to the individual's experience. Cueing gentle, safe movements with minimal instruction can install feelings of safety and trust. As students begin to move well, they will allow further instruction and progress through their exercises, allowing a physical and emotional response to their pain.

### MINDFULNESS
The practice of mindfulness (see p.40) is a powerful yet simple addition to a Pilates session. Being fully present and focussed on the exercises can raise body and mind awareness and reduce the emotional response to pain by accepting the situation there and finding positive ways to navigate it.

### BREATHWORK
The inclusion of specific breathwork (see p.36) gently directs attention away from pain emotions and focusses the mind on the breath. The relaxation response that breathing techniques stimulates is effective at relieving tension within the body, encouraging more comfortable postures, and reducing pain perceptions.

# TO STABILIZE
## OR MOBILIZE?

Identifying the precise cause of pain can be challenging, but assessing the individual as a whole can provide a starting point for what their biggest needs are. For example, do they need stability or mobility more?

Often people are fearful of movement because they preconceive movement to be painful. This creates stiffness within the spine and muscle activation exercises would actually further restrict their movement. These people require education and tuition on safe movement. Mobility exercises are essential here to break the fear barrier and restore normal function.

If a person is lacking in stability, then this should be provided first prior to greater movements, otherwise the localized muscles will never be re-trained and stability never restored.

*Pilates* allows an ***individualized*** *prescription of* **exercise** *for* pain *relief.*

# BREATHING
## TECHNIQUES

**"Above all, learn how to breathe correctly."** Joseph Pilates stated that breathing was of the utmost importance. This was not only to synchronize with the physical Pilates practice, it was also to develop the lungs and optimize the cardiorespiratory system, thus reducing fatigue. He advised a strict breathing pattern for his exercises to reflect its importance for our whole body health, and this ethos echoes the holistic approach Pilates delivers overall.

## WHY DOES **BREATHING MATTER?**

Put simply, we need to breathe for survival. Breathing promotes the circulation of oxygen around the body and up to the brain to ensure optimal body functions. If our breathing is inadequate – if we take lots of short, rapid breaths – then we restrict the oxygen and blood supply to the brain, creating stress and panic. As we panic, supply is further restricted, impacting our brain state and circulation, and unbalancing our hormones and emotions. The release of "fight or flight" hormones increases, while calming hormones reduce.

## PILATES **BREATHING**

Pilates instructors encourage their students to practise a natural breathing pattern, which involves breathing in wide and fully to the sides of the ribcage. This is called "lateral breathing", and it promotes the correct functioning of your ribcage and respiratory muscles.

Like any muscle, those that drive the breathing process need to be exercised to cope with increased physical demands. As you exhale, you should empty your lungs fully and allow relaxation of the muscles and ribcage. This pattern allows the gas exchange of oxygen and carbon dioxide to occur effectively and minimizes any build up of muscular tension.

Efficient respiratory biomechanics – the way we breathe – will reduce any load on your core muscles and allow them to work without additional resistance. The transversus abdominis muscle in the core is primary composed of type I

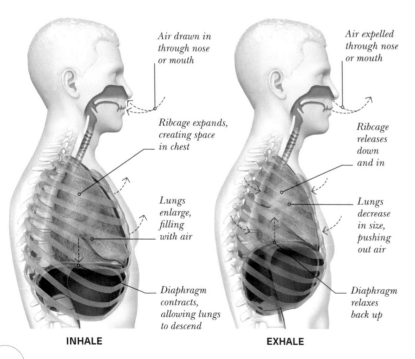

Air drawn in through nose or mouth

Ribcage expands, creating space in chest

Lungs enlarge, filling with air

Diaphragm contracts, allowing lungs to descend

**INHALE**

Air expelled through nose or mouth

Ribcage releases down and in

Lungs decrease in size, pushing out air

Diaphragm relaxes back up

**EXHALE**

# DIFFERENT BREATHING TECHNIQUES

Breathing patterns can be adapted to suit the purpose of the exercise or the practice. This allows for vast variation; the same exercise may be performed for different benefits depending on how you modify the breath.

### Exhale on exertion
This is a predictable pattern that is easy for our brain to follow and focus on the physical aspects. It allows more effective recruitment of the core muscles and removes the resistance of an air-filled abdominal cavity to exercise against.

### Inhale to lengthen
Holding a stretch or mobility movement at its end range and then adding an inhalation to the hold will further expand the body region to provide a deeper stretch. Combine this with the cue to further lengthen, rotate, or twist for most benefit.

### Regular breathing/no pattern
Eliminating a set breathing pattern removes additional elements to think about and will simplify the Pilates exercise. This is ideal for beginners, or for those initially learning complex exercises where the physical technique may take priority.

### To a pattern/rhythm
Inhaling and exhaling for a set number of reps, e.g. inhale for 2 and exhale for 2, maintains a steady breath even when the exercise difficulty is increased. This keeps the exercise speed constant, instead of changing the tempo due to fatigue.

muscle fibres, our slow-twitch fibres which are well oxygenated and work extensively without reaching fatigue. Exhaling as you contract your core muscles allows better recruitment of these type I muscle fibres. If you were to inhale and try to engage your core muscles, you would raise your intra-abdominal pressure, increasing the load on your abdominals. This would involve recruiting type II muscle fibres, the superficial abdominal muscles that will fatigue quickly and not be able to provide muscular support for any length of time.

Good breathing patterns can also improve your lung strength. They teach inhalation through the nose, which provides resistance to the breath from the small nostril hairs inside the nostrils. This trains and strengthens the respiratory muscles specifically as they have to overcome this regular resistance. Athletes who incorporate regular breathwork into their training have shown improved lung function.

**Gives focus**
Your attention is brought to the rise and fall of your breath, the depth of it, and the control of it. This negates thoughts wandering elsewhere.

**Slows movement**
Synchronizing your breathing pattern with your movements encourages the movements to slow down and be executed with precision and concentration rather than a rapid performance.

**Reminds you to breathe**
When our minds are busy, we can focus solely on the physical movement and forget to control our breath. An established breathing pattern prevents breath-holding or hyperventilation.

**Fosters mind/body connection**
Integration of breathing techniques to your Pilates exercises strengthens the connection to your brain, improves body awareness, and activates your relaxation response.

**BENEFITS OF GOOD BREATHING TECHNIQUE**

## Practice exercise for lateral breathing

Sit upright and place your hands on either side of the lower half of your ribcage with your fingertips from each hand lightly touching each other. Take a deep breath in and feel your ribcage widening outwards. Your fingertips will move apart from each other. Now exhale and as the sides of your ribcage sink back inwards, you should feel your fingertips coming back together. Repeat for 5–7 breaths.

*Place hands either side of lower ribcage*

# GUT HEALTH

**Our gut function** is now known to be a vital part of our overall wellbeing. Gut conditions can severely affect our everyday lives and Pilates exercises may be of some benefit.

## ROLE OF **DIGESTION**

Digestion is the system of transporting and breaking down food so that nutrients can be absorbed. Waste is also eliminated. It requires coordination of the muscles from the mouth to the stomach to move food through the body, then the intestines excrete waste from the rectum. Defects in the system can cause symptoms such as bloating, constipation, or heartburn. Most of these are experienced around the abdomen region, and as Pilates focusses on core movement, it can help.

### Role of the vagus nerve

The vagus nerve is the messenger between your body and your brain. It connects to various organs, including the gut and the lungs, and regulates digestion and breathing. It also activates the "rest and digest" parasympathetic nervous system.

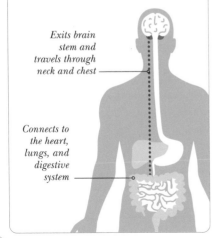

*Exits brain stem and travels through neck and chest*

*Connects to the heart, lungs, and digestive system*

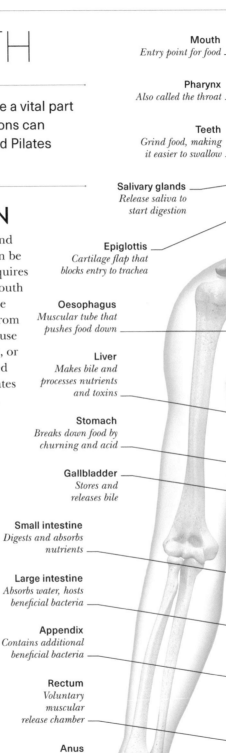

**Mouth**
*Entry point for food*

**Pharynx**
*Also called the throat*

**Teeth**
*Grind food, making it easier to swallow*

**Salivary glands**
*Release saliva to start digestion*

**Epiglottis**
*Cartilage flap that blocks entry to trachea*

**Oesophagus**
*Muscular tube that pushes food down*

**Liver**
*Makes bile and processes nutrients and toxins*

**Stomach**
*Breaks down food by churning and acid*

**Gallbladder**
*Stores and releases bile*

**Small intestine**
*Digests and absorbs nutrients*

**Large intestine**
*Absorbs water, hosts beneficial bacteria*

**Appendix**
*Contains additional beneficial bacteria*

**Rectum**
*Voluntary muscular release chamber*

**Anus**
*Exit point of faeces*

**THE DIGESTIVE TRACT**
Food enters the mouth and is transported through the oesophagus, stomach, small intestine, and large intestine. Waste exits via the anus.

# HOW **PILATES** **CAN** HELP

The positions of Pilates exercises were a deliberate plan. Each exercise was designed away from the upright position, and sometimes literally the opposite – in inverted positions – to relieve the heart and visceral organs from excess strain.

The rolling motions, deep flexions, and rotational exercises are said to physically massage the internal organs. This can increase blood flow to the stomach to aid digestion and encourage peristalsis (see below), as well as relaxing the nervous system. Increased intestinal movement can also regulate bowel movements.

Mobility-based exercises also stretch and lengthen the abdominal cavity to create space and relieve discomfort from gastrointestinal symptoms.

## Exercises for gut health

There are three categories of Pilates exercises that may be beneficial in gut health by massaging the organs and encouraging internal movement through flexion, rotation, and mobility.

| FLEXION | MOBILITY |
|---|---|
| Spine Stretch | Pelvic Tilts |
| Roll Up | Cobra |
| Roll Over | Shoulder Bridge |
| Rolling Back | Swan Dive |
| Seal | Spine Twist |
| Neck Pull | Spine Stretch |
| Scissors | Mermaid |
| Bicycle | Thread the Needle |
| Boomerang | |

**ROTATION**
Hip Twist
Spine Twist
Saw
Corkscrew
Criss Cross

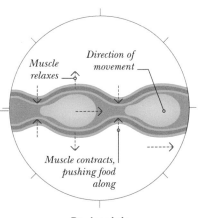

*Muscle relaxes*

*Direction of movement*

*Muscle contracts, pushing food along*

### Peristalsis
Peristalsis is a series of involuntary muscle contractions that propel food along the digestive tract. It is stimulated by the relaxation response via the vagus nerve, and physical exercise such as Pilates can enhance the process.

## How Pilates breathing can help

Regular breathing patterns optimize gas exchange within the lungs, and the elimination of carbon dioxide out of them. This can improve blood flow, nourish the cells, and prevent lethargy. The cleansing of excess air may also reduce bloating. Breathing regulation relaxes the nervous system and, as the gut is controlled by the vagus nerve, it can promote relaxation of the digestive tract.

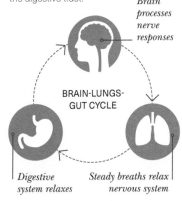

*Brain processes nerve responses*

BRAIN-LUNGS-GUT CYCLE

*Digestive system relaxes*

*Steady breaths relax nervous system*

# PILATES AND MINDFULNESS
## FOR STRESS AND ANXIETY

**"Pilates is the complete coordination of the body, mind, and spirit,"** said Joseph Pilates. From the start, Pilates was much more than a physical practice; research shows that it can help with feelings of depression, anxiety, fatigue, and stress.

## STRESS IN OUR DAILY LIVES

Stress is both a biological and psychological response to an event where we feel we cannot cope with the event or challenge it adequately. We all respond to stress differently, and this varies depending on whether it is a small stress, a big stress, or the accumulation of lots of little stresses that produce ongoing chronic stress.

Small amounts of stress are natural and often positive, as they help us to react quickly to life challenges such as meeting a deadline. But regular exposure to stressful events, or one large stressful event, can be detrimental to our health with greater impact on mental health imbalances, chronic pain, and serious health concerns such as heart disease and stroke.

It is important to recognize the physical signs of heightened stress and to learn coping mechanisms to manage the psychological response in order to minimize the overall stress response on the body. Pilates is an effective stress-reducing method for several reasons.

## THE STRESS RESPONSE

Stress disrupts our natural hormone balance and causes two chemical pathways to occur within the body. These are normal physiological responses that will revert to baseline once the stress is reduced. Chronic exposure, however, causes a prolonged stress response.

### CORTISOL
The brain's hypothalamus stimulates the pituitary gland and a cascade of communications result in the production of cortisol, our stress hormone. This produces a steady supply of blood sugar to allow your body to cope with a stressful event. It also releases stored glucose from the liver to provide energy. The immune system can become suppressed because raised cortisol levels suppress formation and circulation of lymphocytes, and inhibit the making of new antibodies in response to infection. You may feel run down during stressful times.

### ADRENALINE
The hypothalamus also stimulates the adrenal medulla to produce adrenaline, and this brings on our "fight or flight" response, causing increased heart rate, blood pressure, and sweating.

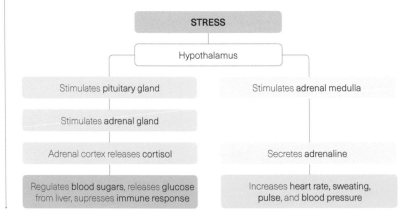

# HOW PILATES CAN HELP
# THE STRESS RESPONSE

The comprehensive and holistic elements of Pilates allow the exercise method to have a beneficial effect on stress. This can occur through movement, breathing, mindfulness, and following a routine.

## MOVEMENT

Physical activity promotes feel-good endorphins in as little as 10 minutes, and brain blood flow is elevated in the hippocampus (emotional processing centre) post-workout, giving us those natural highs. As Pilates exercises are often performed at a slightly slower pace, include breathing control and awareness, and are interspersed with feel-good mobility movements, we often feel an even greater response to a workout.

## BREATHING

The continuous exercise of a Pilates session teaches you to move in a structured and efficient way using the least amount of energy possible. As the exercises become harder, your breathing may increase in speed, so the breathing pattern will teach you to control this and remain calm. Controlled breathing relaxes the autonomic nervous system, which regulates body processes. This becomes further enhanced when you make your exhale longer than your inhale.

## MINDFULNESS

The Pilates routine directs your attention to breathwork and movement control. This focus then relaxes the mind and enforces awareness in that very present moment. This process can mentally clear your thoughts and minimize stress levels.

## ROUTINE

A regular Pilates practice encourages routine in two ways: that of completing your exercises regularly, and also the routine within your practice of sequencing the exercises to cover all body regions, along with strengthening and mobilizing aspects. A regular routine relaxes the brain as this is a "safe" aspect your body becomes accustomed to, eliminating uncertainty and relaxing the body to expect a familiar process.

### Pilates effects on blood pressure

Stress is a major contributing factor for elevated blood pressure (hypertension) and this can increase the risk of cardiovascular disease. Performing a single 60-minute Pilates session can reduce blood pressure by 5–8mmHg within 60 minutes after the class has finished. This immediate response is the same reduction that aerobic exercise could provide. From this evidence, Pilates may be considered a suitable exercise method for lowering blood pressure, especially for those who cannot meet the aerobic exercise guidelines for hypertension, or do not experience a reduction in blood pressure with it.

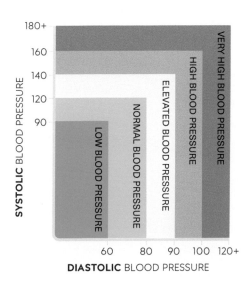

### Mindfulness

Mindfulness is the awareness of the present moment non-judgementally, and accepting the feelings, thoughts, and bodily sensations experienced. Pilates encourages this practice by relating your movement, breath, and thoughts to each other so your mind and body work in sync. Within a Pilates session, the sequences and breathing patterns train awareness and teach every movement to be intentional. We learn to pause, observe, and respond accordingly. This can be applied to situations off the mat where we learn to respond intentionally rather than react automatically. This increased awareness and attention helps to regulate your nervous system by stimulating the vagus nerve, which tells the body to rest. The practice has an anti-inflammatory response on the nervous system, reduces cortisol levels, and lowers blood pressure.

**STABILITY**
pp.50–93

**ROTATORY**
pp.94–119

**STRENGTH**
pp.120–161

**MOBILITY**
pp.162–177

# PILATES
# EXERCISES

**"Physical fitness is the first requisite of happiness."** So said
Joseph Pilates, who firmly believed that if we moved, strengthened,
and mobilized our bodies, we would all be considerably happier.
This exercise section details the original Pilates exercises, giving
a clear description of how to execute each one with the utmost
precision. Numerous variations and tips are included – both to
simplify and occasionally challenge – to make Pilates accessible
to everyone and every ability.

# INTRODUCTION
# TO THE **EXERCISES**

**Demands of the modern day and advances in research** have led to numerous different Pilates schools opening around the world. Each has its own way of teaching the exercises, but the underlying principles remain intact.

*Pilates strives to improve **core stability** and **strength**, whole body strength, and **flexibility**, and has a **positive** impact on the mental health of its participants.*

## SCHOOLS OF THOUGHT

Joseph Pilates believed his method should be available to everyone and supported his students opening their own studios to continue his teachings. In the year 2000 "Pilates" became a generic term, making it available for anyone to offer the exercises. While qualified instruction is preferred, this opened up creativity and innovation of the method.

The Pilates Method was designed and developed for the able body. It consisted of a series of exercises that, rather than increasing repetitions to fatigue, were progressed in difficulty. Today we are more aware than ever of wanting an individualized approach to accommodate for different fitness levels, ability, or health implications. We are often more sedentary and vulnerable to higher levels of stress, both of which can impact our physical and mental wellbeing. Our posture can be affected by lifestyle factors such as carrying children, or even just bad habits of sitting a certain way.

Exercise evolution can cater for each of these scenarios to still allow the benefits of Pilates to be experienced by all. Teaching will still provide the key physical aspects of strengthening, stretching, mobilizing, and rotational elements in a variety of different positions, with the addition of mindfulness and breathwork. Different schools may be classified as classical, matwork, or contemporary.

Classical Pilates preserves Joseph's original matwork repertoire as well as his creations on the larger pieces of equipment and is taught strictly to his instructions.

Matwork Pilates may reflect the original exercise but also offer adaptations to suit the client population and incorporate the use of the small equipment.

Contemporary Pilates combines both classical and matwork exercises with the further addition of incorporating elements of fitness, yoga, and rehabilitation methods. This style will deviate the most from the strict format and be tailored completely to the individual or a particular class group.

Collectively all of these methods still strive to achieve the same goals that were set by Joseph Pilates.

# THINGS MAY **DIFFER**

This book has predominantly displayed the classical Pilates exercises and method, as it is important for readers to learn where the subsequent adaptations came from. These exercises are still equally as beneficial today as they were when the discipline was founded.

A wide range of modern variations have also been chosen to showcase the breadth of Pilates in the current day and make it accessible to every level of fitness, and any age. The exercises have been classified by their function: stability, rotatory, strength, and mobility.

We begin the Pilates journey by teaching some simple posture-based exercises to introduce concepts, mobilize the body, and improve posture.

Take what you wish from each concept of thought. Follow the methods that resonate the most with you. Be aware, too, that should you require a modification for the physical movement, the breathwork, or the technique, there is likely a solution that will work for your unique makeup.

### BREATHING
Original breathwork is still taught and is as relevant now as it was when Joseph Pilates founded the discipline. Some schools have modified the breathing patterns to complement their exercise adaptations or to match changes in scientific research. Sometimes omitting specific breathwork is even suggested to focus more on the movement.

### NAMES
The original names for the exercises are still very prominent, however some schools have changed the names completely or added more stages to the exercises with additional names. The names usually reflect what the exercise represents for easy recognition.

### TECHNIQUES
As the Pilates Method has been passed down through Joseph's direct students and modified along the way, and has had scientific input, techniques will differ depending on who is teaching you. Emphasis may be placed more on breathing, movement, speed, or resembling the traditional exercise. The technique changes make this an adaptable practice.

### EXERCISES
There is an abundance of new exercises now taught within the Pilates Method. These are often designed to simplify the more complex original exercises, or to adapt them for various injuries or conditions. There are also new additions to teach the Pilates principles in different positions, such as standing or sitting on a chair.

## Small equipment

Small Pilates equipment can enhance your matwork practice in a variety of ways, and its use is more accessible when larger studio equipment, such as the Reformer, is not available. Such equipment has become very popular due to the accessibility, portability, and numerous additional exercises it facilitates. Small equipment is also utilized in rehabilitation settings where participants require additional assistance to achieve a full exercise, or in contrast require a greater challenge beyond the matwork.

- **The soft ball** is used to create an unstable base of support for balance challenges. It can also facilitate movement.

- **The resistance band** allows progressive overload for strength gains, or offers additional support if needed.

- **The resistance circle** promotes engagement for the global muscles.

- **The foam roller** provides a balance challenge, and also facilitates more subtle movement control through the shoulder blades and lumbar and pelvic regions.

**RESISTANCE BAND**

**SOFT BALL**

# SIMPLE POSTURE EXERCISES

These exercises teach the foundations of your Pilates practice and are excellent for gentle mobility, as well as for warming up or cooling down. They can also be performed as a short sequence together. Return to these daily for an easy, consistent routine.

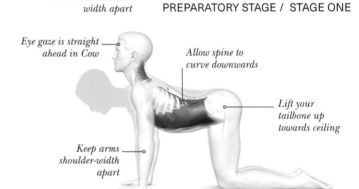

KEY
● Primary target muscle
● Secondary target muscle

## CAT COW

This feel-good spinal mobility exercise creates space in both the front and back of the body, and encourages breath within this space to both warm and relax the body. It engages the abdominal muscles and is a great addition to the start or finish of any Pilates workout.

### PREPARATORY STAGE
Begin in four point kneeling with the shoulders above the wrists and the hips above the knees. Lengthen the spine and keep it neutral. Engage your core.

### STAGE ONE
Exhale as you tuck your tailbone and tilt your pelvis downwards and bring your head and chin towards your chest, rounding your spine upwards towards the ceiling. Ensure you achieve an equal curve through both the upper and lower spine.

### STAGE TWO
Now inhale as you lift your tailbone and breastbone upwards at the same time, and allow your spine to curve downwards, while keeping your abdominals engaged. Repeat the Cat Cow sequence 4–6 times.

*Round the spine upwards towards ceiling*

*Look down at the mat to begin*

*Position hips above knees*

*Bring head towards chest*

*Arms are shoulder-width apart*

PREPARATORY STAGE / STAGE ONE

*Eye gaze is straight ahead in Cow*

*Allow spine to curve downwards*

*Lift your tailbone up towards ceiling*

*Keep arms shoulder-width apart*

STAGE TWO

## DUMB WAITER

This trains shoulder blade control while opening the chest at the front, and the upright position makes it beneficial for posture. Try this sitting upright on a chair to integrate easily into your day.

### PREPARATORY STAGE
Stand upright with your legs hip-distance apart, your spine in neutral, and your arms down by your sides. Bend your elbows to 90 degrees with palms facing upwards. Engage your core, inhale to prepare, and lengthen your spine.

### STAGE ONE
Exhale and open your forearms away from your body, keeping your spine neutral, with ribcage drawn down. Don't squeeze the shoulder blades together – rather let them glide gently. Bring the forearms back into the original position and repeat 6–8 times.

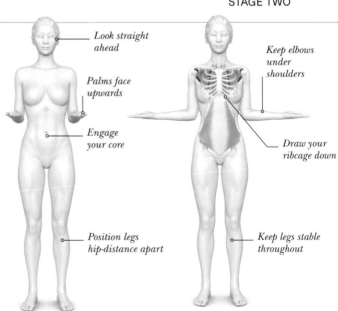

*Look straight ahead*

*Keep elbows under shoulders*

*Palms face upwards*

*Engage your core*

*Draw your ribcage down*

*Position legs hip-distance apart*

*Keep legs stable throughout*

# OVERHEAD ARM CIRCLES

These arm circles mobilize the shoulder joints and upper back while challenging stability of the scapula and thoracic spine. They open the chest, teaching ribcage and core control when the arms are overhead.

### PREPARATORY STAGE
Lie on your back with your spine and pelvis in neutral and your legs hip-distance apart. Place your arms down by your sides with palms facing downwards. Make sure your shoulders are relaxed and engage your core. Exhale as you lift your arms up above your shoulders and inhale to hold.

### STAGE ONE
Exhale as you continue moving your arms overhead as far as you can without disturbing your neutral spine. Inhale as you bring your arms out to the sides to make a circle and return the arms back to the start directly above your shoulders. Repeat 6–8 times.

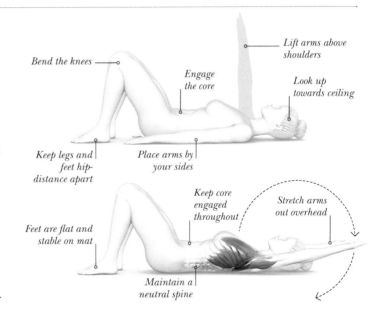

*Bend the knees*

*Engage the core*

*Lift arms above shoulders*

*Look up towards ceiling*

*Keep legs and feet hip-distance apart*

*Place arms by your sides*

*Feet are flat and stable on mat*

*Keep core engaged throughout*

*Stretch arms out overhead*

*Maintain a neutral spine*

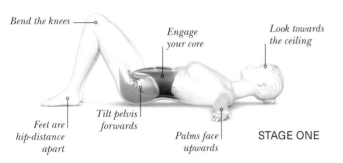

*Bend the knees*

*Engage your core*

*Look towards the ceiling*

*Feet are hip-distance apart*

*Tilt pelvis forwards*

*Palms face upwards*

STAGE ONE

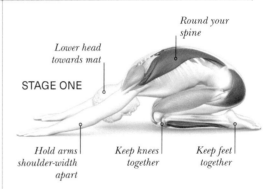

*Lower head towards mat*

*Round your spine*

STAGE ONE

*Hold arms shoulder-width apart*

*Keep knees together*

*Keep feet together*

# PELVIC TILTS

This basic movement mobilizes the spine and teaches control of the pelvis while gently engaging the abdominal muscles. It is a great preparatory exercise to warm the body up and find your neutral starting position prior to beginning matwork exercises.

### PREPARATORY STAGE
Lie on your back with your spine and pelvis in neutral and your legs hip-distance apart. Bring your arms out to the side with palms facing upwards. Make sure your shoulders are relaxed.

### STAGE ONE
Exhale as you gently tilt your pelvis forwards and notice your lower spine lifting up off the mat. Ensure your abdominals and ribcage do not flare upwards. Inhale as you return back to the neutral preparatory stage.

### STAGE TWO
Exhale as you then tilt your pelvis backwards and notice your lower spine flattening into the mat. Inhale to return to the neutral position and repeat the sequence 6–8 times.

# SHELL STRETCH

This is an easy go-to exercise to relieve tight back muscles, restore calmness, or provide a moment of relaxation. It is complementary to any matwork Pilates exercise and is suitable for everyone.

### PREPARATORY STAGE
Sit upright in a low kneeling position with your bottom resting on your heels, knees together, and spine lengthened. Rest your palms on your knees with your shoulders relaxed.

### STAGE ONE
Exhale and reach your chest and trunk towards your thighs, extending your arms out in front of you along the mat. Your hips reach behind you and remain rested on top of your ankles and heels. Your spine rounds and you lower your forehead to rest on the mat, tucking your chin in. Stay here for 3–4 counts, or longer if your aim is greater relaxation.

# ABDOMINAL CURLS

These curls are an isolated abdominal strengthening exercise. They mobilize your spine into flexion and build abdominal awareness. They are also useful to teach control of abdominal doming (caused by a weakened abdomen) and diastasis: separation of the rectus abdominis muscles, which can both occur after a pregnancy; see page 200 in the Pilates Training section for further postpartum exercise advice.

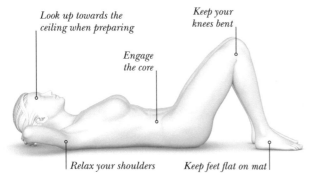

*Look up towards the ceiling when preparing*

*Keep your knees bent*

*Engage the core*

*Relax your shoulders*

*Keep feet flat on mat*

**PREPARATORY STAGE**

Lie on your back with your hips and knees bent, hip-distance apart, and your feet flat on the floor. Interlace your fingertips and place your hands behind your head. Relax your shoulders and glide your ribcage downwards towards your hips. Inhale to prepare.

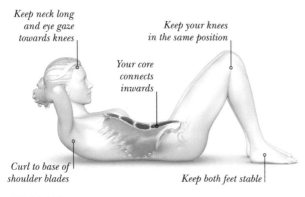

*Keep neck long and eye gaze towards knees*

*Keep your knees in the same position*

*Your core connects inwards*

*Curl to base of shoulder blades*

*Keep both feet stable*

**STAGE ONE**

Exhale as you lift your head, neck, and upper body upwards and forwards off the mat, sequentially curling your spine up until you reach the base of your shoulder blades. Inhale to hold this position, and exhale as you lower back down sequentially through your spine, upper body, and head again. Repeat up to 10 times.

## Progression tips

To progress both of these exercises once you are used to them, try some of these variations:

- **Hold the curled up position** for a short period of time (3–10 seconds) to build abdominal endurance.

- **Perform the same exercise** but with the legs in double table top (see p.54).

- **Add a resistance circle** (see p.45) between your knees to increase the adductor work and challenge the anterior oblique sling further.

- **Hold a small weight** in each hand.

- **Extend one leg outwards** as you perform the curl up movement. Return the leg as you lower back down.

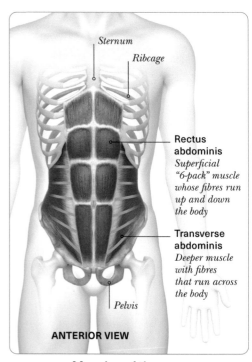

*Sternum*

*Ribcage*

**Rectus abdominis**
*Superficial "6-pack" muscle whose fibres run up and down the body*

**Transverse abdominis**
*Deeper muscle with fibres that run across the body*

*Pelvis*

**ANTERIOR VIEW**

### Muscles of the core

The transversus abdominis is the innermost abdominal muscle, and provides localized spine stability and support. It works with the other core muscles, the pelvic floor, the diaphragm, and the multifidus. The rectus abdominis is the most superficial abdominal muscle, and its vertically orientated muscle fibres produce trunk flexion.

# OBLIQUE CURLS

These isolated oblique abdominal strengthening exercises mobilize your spine into flexion with rotation and require a high level of pelvic stability. They are often prescribed for sports that demand this rotational control, such as running, racquet sports, football, and rugby.

## Caution

Those with osteoporosis should use caution when performing oblique and abdominal curls, as repetitive flexion-based exercises can increase the risk of a compression fracture in the spine.

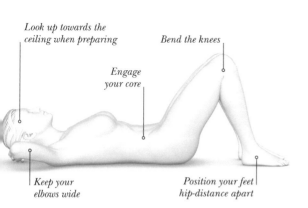

*Look up towards the ceiling when preparing*

*Bend the knees*

*Engage your core*

*Keep your elbows wide*

*Position your feet hip-distance apart*

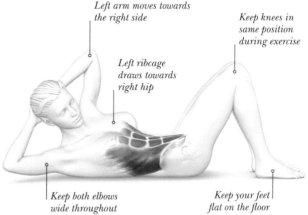

*Left arm moves towards the right side*

*Keep knees in same position during exercise*

*Left ribcage draws towards right hip*

*Keep both elbows wide throughout*

*Keep your feet flat on the floor*

**PREPARATORY STAGE**

Lie on your back with your hips and knees bent, hip-distance apart, and your feet flat on the floor. Interlace your fingertips and place your hands behind your head. Relax your shoulders and glide your ribcage downwards towards your hips. Inhale to prepare.

**STAGE ONE**

Exhale as you lift your head, neck, and upper body upwards and off the mat on the diagonal towards your right side so that your left ribcage draws towards your right hip. Inhale to hold this position and exhale as you lower back down. Repeat up to 10 times, then change sides.

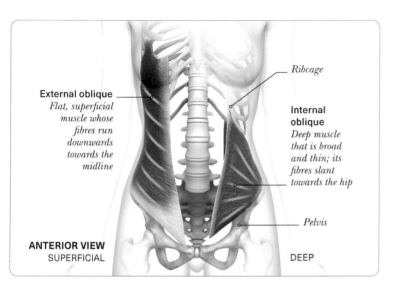

**External oblique**
*Flat, superficial muscle whose fibres run downwards towards the midline*

*Ribcage*

**Internal oblique**
*Deep muscle that is broad and thin; its fibres slant towards the hip*

*Pelvis*

**ANTERIOR VIEW**
SUPERFICIAL

DEEP

**KEY**

● Primary target muscle

● Secondary target muscle

## Internal / external obliques

The muscle fibres of these two muscles run perpendicular to each other and work together to produce trunk rotation. The right external oblique and left internal oblique will produce left-sided rotation; the reverse of this will produce right-sided rotation. Bilateral contraction (using both obliques at once) will produce trunk flexion.

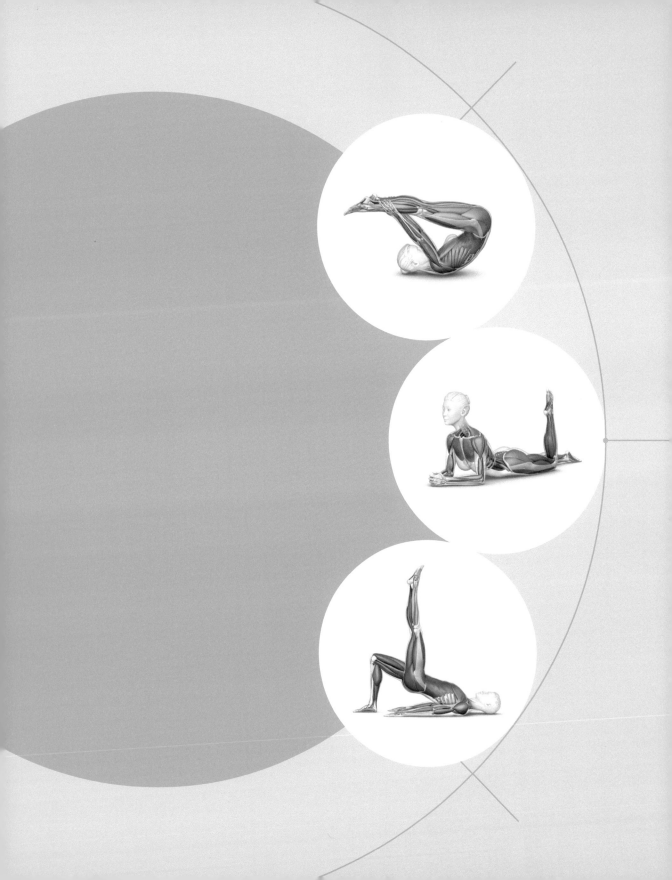

# STABILITY
# EXERCISES

**Stabilizing exercises are the foundation of your Pilates practice.**
They provide the connection to your inner core, working the localized
musculature, and teaching the alignment and movement patterns that
allow you to move beyond this level. If you are ever in doubt about your
practice, return to your stability-based exercises as your base.

# HUNDRED

**Named for the hundred beats you make** with the arms, this classic Pilates exercise promotes abdominal strength and endurance, as well stability in the back and pelvis. It is often used to build strength during a session in preparation for more abdominal exercises.

## THE **BIG PICTURE**

Hundred requires a good connection through your core to withstand the endurance and maintain good technique. The arms should be pulsed 100 times, counted as 5 pulses for an inhale, 5 pulses for an exhale, and repeated 10 times in total. Begin with just 20 pulses and gradually build up. For a less challenging version if your abdominals or hamstrings are impacted, try the Double Table Top Hundred variation (see p.54).

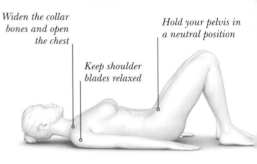

*Widen the collar bones and open the chest*

*Keep shoulder blades relaxed*

*Hold your pelvis in a neutral position*

### PREPARATORY STAGE
Lie on the mat with a neutral spine and pelvis and knees bent, feet hip-distance apart, and arms resting by your sides with palms downwards. Lengthen through the neck to prepare.

### Chest, torso, and hips
Your **pectoralis major** and **rectus abdominis** engage to form the position. Your **triceps** extend your elbows while your pronators turn your arms palm downwards. The **biceps** are engaged and lengthened. The **gluteals** engage to support the elevated legs. The **hip flexors** contract to hold the legs upwards.

**LATERAL VIEW**

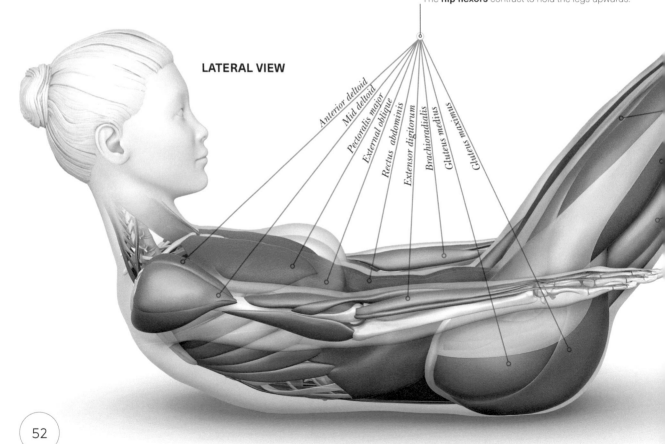

Anterior deltoid
Mid deltoid
Pectoralis major
External oblique
Rectus abdominis
Extensor digitorum
Brachioradialis
Gluteus medius
Gluteus maximus

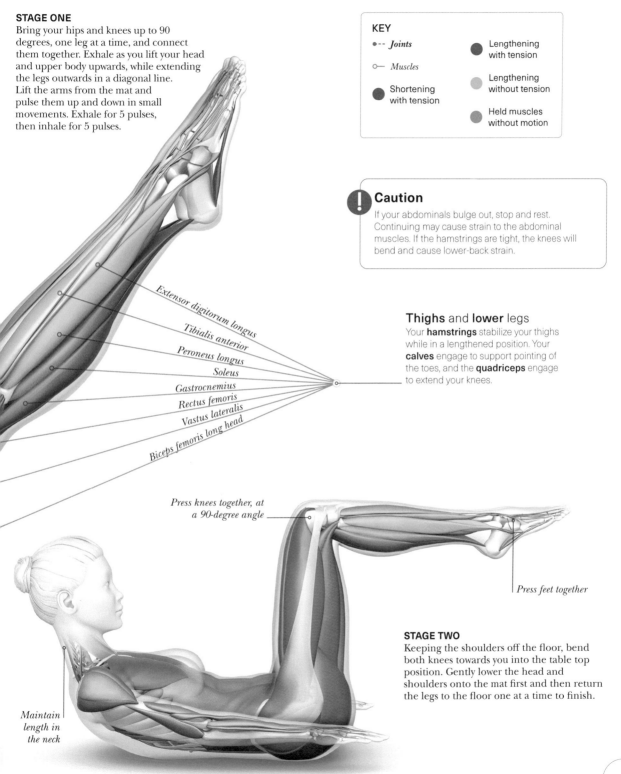

**STAGE ONE**
Bring your hips and knees up to 90 degrees, one leg at a time, and connect them together. Exhale as you lift your head and upper body upwards, while extending the legs outwards in a diagonal line. Lift the arms from the mat and pulse them up and down in small movements. Exhale for 5 pulses, then inhale for 5 pulses.

**KEY**
•-- *Joints*
o— *Muscles*
● Shortening with tension
● Lengthening with tension
● Lengthening without tension
● Held muscles without motion

**! Caution**
If your abdominals bulge out, stop and rest. Continuing may cause strain to the abdominal muscles. If the hamstrings are tight, the knees will bend and cause lower-back strain.

Extensor digitorum longus
Tibialis anterior
Peroneus longus
Soleus
Gastrocnemius
Rectus femoris
Vastus lateralis
Biceps femoris long head

**Thighs** and **lower** legs
Your **hamstrings** stabilize your thighs while in a lengthened position. Your **calves** engage to support pointing of the toes, and the **quadriceps** engage to extend your knees.

Press knees together, at a 90-degree angle

Press feet together

**STAGE TWO**
Keeping the shoulders off the floor, bend both knees towards you into the table top position. Gently lower the head and shoulders onto the mat first and then return the legs to the floor one at a time to finish.

*Maintain length in the neck*

## » VARIATIONS

These variations offer shorter leg levers and more relaxed head and neck positions, both of which reduce the abdominal load. They are great starting points to build core endurance safely and perfect core engagement technique before progressing to the main Hundred. Try 10 repetitions of each for a varied circuit.

*Single table top has one leg raised with **hip** and **knee** to 90 degrees; **double** table top is the same but with both legs raised.*

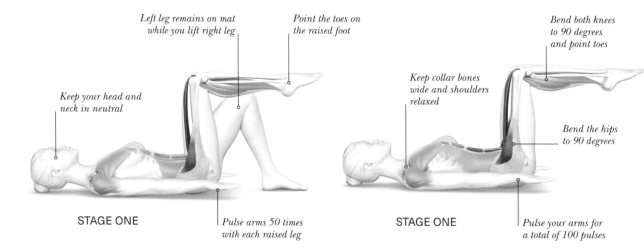

Keep your head and neck in neutral

Left leg remains on mat while you lift right leg

Point the toes on the raised foot

STAGE ONE

Pulse arms 50 times with each raised leg

Keep collar bones wide and shoulders relaxed

Bend both knees to 90 degrees and point toes

Bend the hips to 90 degrees

STAGE ONE

Pulse your arms for a total of 100 pulses

### SINGLE LEG HUNDRED

Keep your raised leg fixed at 90 degrees at the hip and knee while you pulse your arms, and keep your pelvis in neutral. Pulse the arms for 10–20 repetitions to start with, until you build up the endurance to pulse 100 times.

#### PREPARATORY STAGE
Start in the Hundred preparatory position, with both knees bent, feet hip-distance apart, and arms by your sides with palms downwards.

#### STAGE ONE
Bring one leg up to the table top position. Raise your arms slightly off the mat and pulse them up and down, inhaling for 5 pulses and exhaling for 5 pulses Repeat with the opposite leg, completing a total of 100 pulses.

#### STAGE TWO
Once you have completed 50 pulses with each leg in the table top position, return to the preparatory position, with both feet on the floor.

### DOUBLE TABLE TOP HUNDRED

Control your abdominals as you raise each leg up to table top position. If you feel the increased load here or your abdominals appear to bulge outwards, try to engage your core a little deeper for more support.

#### PREPARATORY STAGE
Lie on the floor in the Hundred preparatory position, knees bent, feet hip-distance apart, and arms by your sides with palms facing downwards.

#### STAGE ONE
Bring both legs up to the table top position one at a time. Raise your arms slightly off the mat and pulse them up and down, inhaling for 5 pulses and exhaling for 5 pulses. Repeat this sequence for a total of 100 pulses.

#### STAGE TWO
Return to the preparatory position, lowering your legs to the floor one at a time.

**KEY**
● Primary target muscle
● Secondary target muscle

# DOUBLE TABLE TOP AND
## ABDOMINAL CURL HUNDRED

Keep your eye gaze forwards and your shoulders relaxed throughout this exercise. The head and upper body lift is moderate, with the base of your shoulder blades remaining on the mat. Ensure you do not flatten your spine against the mat.

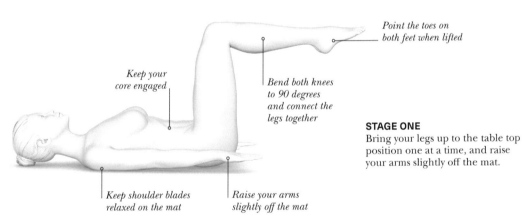

*Bend both knees*

*Keep your head and neck in neutral*

*Engage your core to prepare*

*Relax your shoulder blades on the mat*

*Position your feet hip-distance apart*

### PREPARATORY STAGE
Start in the Hundred preparatory position, knees bent, feet hip-distance apart, and arms by your sides with palms facing downwards.

*Point the toes on both feet when lifted*

*Keep your core engaged*

*Bend both knees to 90 degrees and connect the legs together*

*Keep shoulder blades relaxed on the mat*

*Raise your arms slightly off the mat*

### STAGE ONE
Bring your legs up to the table top position one at a time, and raise your arms slightly off the mat.

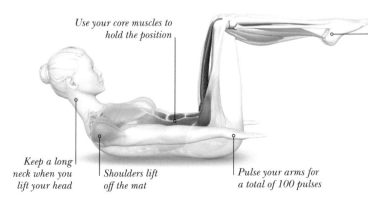

*Use your core muscles to hold the position*

*Keep the toes pointed throughout exercise*

*Keep a long neck when you lift your head*

*Shoulders lift off the mat*

*Pulse your arms for a total of 100 pulses*

### STAGE TWO
Lift your head, neck, and upper body off the mat and pulse your arms up and down, inhaling for 5 pulses and exhaling for 5 pulses. Repeat for a total of 100 pulses, then return to the preparatory position, gently lowering the head and shoulders, followed by the legs, one leg at a time.

# ROLLING BACK

**This dynamic and fun exercise**, also known as Rolling Like a Ball, mobilizes the lumbar spine into flexion and challenges your abdominal strength. The key to a good rolling technique is to control the movement with your muscles rather than use momentum. This exercise requires a good warm up prior to attempting it.

## THE BIG **PICTURE**

Rolling Back requires a deep core connection to support your spine and maintain integrity of its C-shape, and to maintain the relationship between your trunk and legs. You should roll directly backwards and avoid rotating or leaning to one side. Your breath should flow with each movement and your roll back and roll up motions should be of equal duration. Practise by curving your spine backwards with your hands behind your knees.

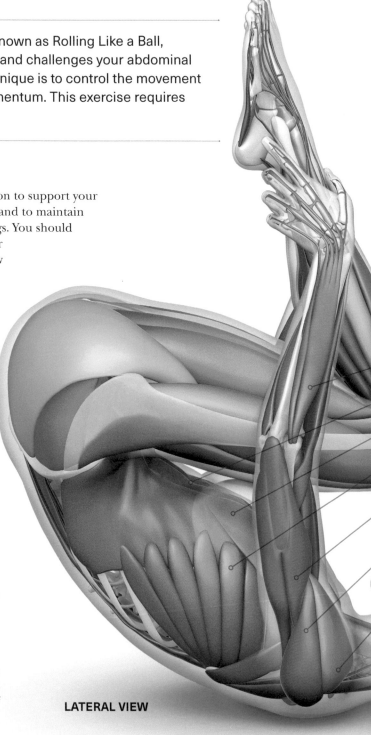

**LATERAL VIEW**

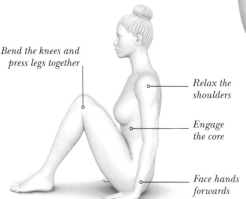

Bend the knees and press legs together

Relax the shoulders

Engage the core

Face hands forwards

**PREPARATORY STAGE**
Sit at the front of your mat with your pelvis slightly tucked under so that your spine is curved. Place both feet flat on the floor with your legs connected together and your arms by your sides. Inhale as you raise both legs and bend to lightly clasp the outside of your shins with your hands.

**KEY**

•-- *Joints*

○— *Muscles*

● Shortening
with tension

● Lengthening
with tension

● Lengthening
without tension

● Held muscles
without motion

## Upper **body**

The **pectoralis major** and **rectus
abdominis** engage to form the position.
The **triceps** extend the elbows. The
**extensor digitorum longus** lengthens.

Extensor digitorum

Rectus abdominis

Pectoralis major

Serratus anterior

Triceps brachii

Posterior deltoid

Mid deltoid

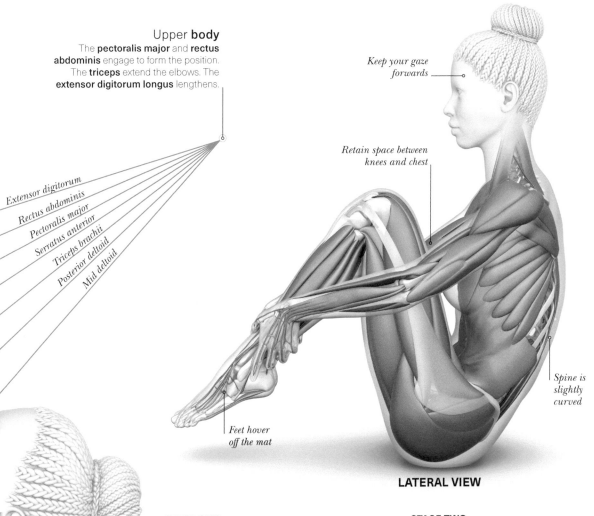

*Keep your gaze
forwards*

*Retain space between
knees and chest*

*Spine is
slightly
curved*

*Feet hover
off the mat*

**LATERAL VIEW**

### STAGE ONE
Roll back with control while keeping
the same space between your shins
and your thighs, and your knees and
your chest. Roll back until you are
on your shoulders.

### STAGE TWO
Exhale as you roll forwards and return
upright, keeping your feet raised slightly
off the mat and finding your balance to
steady yourself. Complete 6–8 repetitions
of Rolling Back.

## » VARIATIONS

These variations are all very similar to the main Rolling Back, but the subtle changes are an excellent starting point for those with less experience. They can help build confidence and improve technique, teaching you to use your core correctly to roll without momentum and to stay tightly curled in a ball.

*Rolling Back is a **fun way** to finish your workout and **transition** back to standing.*

### HAND SUPPORT

This variation teaches you the technique of Rolling Back through your spine but allows you to use your hands to control the movement until you can engage your core and hold the shape correctly. Press equally through both hands to continue rolling through your midline and keep your shoulders relaxed.

**KEY**

● Primary target muscle
● Secondary target muscle

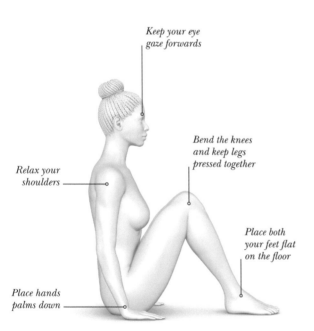

*Keep your eye gaze forwards*

*Relax your shoulders*

*Bend the knees and keep legs pressed together*

*Place both your feet flat on the floor*

*Place hands palms down*

PREPARATORY STAGE

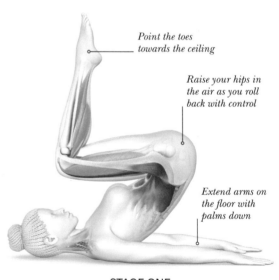

*Point the toes towards the ceiling*

*Raise your hips in the air as you roll back with control*

*Extend arms on the floor with palms down*

STAGE ONE

**PREPARATORY STAGE**
Sit up tall at the front of your mat with your pelvis slightly tucked under. Place both feet flat on the floor with your knees bent and legs together and rest your arms by your sides with hands lightly on the floor. Engage your core.

**STAGE ONE**
Inhale as you roll up and back, using your arms to control the movement. Roll back until you are on your shoulders, with your arms extended on the floor and palms facing downwards.

**STAGE TWO**
Exhale and roll forwards up to sitting. Repeat the entire sequence 6–8 times.

# **TIPTOE** BALANCE

Using your tiptoes provides extra stability and an end point to balance
each time you roll up to sitting. Use this moment to stabilize yourself
before rolling back again. Once you achieve this consistently,
progress to the main Rolling Back exercise (see p.56), where you rely
completely on your core to balance yourself.

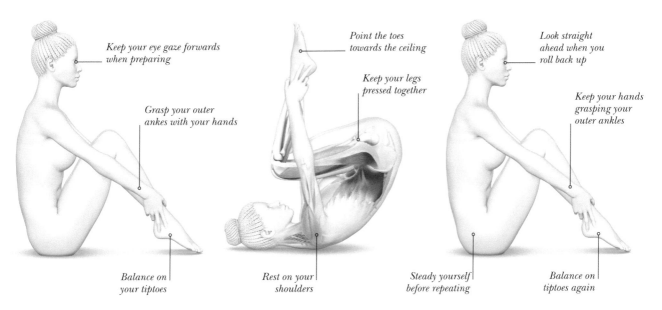

*Keep your eye gaze forwards
when preparing*

*Point the toes
towards the ceiling*

*Look straight
ahead when you
roll back up*

*Grasp your outer
ankes with your hands*

*Keep your legs
pressed together*

*Keep your hands
grasping your
outer ankles*

*Balance on
your tiptoes*

*Rest on your
shoulders*

*Steady yourself
before repeating*

*Balance on
tiptoes again*

**PREPARATORY STAGE**

Sit up tall at the front of your mat with your
knees bent and pelvis slightly tucked under.
Raise your heels to balance on your tiptoes,
and extend your hands to grasp your outer
ankles. Engage the core.

**STAGE ONE**

Inhale as you control rolling backwards
while keeping the space between your
shins and your thighs, and your knees
and your chest consistent. Roll back until
you are on your shoulders.

**STAGE TWO**

Exhale as you roll forwards and
return upright, balancing on your
tiptoes and finding your centre to
steady yourself. Inhale, and
complete 6–8 repetitions.

## **Rolling Back on the ball**

If the full option of Rolling Back is not suitable,
you can use a large gym ball for extra support
and to avoid actually having to roll. It can be
used as an easier exercise version to practise
controlling the movement with the core while
maintaining good posture. Sit on the ball
with your feet flat on the floor and carefully
lie back so that the ball is underneath your
pelvis and spine with your head, neck, and
upper chest still slightly elevated upwards.
Exhale to flex your trunk forwards, using your
core and abdominals, until you reach the
position shown here. Inhale to return back
down, using your core to control the
movement. Complete 6–8 times.

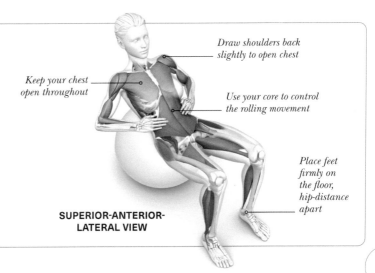

*Keep your chest
open throughout*

*Draw shoulders back
slightly to open chest*

*Use your core to control
the rolling movement*

*Place feet
firmly on
the floor,
hip-distance
apart*

**SUPERIOR-ANTERIOR-
LATERAL VIEW**

# **ONE LEG** STRETCH

**This beginner-level exercise strengthens the abdominal muscles** with a mixture of coordination and reciprocal leg movements. Performing this exercise creates a base for our everyday lower-limb movements such as walking, running, and cycling.

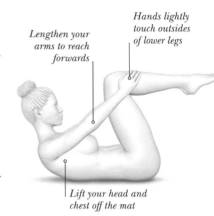

*Lengthen your arms to reach forwards*

*Hands lightly touch outsides of lower legs*

*Lift your head and chest off the mat*

## THE **BIG PICTURE**

This exercise works your core strength in relation to the long leg levers. It can be used to prepare for Double Leg Stretch (see p.64). Maintain your head, trunk, and pelvic position throughout the exercise and ensure you do not rotate to the side. Become familiar with the movement first before adding in the breathing. Complete 8–10 repetitions.

**PREPARATORY STAGE**
Lie flat on your mat with hips and knees bent and hip-distance apart, feet flat on the mat and arms extended by your sides. Float each leg up to the table top position (thighs perpendicular to mat), with toes pointed. Exhale as you lift your head and chest upwards, and reach your hands to touch the outsides of your lower legs, with palms facing inwards. Inhale to prepare.

### Upper body

The **neck flexors** are slightly engaged to keep the head upright, while the **neck extensors** are lengthened. The **pectoralis major** contracts to bring the arms in towards the legs. The **rectus abdominis** and **internal** and **external obliques** contract to keep the upper body lifted upwards.

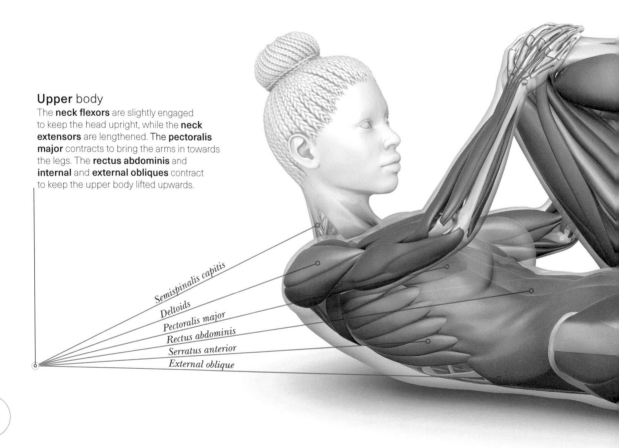

*Semispinalis capitis*
*Deltoids*
*Pectoralis major*
*Rectus abdominis*
*Serratus anterior*
*External oblique*

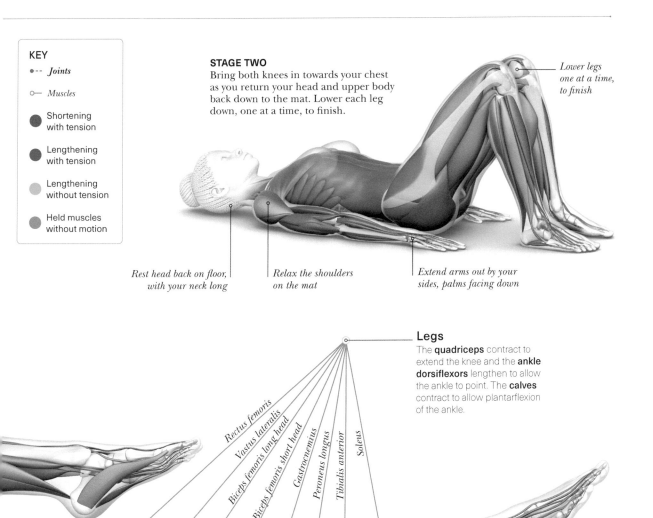

## KEY

•-- *Joints*

○— *Muscles*

⬤ Shortening with tension

⬤ Lengthening with tension

⬤ Lengthening without tension

⬤ Held muscles without motion

**STAGE TWO**
Bring both knees in towards your chest as you return your head and upper body back down to the mat. Lower each leg down, one at a time, to finish.

*Lower legs one at a time, to finish*

*Rest head back on floor, with your neck long*

*Relax the shoulders on the mat*

*Extend arms out by your sides, palms facing down*

## Legs

The **quadriceps** contract to extend the knee and the **ankle dorsiflexors** lengthen to allow the ankle to point. The **calves** contract to allow plantarflexion of the ankle.

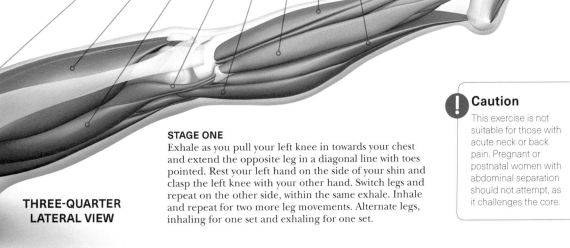

*Rectus femoris*

*Vastus lateralis*

*Biceps femoris long head*

*Biceps femoris short head*

*Gastrocnemius*

*Peroneus longus*

*Tibialis anterior*

*Soleus*

**THREE-QUARTER LATERAL VIEW**

**STAGE ONE**
Exhale as you pull your left knee in towards your chest and extend the opposite leg in a diagonal line with toes pointed. Rest your left hand on the side of your shin and clasp the left knee with your other hand. Switch legs and repeat on the other side, within the same exhale. Inhale and repeat for two more leg movements. Alternate legs, inhaling for one set and exhaling for one set.

> **! Caution**
> This exercise is not suitable for those with acute neck or back pain. Pregnant or postnatal women with abdominal separation should not attempt, as it challenges the core.

# » VARIATIONS

These simple variations encourage you to keep the leg in line from the hip to the knee and ankle, and to maintain the hip-distance space for correct alignment. They allow you to progress slowly to build pelvic stability and core control.

KEY
● Primary target muscle
● Secondary target muscle

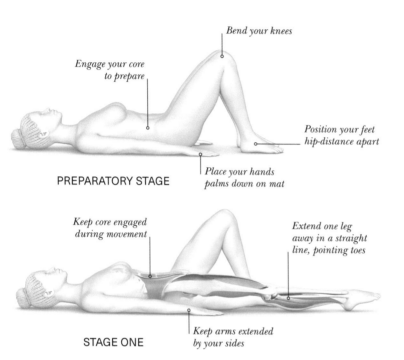

*Bend your knees*

*Engage your core to prepare*

*Position your feet hip-distance apart*

*Place your hands palms down on mat*

PREPARATORY STAGE

*Keep core engaged during movement*

*Extend one leg away in a straight line, pointing toes*

*Keep arms extended by your sides*

STAGE ONE

## BEGINNER LEVEL

In this variation, you keep the leg on the mat, making it closed-chain. This is more supportive to the back and less demanding on your core. Learn leg alignment before progressing to lifting the legs off the mat.

**PREPARATORY STAGE**
Lie flat on your mat with your spine and pelvis neutral, both legs flexed at your hips and knees, hip-distance apart with feet flat on the mat. Extend your arms by your sides.

**STAGE ONE**
Exhale as you extend one leg away in a straight line from your body, keeping contact with your mat.

**STAGE TWO**
Inhale to return the leg back to the start. Repeat on the opposite leg and continue to alternate legs for 8–10 repetitions.

## SINGLE LEG OPTION

Use your static leg to press into the mat for stability while your moving leg reaches away. Focus on core engagement as you press the leg outwards on the diagonal.

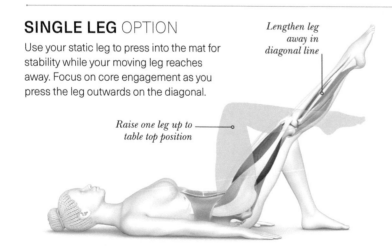

*Lengthen leg away in diagonal line*

*Raise one leg up to table top position*

PREPARATORY STAGE / STAGE ONE

**PREPARATORY STAGE**
Lie flat on the mat with your spine and pelvis neutral, both legs flexed at your hips and knees, hip-distance apart with feet flat on the mat. Extend your arms by your sides.

**STAGE ONE**
Exhale as you raise one leg up to the table top position. Lengthen it away from your body in a diagonal line with toes pointed.

**STAGE TWO**
Inhale to return the leg back to table top and then down to the mat. Repeat on the opposite leg and continue to alternate legs for 8–10 repetitions.

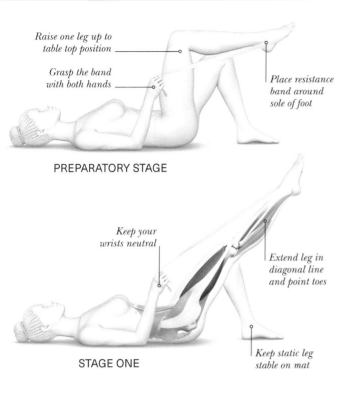

*Raise one leg up to table top position*

*Grasp the band with both hands*

*Place resistance band around sole of foot*

PREPARATORY STAGE

*Keep your wrists neutral*

*Extend leg in diagonal line and point toes*

STAGE ONE

*Keep static leg stable on mat*

# WITH BAND SUPPORT

Using a band provides extra stability to the hip and leg as you press into it. This also allows you to press against resistance, which provides useful feedback on leg position and increases your core engagement too.

### PREPARATORY STAGE
Lie flat on your mat with both legs flexed at your hips and knees, hip-distance apart with feet flat on the mat. Extend your arms by your sides. Raise one leg up to the table top position and place a resistance band around the sole of your foot.

### STAGE ONE
Exhale as you lengthen the leg away from your body in a diagonal line with toes pointed, pressing your foot into the band.

### STAGE TWO
Inhale to return the leg back to the table top position. Complete 8–10 repetitions before switching to the other leg.

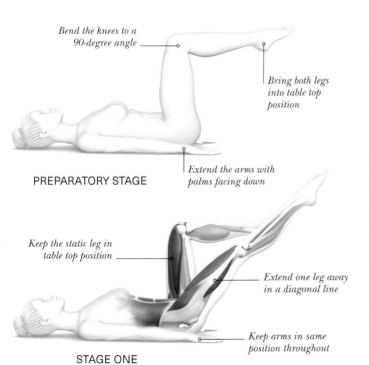

*Bend the knees to a 90-degree angle*

*Bring both legs into table top position*

PREPARATORY STAGE

*Extend the arms with palms facing down*

*Keep the static leg in table top position*

*Extend one leg away in a diagonal line*

STAGE ONE

*Keep arms in same position throughout*

# DOUBLE TABLE TOP

This increases your core challenge by having both legs raised throughout, with the addition of a long leg lever. Control your abdominals as you extend the leg away from you and ensure your pelvis does not tilt forwards.

### PREPARATORY STAGE
Lie flat on your mat with your spine and pelvis neutral and both legs flexed at your hips and knees in the table top position, hip-distance apart. Extend your arms by your sides with palms down.

### STAGE ONE
Exhale as you lengthen one leg away from your body in a diagonal line with toes pointed. Keep your head and neck long and your core engaged during this movement.

### STAGE TWO
Inhale to return the leg back to the table top position. Repeat on the opposite leg and continue to alternate for 8–10 repetitions.

# DOUBLE LEG STRETCH

**This coordination-based exercise** requires control of both your upper and lower limbs, as well as good abdominal strength. It also mobilizes your shoulders, hips, and knees. As you develop more strength, you can lower your legs further towards the mat and bring your arms further overhead for an extra challenge.

## THE **BIG PICTURE**

First master One Leg Stretch (see p.60) before adding the extra load of the upper limbs with this exercise. Squeeze your inner thighs together for increased anterior oblique sling activation (see p.18) and support for your spine. For an easier option, stretch the feet towards the ceiling and, as you lower them into the diagonal, ensure the abdominals do not dome outwards. Relax your neck and shoulders to avoid tension.

KEY

•-- *Joints*

○— *Muscles*

● Shortening with tension

● Lengthening with tension

● Lengthening without tension

● Held muscles without motion

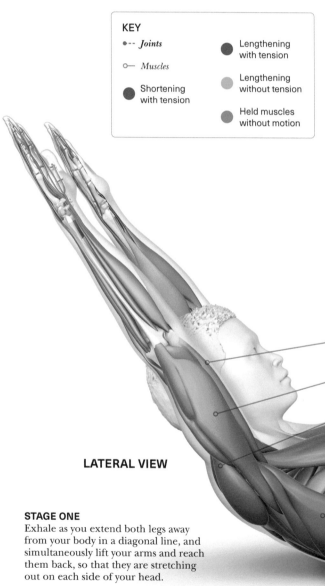

**LATERAL VIEW**

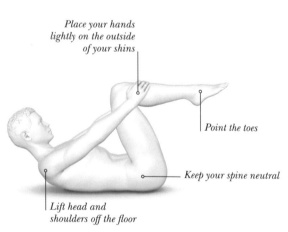

*Place your hands lightly on the outside of your shins*

*Point the toes*

*Keep your spine neutral*

*Lift head and shoulders off the floor*

**PREPARATORY STAGE**
Lie on your back with your hips and knees bent and feet flat on the mat. Lift your head and chest upwards at the same time as bringing your knees in towards your chest. Reach your arms long so that your hands clasp the outside of your shins. Engage your core.

**STAGE ONE**
Exhale as you extend both legs away from your body in a diagonal line, and simultaneously lift your arms and reach them back, so that they are stretching out on each side of your head.

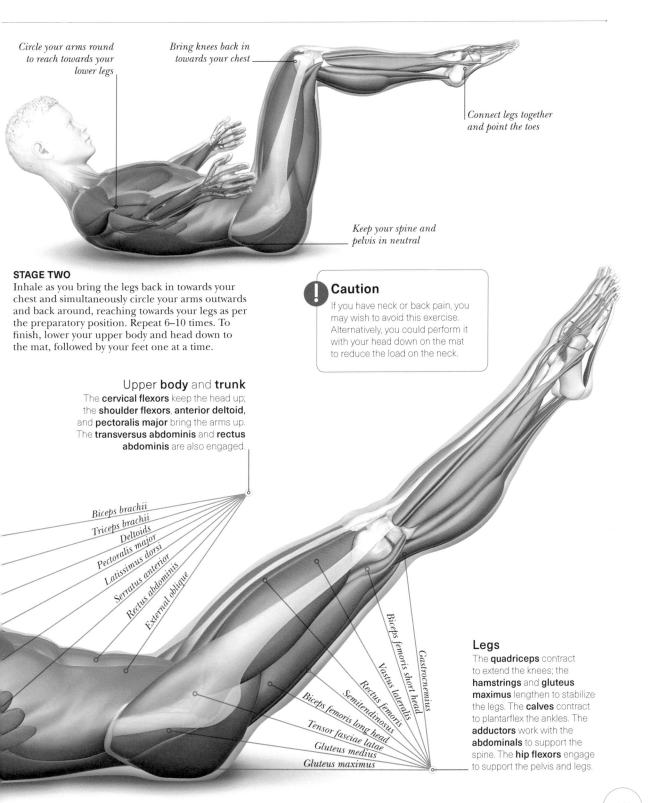

*Circle your arms round to reach towards your lower legs*

*Bring knees back in towards your chest*

*Connect legs together and point the toes*

*Keep your spine and pelvis in neutral*

## STAGE TWO

Inhale as you bring the legs back in towards your chest and simultaneously circle your arms outwards and back around, reaching towards your legs as per the preparatory position. Repeat 6–10 times. To finish, lower your upper body and head down to the mat, followed by your feet one at a time.

### ! Caution

If you have neck or back pain, you may wish to avoid this exercise. Alternatively, you could perform it with your head down on the mat to reduce the load on the neck.

### Upper **body** and **trunk**

The **cervical flexors** keep the head up; the **shoulder flexors**, anterior deltoid, and **pectoralis major** bring the arms up. The **transversus abdominis** and **rectus abdominis** are also engaged.

*Biceps brachii*
*Triceps brachii*
*Deltoids*
*Pectoralis major*
*Latissimus dorsi*
*Serratus anterior*
*Rectus abdominis*
*External oblique*

*Biceps femoris short head*
*Gastrocnemius*
*Vastus lateralis*
*Rectus femoris*
*Semitendinosus*
*Biceps femoris long head*
*Tensor fasciae latae*
*Gluteus medius*
*Gluteus maximus*

### Legs

The **quadriceps** contract to extend the knees; the **hamstrings** and **gluteus maximus** lengthen to stabilize the legs. The **calves** contract to plantarflex the ankles. The **adductors** work with the **abdominals** to support the spine. The **hip flexors** engage to support the pelvis and legs.

# » VARIATIONS

These variations allow you to practise the long arm and leg levers at different intensities, and then with the addition of Abdominal Curls (see p.48). Make sure you have perfected the breathing pattern before progressing to the challenging Double Leg Stretch.

**KEY**
● Primary target muscle
● Secondary target muscle

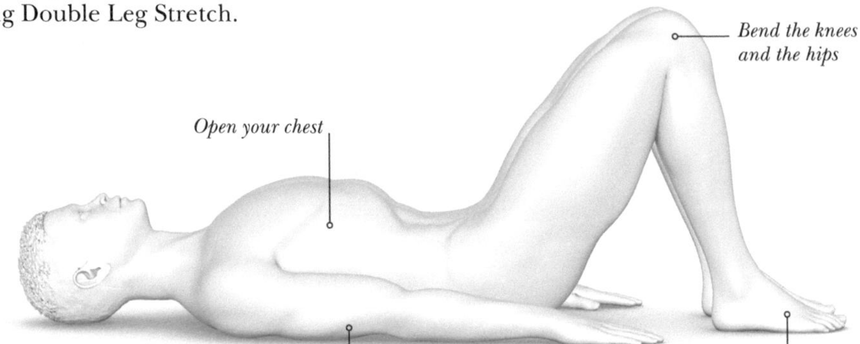

*Open your chest*

*Bend the knees and the hips*

**PREPARATORY STAGE**

*Reach both your arms overhead*

*Lengthen your arms by your sides, palms down*

*Connect your feet and legs together*

*Engage the core to help raise you up*

*Lengthen both legs away from the body*

*Lift your upper body off the mat*

*Keep spine and pelvis in neutral*

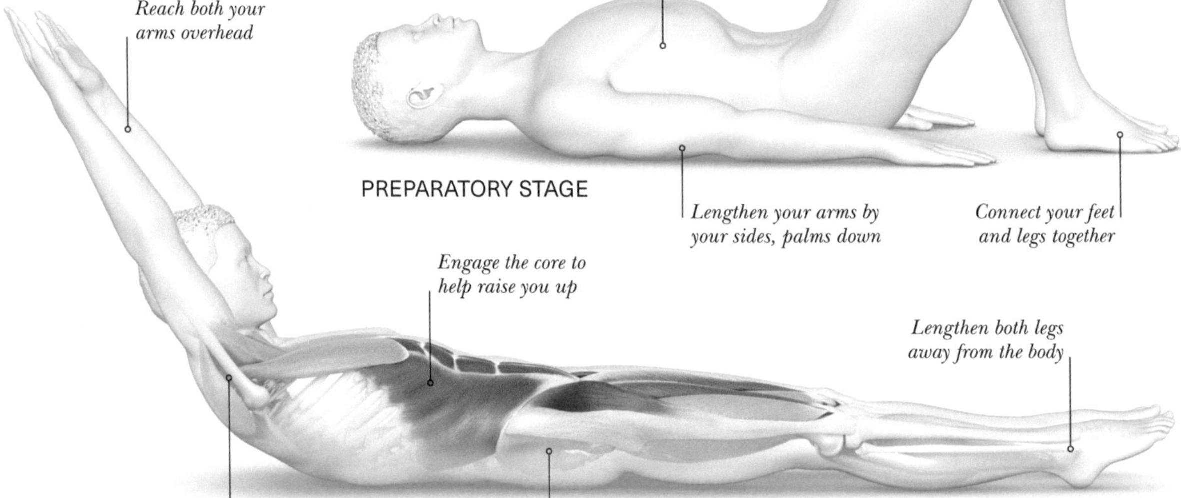

**STAGE ONE**

## DOUBLE LEG STRETCH
### PREPARATION

Although the legs remain in contact with the mat, this exercise requires good core activation to maintain a neutral spine as you extend the legs away from you. You can perform the exercise keeping your head and upper body flat on the mat, to reduce the challenge.

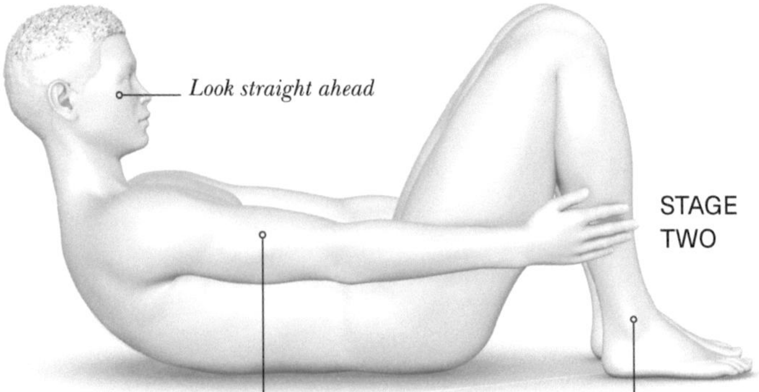

*Look straight ahead*

**STAGE TWO**

*Bring arms forward to touch your shins*

*Raise knees back up to the start position*

**PREPARATORY STAGE**
Lie on your back with your spine and pelvis in neutral, your hips and knees flexed, and your inner thighs connected. Lengthen your arms by your sides.

**STAGE ONE**
Lift your head, neck, and upper body up off the mat and reach your arms forwards. Exhale as you extend both legs away from your body along the mat and at the same time reach your arms overhead.

**STAGE TWO**
Inhale as you circle the arms around and bring your legs back in towards you to the start position, hands lightly touching the shins as you do so. Repeat 6–10 times.

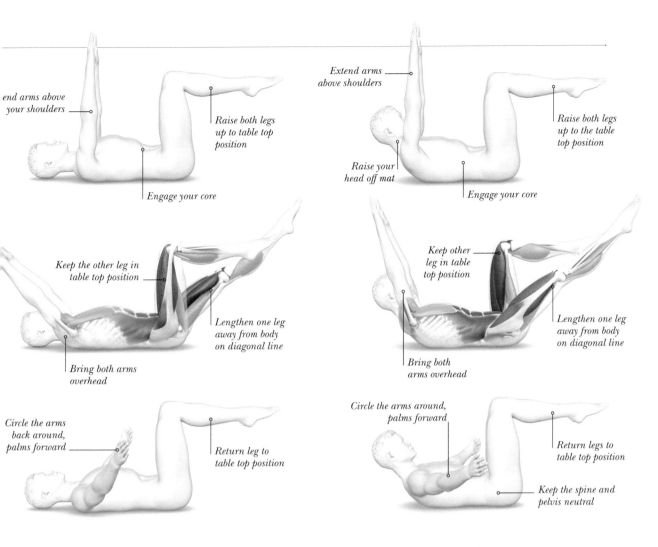

*end arms above your shoulders*

*Raise both legs up to table top position*

*Engage your core*

*Extend arms above shoulders*

*Raise your head off mat*

*Raise both legs up to the table top position*

*Engage your core*

*Keep the other leg in table top position*

*Lengthen one leg away from body on diagonal line*

*Bring both arms overhead*

*Keep other leg in table top position*

*Lengthen one leg away from body on diagonal line*

*Bring both arms overhead*

*Circle the arms back around, palms forward*

*Return leg to table top position*

*Circle the arms around, palms forward*

*Return legs to table top position*

*Keep the spine and pelvis neutral*

## SINGLE LEG COORDINATION

This variation provides a challenge of coordination, because you move both arms but only one leg at a time. Your core supports you further as you reach away. Keep the lengthened leg on a high diagonal.

### PREPARATORY STAGE
Lie on your back with your spine and pelvis in neutral and both legs raised up to the table top position, hip-distance apart, and your arms raised up extended above your shoulders. Engage your core.

### STAGE ONE
Exhale as you lengthen one leg away from your body on a diagonal line, and simultaneously bring your arms overhead.

### STAGE TWO
Inhale as you circle the arms back around and bring the leg back to the table top position. Repeat on the opposite leg and continue to alternate for 6–10 repetitions. Return to the preparatory position.

## WITH ABDOMINAL CURL

This variation is the same as Single Leg Coordination but with the head and upper body lifted to increase the load on your abdominals. Lengthen your neck and gaze towards your knees.

### PREPARATORY STAGE
Lie on your back with your spine and pelvis in neutral and both legs raised up to the table top position, hip-distance apart. Raise your upper body and head up off the mat and extend your arms above your shoulders.

### STAGE ONE
Engage your core. Exhale as you lengthen one leg away from your body on a diagonal line, and simultaneously bring your arms overhead.

### STAGE TWO
Inhale as you circle the arms back around and bring the leg back to the table top position. Repeat on the opposite leg and continue to alternate for 6–10 repetitions.

# ROCKER WITH OPEN LEGS

**This exercise provides the challenge of rocking back and forth smoothly** while maintaining the same basic position. It requires abdominal strength and length in both the spine and hamstrings, and is a great intermediate exercise for those requiring both strength and flexibility.

## THE **BIG PICTURE**

Rocker with Open Legs works best when space and connection are maintained throughout several areas. The first connection is between the arms and the legs, to prevent the legs collapsing when they reach overhead. The second connection is within the abdominal muscles, to stabilize the trunk on the return to the upright pose and to prevent collapse through the trunk.

**KEY**

●--- *Joints*

○— *Muscles*

● Shortening with tension

● Lengthening with tension

● Lengthening without tension

● Held muscles without motion

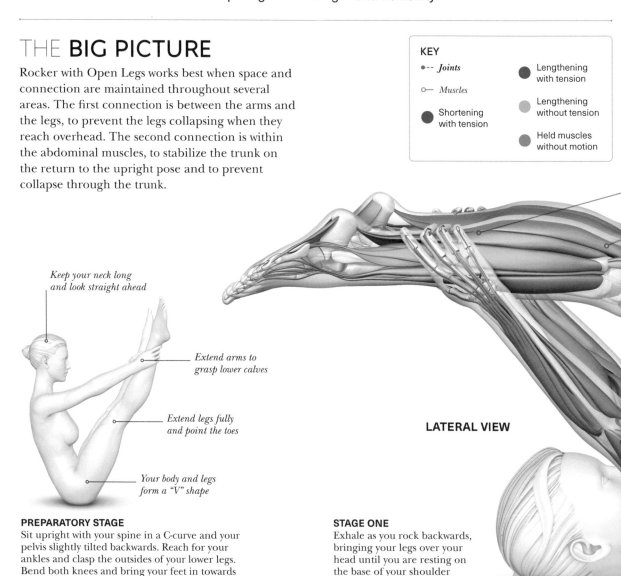

*Keep your neck long and look straight ahead*

*Extend arms to grasp lower calves*

*Extend legs fully and point the toes*

*Your body and legs form a "V" shape*

**LATERAL VIEW**

### PREPARATORY STAGE
Sit upright with your spine in a C-curve and your pelvis slightly tilted backwards. Reach for your ankles and clasp the outsides of your lower legs. Bend both knees and bring your feet in towards your buttocks with your knees wide, then on an inhale extend both legs upwards, extending your arms at the same time. Find your balance.

### STAGE ONE
Exhale as you rock backwards, bringing your legs over your head until you are resting on the base of your shoulder blades. Inhale to return back upright to the preparatory position. Repeat 6–8 times.

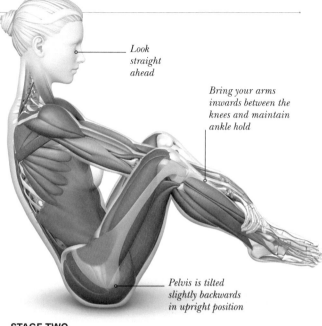

Look straight ahead

Bring your arms inwards between the knees and maintain ankle hold

Pelvis is tilted slightly backwards in upright position

## Legs

The **hamstrings** extend the knees and the **quadriceps** stabilize the thighs. The **calves** contract to point your toes down. The **hip abductors** keep the legs apart, while the **adductors** are lengthened.

Soleus
Gastrocnemius
Semitendinosus
Biceps femoris long head
Vastus lateralis
Rectus femoris
Tensor fasciae latae
Gluteus maximus
Gluteus medius

### STAGE TWO

Bend your knees, keeping them wide, and lower both feet to your mat with control. As you bend the knees, allow your arms to come inwards between the knees, maintaining the hold on your ankles. Release your hands to finish.

66 99

*Perform a smooth **roll through** your spine and keep your legs rigid and apart to hold **the position**.*

Quadratus lumborum
External oblique
Iliocostalis
Rectus abdominis
Pectoralis major
Triceps brachii
Serratus anterior
Teres major
Deltoids

## Upper body

The **pectoralis major** engages as your arms are adducted to clasp your ankles, and your **triceps** maintain elbow extension. Your **transversus abdominis** engages to stabilize the spine, while your **rectus abdominis** is activated to flex the spine. Your **spinal extensors** are stretched.

69

# SWAN DIVE

**This graceful, advanced exercise** requires a strong control of momentum. It strengthens the back of the body, and opens the chest and front of the body. Perform a set of the Cobra exercise (see p.170) before you try this, to prepare your spine for the large extension movement.

## THE **BIG PICTURE**

This exercise requires full engagement of the muscles throughout the back of the body, from the upper back down to the feet, to maintain the shape and rigidity required to perform the large rocking motion. To prevent uncoordinated movement, or falling forwards, strive for a consistent rhythm, and trust your body as you move between the two extreme rocking positions. It's a good idea to counteract this spinal extension exercise with a Shell Stretch afterwards (see p.47).

**Thighs** and **lower** legs
Your **hip extensors** help raise your legs; your **hip flexors** stretch. Your **quadriceps** extend your knees, and your **hamstrings** are active. The **calf muscles** are active to help flex the ankles down.

*Peroneus longus*
*Soleus*
*Gastrocnemius*
*Biceps femoris short head*
*Biceps femoris long head*
*Vastus lateralis*
*Tensor fasciae latae*
*Gluteus maximus*

*Keep your gaze forwards*

*Extend your arms at the top of the Cobra position*

*Position legs hip-distance apart*

**PREPARATORY STAGE**
Lie on your front with your spine and pelvis in neutral, and your hands resting underneath your shoulders with elbows flexed. Inhale to lift and lengthen your head and upper body up off of the mat into a Cobra position, arms stretched out.

**STAGE ONE**
Exhale as you release your hands and reach your arms forwards with your palms facing inwards. Rock forwards onto your ribcage and chest, raising and lengthening both legs upwards behind you.

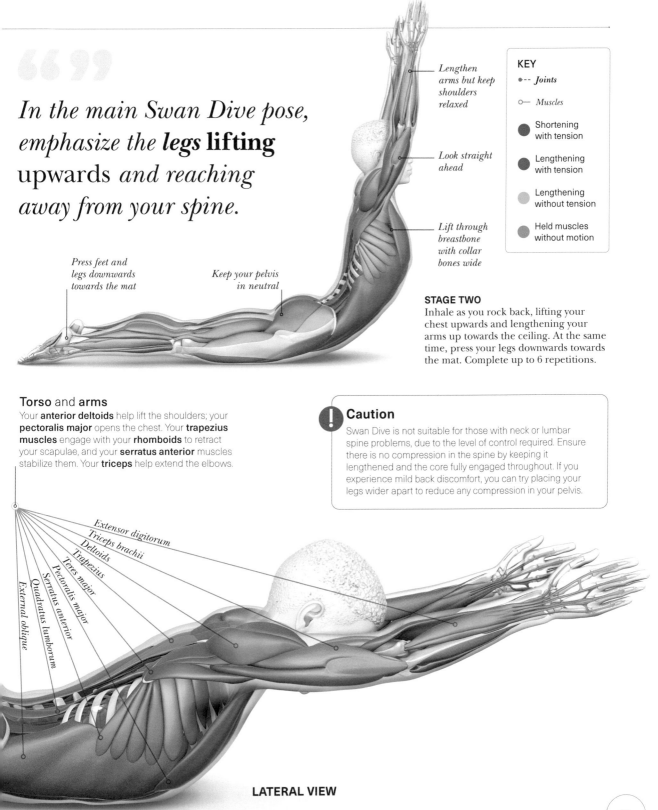

*In the main Swan Dive pose, emphasize the **legs** lifting upwards *and reaching* away from your spine.*

Lengthen arms but keep shoulders relaxed

Look straight ahead

Lift through breastbone with collar bones wide

Press feet and legs downwards towards the mat

Keep your pelvis in neutral

### STAGE TWO
Inhale as you rock back, lifting your chest upwards and lengthening your arms up towards the ceiling. At the same time, press your legs downwards towards the mat. Complete up to 6 repetitions.

### Torso and arms
Your **anterior deltoids** help lift the shoulders; your **pectoralis major** opens the chest. Your **trapezius muscles** engage with your **rhomboids** to retract your scapulae, and your **serratus anterior** muscles stabilize them. Your **triceps** help extend the elbows.

### ! Caution
Swan Dive is not suitable for those with neck or lumbar spine problems, due to the level of control required. Ensure there is no compression in the spine by keeping it lengthened and the core fully engaged throughout. If you experience mild back discomfort, you can try placing your legs wider apart to reduce any compression in your pelvis.

Extensor digitorum
Triceps brachii
Deltoids
Trapezius
Teres major
Pectoralis major
Serratus anterior
Quadratus lumborum
External oblique

**LATERAL VIEW**

## » VARIATIONS

The first two variations focus on neck and shoulder blade muscle activation, which is an essential skill required to support the upper body in the rocking motion of the main exercise. Swan Dive Preparation allows you to practise a more gentle rocking motion with control.

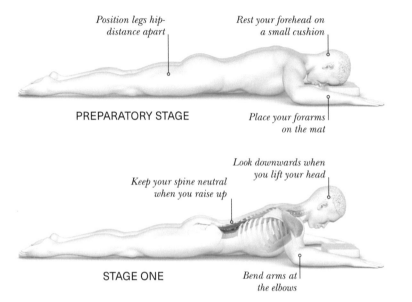

Position legs hip-distance apart

Rest your forehead on a small cushion

PREPARATORY STAGE

Place your forearms on the mat

Look downwards when you lift your head

Keep your spine neutral when you raise up

STAGE ONE

Bend arms at the elbows

### UPPER BODY ONLY

As you lift your head upwards, keep your chin lightly tucked in and your neck lengthened. Relax your shoulder blades down your back and keep them that way throughout the exercise. Apply light pressure only through the arms.

**PREPARATORY STAGE**
Lie on your front with your spine and pelvis in neutral and legs hip-distance apart. Place your arms in front of you with elbows bent, forearms on mat, and palms facing down. Rest your forehead on a small cushion to keep your neck neutral.

**STAGE ONE**
Exhale as you lift your chest, head, and neck up off the mat and hold for an inhale.

**STAGE TWO**
Exhale as you lower your chest, head, and neck down to the mat, and repeat 6–8 times.

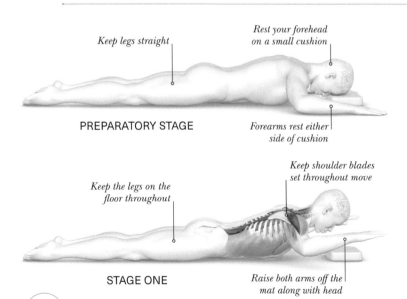

Keep legs straight

Rest your forehead on a small cushion

PREPARATORY STAGE

Forearms rest either side of cushion

Keep shoulder blades set throughout move

Keep the legs on the floor throughout

STAGE ONE

Raise both arms off the mat along with head

### UPPER BODY AND ARMS

Focus on engaging your core a little more as you lift both the head and arms upwards. Be careful not to extend your lower back when performing this variation.

**PREPARATORY STAGE**
Lie on your front with your spine and pelvis in neutral, and legs hip-distance apart. Place your arms in front of you with elbows bent, forearms on the mat, and palms downwards. Remember to keep the neck long.

**STAGE ONE**
Exhale to lift your chest, head, and neck up off the mat, as well as both arms. Hold for an inhale.

**STAGE TWO**
Exhale as you lower your chest, head, neck, and arms back to the mat. Repeat 6–8 times.

# SWAN DIVE PREPARATION

Maintain length through your spine to avoid compression in your lower back and reach your legs away from you. As you rock forwards, continue reaching your legs away and upwards and use your core and gluteals to support you further. Support your upper body lightly through both arms.

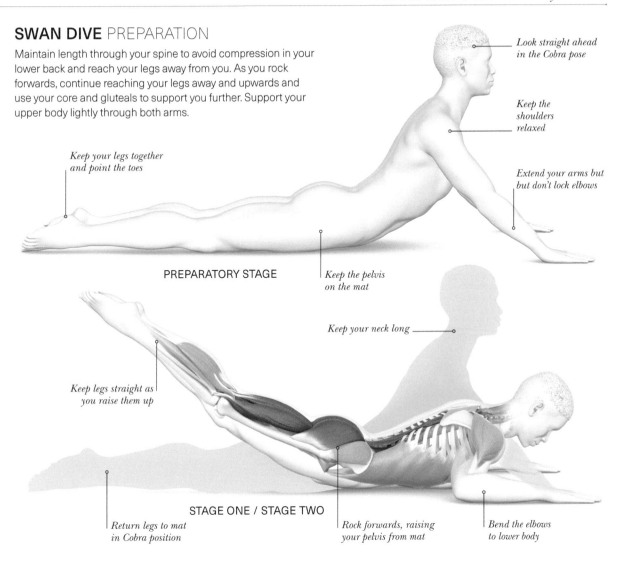

*Look straight ahead in the Cobra pose*

*Keep the shoulders relaxed*

*Keep your legs together and point the toes*

*Extend your arms but but don't lock elbows*

PREPARATORY STAGE

*Keep the pelvis on the mat*

*Keep your neck long*

*Keep legs straight as you raise them up*

STAGE ONE / STAGE TWO

*Return legs to mat in Cobra position*

*Rock forwards, raising your pelvis from mat*

*Bend the elbows to lower body*

### PREPARATORY STAGE
Lie on your front on the mat and raise your trunk up into the Cobra position (see p.170).

### STAGE ONE
Exhale as you bend your elbows and lower your upper body towards the mat. Rock forwards on to your ribcage and chest, raising and lengthening both legs upwards behind you.

### STAGE TWO
Inhale as you rock back, returning to the Cobra position, pressing up through your hands, lifting your chest upwards, and lowering your legs down to the mat. Repeat for up to 6 repetitions.

*Keeping a **strong shape** and steady breath will allow you to maintain a consistent rhythm of movement as you **rock** forwards and backwards.*

# ONE LEG KICK

**This lower limb exercise** primarily strengthens the gluteal and hamstring muscles, while also lengthening the hips and stretching the quadricep muscles. It requires pelvic stability to isolate the leg movement from the spine, and is ideal for those who need training in lower-limb strength and posterior pelvic stability.

## THE **BIG PICTURE**

Elongate your spine by reaching the crown of your head away from your tailbone and focussing on the connection to your core. Your core remains engaged to prevent collapsing down through your torso and pelvis region, and to avoid compression of the lower back. Your arms remain active throughout the exercise to press down into the mat to stabilize, while your upper back activates to raise open the chest. If you find it hard to keep the chest raised, start with the modified version, where the head rests on your forearms.

### KEY

- •-- *Joints*
- o— *Muscles*
- ● Shortening with tension
- ● Lengthening with tension
- ● Lengthening without tension
- ● Held muscles without motion

Keep your gaze facing forwards

Keep your pelvis neutral, with hip bones slightly raised

Point the toes

Rest elbows on floor and clasp hands

Position your legs hip-distance apart

**PREPARATORY STAGE**
Lie on your front with chest raised and your elbows underneath your shoulders, slightly wider than shoulder-width apart. Keep your spine long, with the ribcage and front hip bones lifted up off the mat. Your legs extend behind you, hip-distance apart with toes pointed. Clasp your hands in front of you.

## Caution

This is generally safe for all, but those with acute back pain should be careful in case the leg pulses jolt the spine. If you cannot maintain a neutral pelvis in this position, try placing a small cushion underneath your pelvis to bring your pelvis and spine into neutral and offer more support to your spine.

# VARIATION: **MODIFIED ONE LEG** KICK

*Rest your head on your forearms*

STAGE ONE

### PREPARATORY STAGE

Lie on your front with your forearms stacked on top of each other and your forehead resting on top. Keep your pelvis and spine neutral. Your legs are extended behind you, hip-distance apart, with the toes pointed.

### STAGE ONE

Exhale as you bend your left knee and bring your heel towards your buttock, then pulse the leg 3 times.

### STAGE TWO

Inhale as you lower the left leg back down to the mat. Repeat with the right leg, and complete the full sequence 6 times, alternating legs each time.

## **Upper** body

Your **cervical extensors** help extend the neck; your **cervical flexors** support the head. Your **pectoralis major** stretches to open the chest. Your **lower trapezius** muscles retract your scapulae, and your **serratus anterior** muscles stabilize them.

Iliocostalis
Splenius cervicis
Anterior deltoid
Mid deltoid
Pectoralis major
Brachialis

## **Thighs** and **lower** legs

Your **glutes** stabilize your pelvis. Your **hamstrings** engage to flex the knee; and your **hip flexors** and **quadriceps** stretch. Your **calf muscles** help point your foot down and your **ankle dorsiflexors** stretch.

Peroneus longus
Gastrocnemius
Gluteus maximus
Biceps femoris long head
Tensor fasciae latae
Vastus lateralis

### STAGE ONE

Exhale as you bend your left knee and bring your heel towards your left buttock, then pulse the leg 3 times. Inhale as you lower the left leg back down to the mat. Repeat with the right leg, then complete the full sequence 6 times on each leg, alternating the legs each time.

**THREE-QUARTER LATERAL VIEW**

# DOUBLE LEG KICK

**This full body energizing exercise** strengthens both the upper back and hip extensors, as well as opening the chest. It requires coordination between the upper and lower body to keep a steady rhythm.

## THE BIG PICTURE

Keep your pelvis level throughout this exercise by activating your core and learning to dissociate your upper and lower body from your trunk. Make sure you lower your legs down with control to fully work the hamstrings and prevent any rocking of the pelvis. When you come to stage 2, focus on lifting from your chest and keep your neck in line with your spine to avoid over-extending and straining the neck.

**KEY**

●--  *Joints*

○—  *Muscles*

● Shortening
   with tension

● Lengthening
   with tension

● Lengthening
   without tension

● Held muscles
   without motion

Rest one side
of your head
on the mat

Hold your pelvis and
spine in neutral

Connect legs
together and
point toes

Clasp hands behind
you, resting on back

### PREPARATORY STAGE
Lie on your front with your head turned to one side resting on the mat. Extend your legs with inner thighs connected and toes pointed. Clasp your hands behind you, resting them on your mid-back with your palms facing upwards.

### LATERAL VIEW

### STAGE ONE
Exhale as you bend both knees and bring your heels towards your buttocks to approximately 90 degrees. Pulse the legs in towards you 3 times.

### Upper body
The **middle** to **lower trapezius** and **rhomboids** stretch, but will retract your scapulae in stage 2, along with the **posterior deltoid** and **latissimus dorsi**, which will extend the shoulders. The arms are rotated around fully, with the **biceps** engaged to flex and the **triceps** lengthened.

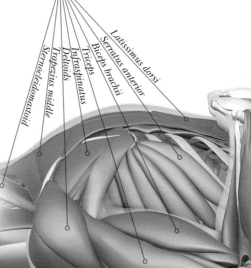

Sternocleidomastoid
Trapezius middle
Deltoids
Infraspinatus
Triceps
Biceps brachii
Serratus anterior
Latissimus dorsi

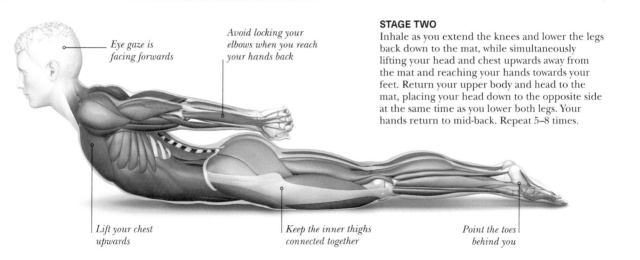

*Eye gaze is facing forwards*

*Avoid locking your elbows when you reach your hands back*

*Lift your chest upwards*

*Keep the inner thighs connected together*

*Point the toes behind you*

## STAGE TWO
Inhale as you extend the knees and lower the legs back down to the mat, while simultaneously lifting your head and chest upwards away from the mat and reaching your hands towards your feet. Return your upper body and head to the mat, placing your head down to the opposite side at the same time as you lower both legs. Your hands return to mid-back. Repeat 5–8 times.

## Legs
Your **gluteal muscles** engage to stabilize the pelvis. Your **hamstring muscles** engage to flex the knees, while your **hip flexors** and **quadriceps** stretch. Your **calf muscles** engage to point your foot downwards, and your **ankle dorsiflexors** stretch.

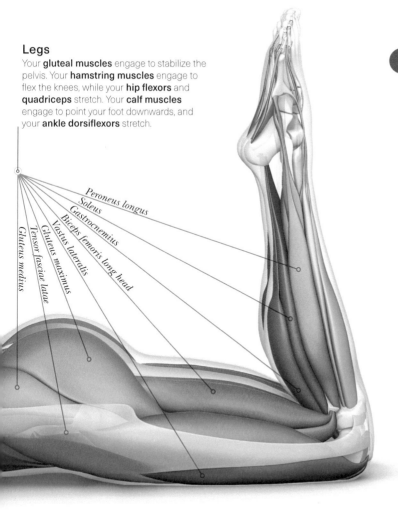

Peroneus longus
Soleus
Gastrocnemius
Biceps femoris long head
Vastus lateralis
Gluteus maximus
Tensor fasciae latae
Gluteus medius

### ⚠ Caution
Avoid this exercise if you have lower-back pain. As it is a deep extension-based exercise, you can counter it with a flexion-based exercise such as Spine Stretch (see p.164).

*Focus on **matching** your breath to the **movements** to help keep the steady rhythm and **flow** of the exercise.*

# SCISSORS

**Named for the open scissors shape the legs make**, this is a principal Pilates exercise that promotes core and pelvic stability. The inverted position and long leg levers make this an advanced exercise, but there are several variation options that offer easier alternatives.

> **⚠ Caution**
> The Single Leg Lifts and Reciprocal Legs would be the most suitable variations if you struggle with lower back pain. Good hamstring length is required for the stage 1 (below) and Reciprocal With Legs Extended options (see p.81).

## THE BIG PICTURE

Find your balance and make sure you feel stable in the preparatory stage before progressing to the leg movements. Stretch the legs equally in opposition from each other. Ensure your weight is evenly distributed across the shoulder blades, and not in the head and neck. Use your core to maintain the trunk position and avoid reclining into your hands.

**Upper** body **and** torso
Your **pectoralis major** and **serratus anterior** open the chest. Your **spinal extensors** lengthen with slight engagement to support the lifting of the trunk. Your **abdominal muscles** contract to maintain the position.

Legs come forwards in shoulder stand

Legs point up over the pelvis with toes pointed

Support your pelvis with both hands

Lengthen your arms by your sides, palms down

**PREPARATORY STAGE**
Lie down with your hips and knees bent in the double table top position. Extend your legs upwards, inhale, then lift your pelvis to rest on your shoulder blades. Support with both hands.

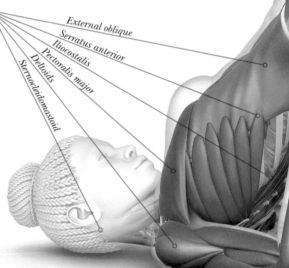

External oblique
Serratus anterior
Iliocostalis
Pectoralis major
Deltoids
Sternocleidomastoid

**STAGE ONE**
Exhale as you separate your legs, bringing one leg forwards overhead and extending the other leg away from your body.

## Legs

Your **hip flexors** engage to stabilize your hips. Your **quadriceps** contract to extend your knees, while your **hamstrings** and **gluteus maximus** support your hips while lengthening. Your **adductors** keep your legs apart.

Soleus
Gastrocnemius
Peroneus longus

medialis
tor magnus
Gluteus maximus
Rectus femoris
Biceps femoris long head
Vastus lateralis

**THREE-QUARTER LATERAL VIEW**

66 99

*Good hamstring length is **required to perform** Scissors correctly.*

Keep the toes pointed on both feet

Reach and lengthen the legs in opposite directions

Keep pelvis level and steady

**STAGE TWO**
Inhale as you directly swap the legs over, bringing them over your pelvis to pass each other. Repeat up to 6 times and then connect your legs together, roll them overhead, and sequentially roll down through your spine to return to the mat to finish.

Elbows and upper arms rest on mat

79

# » VARIATIONS

These teach control with alternate leg movements but without the inverted position of main Scissors. They are therefore ideal for beginners (the first two especially), or for anyone who is not able or has been advised not to attempt inversions, for example if you are pregnant, have high blood pressure, or suffer from spinal issues.

**KEY**
● Primary target muscle
● Secondary target muscle

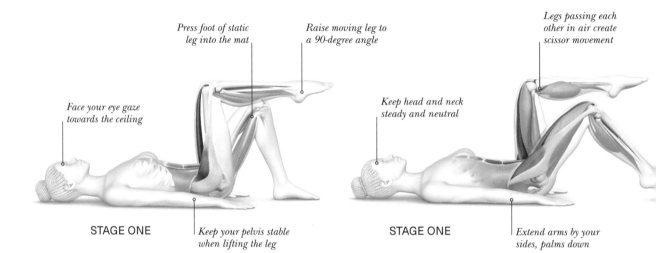

*Press foot of static leg into the mat*

*Raise moving leg to a 90-degree angle*

*Face your eye gaze towards the ceiling*

STAGE ONE

*Keep your pelvis stable when lifting the leg*

*Legs passing each other in air create scissor movement*

*Keep head and neck steady and neutral*

STAGE ONE

*Extend arms by your sides, palms down*

## SINGLE LEG LIFTS

This variation is a great starting point for any core and pelvic stability work. Raising the leg off the mat makes this an open-chain exercise and teaches control in a way that is suitable for all.

**PREPARATORY STAGE**
Lie on your back with your knees bent, feet hip-distance apart and flat on the floor, arms by your sides with palms facing downwards.

**STAGE ONE**
Exhale as you float one leg up to the table top position, forming a 90-degree angle with the moving leg and pressing the static foot into the mat.

**STAGE TWO**
Inhale as you return the leg back to the mat. Continue to alternate legs for 8–10 repetitions.

## RECIPROCAL LEGS

The constant movement of both legs here increases the core challenge and builds endurance as you keep moving. Tap the feet closer to your bottom for ease or move them further away for increased difficulty.

**PREPARATORY STAGE**
Lie on your back on the mat with your knees bent, and one at a time, float your legs up into the double table top position.

**STAGE ONE**
Exhale as you lower one foot towards the mat, and as you return this leg back to table top, simultaneously lower the opposite leg so that they pass each other and create a scissor movement.

**STAGE TWO**
Continue alternating for 8–10 repetitions, exhaling for two movements and inhaling for two movements.

# *Scissors is **useful for hip and leg mobility** as it stretches both the* back *of the top leg and the* front *of the* **bottom leg**.

Look forwards
at your knees

Point the toes

Reach your arms
forward to touch calves

aze upwards
to start

REPARATORY STAGE / STAGE ONE

Engage your core

Pull the elevated
leg towards you
in 2 short pulses

Clasp your shin with
both hands

Raise upper body in
abdominal curl pose

STAGE TWO

Point the toes
on both feet

## RECIPROCAL LEGS EXTENDED

Keep your pelvis neutral as you reach your legs in opposing directions. Feel the length in the legs and engage your core to match the demand of these long levers. Switch the legs over quickly to spend longer in the Scissors position.

### PREPARATORY STAGE
Lie on your back on the mat with your knees bent, and one at a time, float your legs up into the double table top position. Position your arms along your sides, with palms facing downwards.

### STAGE ONE
Raise your head and upper body upwards into an abdominal curl position, reaching your arms forward to lightly touch the sides of your calves.

### STAGE TWO
Simultaneously extend one leg upwards towards the ceiling, clasping your shin with both hands. At the same time, extend the opposite leg down towards the mat. Inhale as you draw the top leg in towards you with 2 small pulses, gently pulling the leg inwards with both hands, and exhale as you switch legs over. Continue alternating for 8–10 repetitions.

# BICYCLE

**This exercise mimics a cycling movement** – a direct progression from Scissors in the Pilates repertoire (see p.78). It strengthens your pelvic and core stability in the inverted position with coordination of the long leg levers, making it an advanced exercise.

## THE **BIG PICTURE**

Focus on the connection of your core and pelvis to stabilize the trunk position. Maintain the space between your chest and the extended top leg to ensure this leg does not lower towards you or flex at the knee. Activate your posterior oblique sling (see p.18) by pressing your upper arms into the mat for extra stability. Perform the Bicycle sequence for a total of 5 times on each leg. Those who struggle with the shoulder stand can start with the modified version.

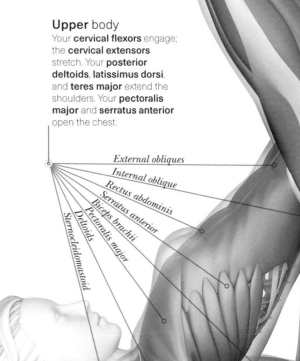

**Upper** body
Your **cervical flexors** engage; the **cervical extensors** stretch. Your **posterior deltoids**, **latissimus dorsi**, and **teres major** extend the shoulders. Your **pectoralis major** and **serratus anterior** open the chest.

*External obliques*
*Internal oblique*
*Rectus abdominis*
*Serratus anterior*
*Biceps brachii*
*Pectoralis major*
*Deltoids*
*Sternocleidomastoid*

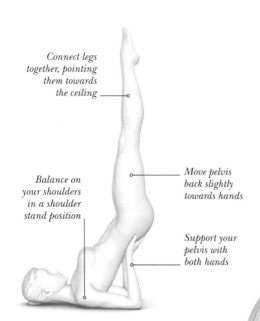

*Connect legs together, pointing them towards the ceiling*

*Balance on your shoulders in a shoulder stand position*

*Move pelvis back slightly towards hands*

*Support your pelvis with both hands*

**PREPARATORY STAGE**
Lie on your back with your hips and knees bent in the double table top position, thighs perpendicular to the mat. Extend your legs upwards above your pelvis, inhale, then lift your pelvis and peel your spine upwards to rest on your shoulder blades. Place hands on the pelvis.

82

## Legs

Your **hip flexors** engage to stabilize your hips on the extended leg, lengthening under tension on the flexed leg. Your **quadriceps** contract to extend your knee; your **hamstrings** and **glutes** support your hips. Your hamstrings engage to flex the lower leg. Your **adductors** engage to stabilize the legs and the **calves** contract to point the toes downwards.

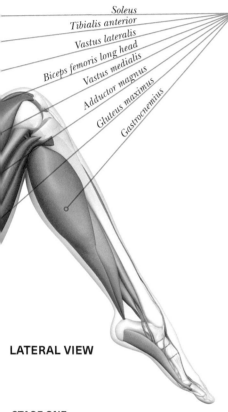

Soleus
Tibialis anterior
Vastus lateralis
Biceps femoris long head
Vastus medialis
Adductor magnus
Gluteus maximus
Gastrocnemius

**LATERAL VIEW**

### STAGE ONE
Exhale as you part your legs so that the left leg reaches downwards towards the mat and the right leg reaches overhead towards your body. Bend your left knee and bring your heel towards your buttocks, while your right leg continues to reach upwards.

### STAGE TWO
Inhale as you bring your left knee in towards you until your left knee is over your left hip. Simultaneously lower your right leg down towards the mat. Continue alternating legs to mimic a cycling motion by bending your right knee and reaching the left leg up.

**KEY**

•-- *Joints*

o— *Muscles*

● Shortening with tension

● Lengthening with tension

● Lengthening without tension

● Held muscles without motion

# VARIATION: **MODIFIED** BICYCLE

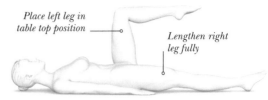

*Place left leg in table top position*

*Lengthen right leg fully*

**PREPARATORY STAGE**

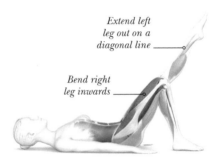

*Extend left leg out on a diagonal line*

*Bend right leg inwards*

**STAGE ONE**

**PREPARATORY STAGE**
Lie on your back with your spine and pelvis in neutral and your hips and knees bent, with feet flat on the floor. Bring your left leg up to table top position and lengthen the right leg out fully along the mat.

**STAGE ONE**
Exhale as you extend the left leg out on a diagonal line while simultaneously bending the right leg inwards, bringing your heel towards your buttock.

**STAGE TWO**
Inhale to return the left leg back to table top, and the right leg back to the extended position along the mat. Repeat 6–8 times, then swap the legs over and complete on the other side.

**! Caution**
Do not attempt this exercise if you have back or neck pain, or lack in full hamstring length, as this could tilt the pelvis and strain the lower back.

# SHOULDER BRIDGE

**This exercise targets almost all of the muscle slings** while being accessible to both beginners and advanced participants. It sequentially mobilizes the spine, and strengthens the core through movement. The glutes are also targeted for strength and endurance.

## THE BIG PICTURE

Initiate the movement from your pelvis to rise up to a neutral bridge position. This opens the chest and hips and activates the entire back of your body. Avoid over-extending the lumbar spine as this may cause strain. The weight should rest on the shoulder blades to avoid tension in the neck. Place a block between your knees to increase stability, or press your hands firmly into the mat to activate the back for additional support. Move the feet further outwards for more hamstring muscle bias.

*The shoulder bridge promotes a **strong core**, which will improve your **posture** and minimize lower back pain.*

**Lower** body
The **hamstrings** lengthen to stabilize the elevated leg. The **calves** contract to point the ankle. The **quadriceps** activate to stabilize the lower leg and the **adductors** engage to bring the thighs towards parallel. The **glutes** engage to hold the bridge.

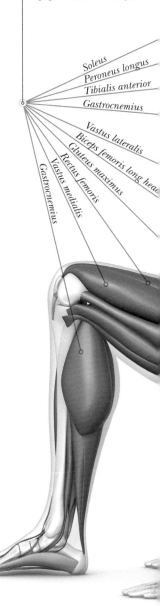

Soleus
Peroneus longus
Tibialis anterior
Gastrocnemius
Vastus lateralis
Biceps femoris long head
Gluteus maximus
Rectus femoris
Vastus medialis
Gastrocnemius

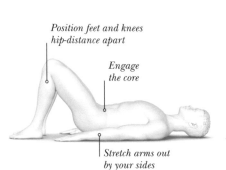

*Position feet and knees hip-distance apart*

*Engage the core*

*Stretch arms out by your sides*

**PREPARATORY STAGE ONE**
Lie on your back with knees and feet hip-distance apart and arms by your sides. Face palms downwards on the floor and keep the head and neck neutral. Gently engage your core.

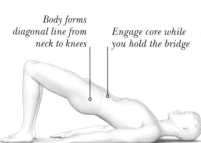

*Body forms diagonal line from neck to knees*

*Engage core while you hold the bridge*

**PREPARATORY STAGE TWO**
Exhale, and slowly peel your spine off the mat one vertebra at a time until you are resting on your shoulder blades, your body forming a diagonal line.

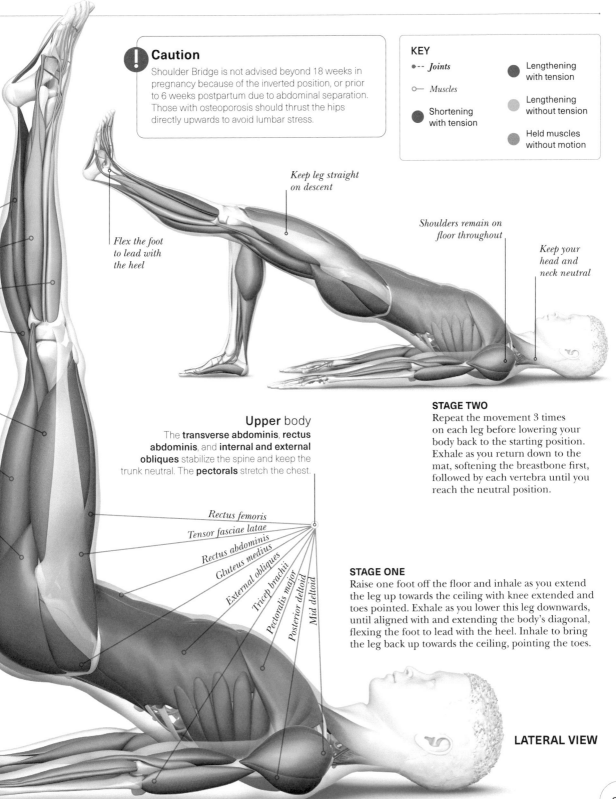

**KEY**

•-- *Joints*

o— *Muscles*

● Shortening with tension

● Lengthening with tension

● Lengthening without tension

● Held muscles without motion

*Keep leg straight on descent*

*Flex the foot to lead with the heel*

*Shoulders remain on floor throughout*

*Keep your head and neck neutral*

**Upper** body

The **transverse abdominis**, **rectus abdominis**, and **internal and external obliques** stabilize the spine and keep the trunk neutral. The **pectorals** stretch the chest.

**STAGE TWO**

Repeat the movement 3 times on each leg before lowering your body back to the starting position. Exhale as you return down to the mat, softening the breastbone first, followed by each vertebra until you reach the neutral position.

Rectus femoris
Tensor fasciae latae
Rectus abdominis
Gluteus medius
External obliques
Tricep brachii
Pectoralis major
Posterior deltoid
Mid deltoid

**STAGE ONE**

Raise one foot off the floor and inhale as you extend the leg up towards the ceiling with knee extended and toes pointed. Exhale as you lower this leg downwards, until aligned with and extending the body's diagonal, flexing the foot to lead with the heel. Inhale to bring the leg back up towards the ceiling, pointing the toes.

**LATERAL VIEW**

85

## » VARIATIONS

These variations allow you to practise the Shoulder Bridge movement, develop endurance, build the lateral gluteals, and then finally progress to single leg options at a lower intensity than the main exercise. These building blocks are key to any Pilates workout as the core, gluteals, and legs are all engaged.

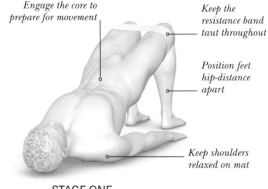

*Engage the core to prepare for movement*

*Keep the resistance band taut throughout*

*Position feet hip-distance apart*

*Keep shoulders relaxed on mat*

**STAGE ONE**

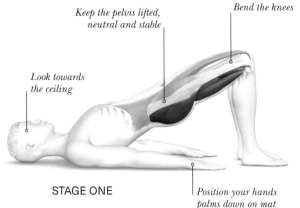

*Keep the pelvis lifted, neutral and stable*

*Bend the knees*

*Look towards the ceiling*

**STAGE ONE**

*Position your hands palms down on mat*

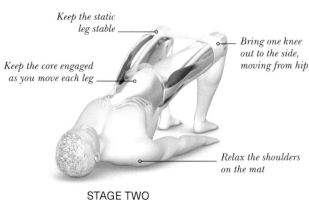

*Keep the static leg stable*

*Bring one knee out to the side, moving from hip*

*Keep the core engaged as you move each leg*

*Relax the shoulders on the mat*

**STAGE TWO**

## **BASIC** SHOULDER BRIDGE

This option focusses on spinal mobility and mastering the sequential movement rather than moving as a whole. Imagine a strip of velcro down your spine and try to peel it off in sequence, and then return back down in order.

### PREPARATORY STAGE
Start in the neutral position with your knees and feet hip-distance apart and arms by your sides. Make sure your head and neck are neutral, and gently engage your core.

### STAGE ONE
Exhale as you gently roll the lower back into the mat and peel your spine off the mat one vertebra at a time until you are resting on your shoulder blades.

### STAGE TWO
Inhale to hold the position, then exhale to lower back down one vertebra at a time. Complete 6 repetitions of the sequence.

## **HIP** ABDUCTIONS

The resistance band used in this variation increases the effort on the lateral hip rotators bilaterally. This is because one leg has to push against the band to abduct the hip, while the other leg has to stay stationary and avoid being pulled over with the band.

### PREPARATORY STAGE
Place a resistance band around your legs, just above the knees. Start in the neutral position with your knees and feet hip-distance apart and arms extended by your sides.

### STAGE ONE
Peel your spine off the mat one vertebra at a time until you are resting on your shoulder blades, keeping the band taut. Inhale to hold the position.

### STAGE TWO
Exhale and bring one knee out to the side, moving from your hip joint. Move as far as able, keeping your trunk and pelvis stable. Inhale to return the leg to the start, and alternate legs for 6 repetitions.

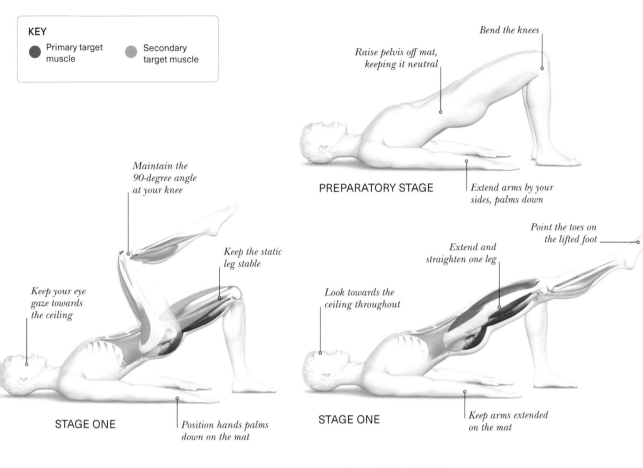

KEY
● Primary target muscle
● Secondary target muscle

*Bend the knees*

*Raise pelvis off mat, keeping it neutral*

PREPARATORY STAGE

*Extend arms by your sides, palms down*

*Maintain the 90-degree angle at your knee*

*Keep the static leg stable*

*Keep your eye gaze towards the ceiling*

STAGE ONE

*Position hands palms down on the mat*

*Point the toes on the lifted foot*

*Extend and straighten one leg*

*Look towards the ceiling throughout*

STAGE ONE

*Keep arms extended on the mat*

# KNEE RAISES

This exercise introduces the removal of the foot from the mat and requires good balance and stability. Find your balance, lift the foot carefully, and press upwards through the opposite gluteals to avoid dropping the hip down at that side.

### PREPARATORY STAGE
Start in the neutral position with your knees and feet hip-distance apart and your arms by your sides. Make sure your head and neck are neutral, and gently engage your core.

### STAGE ONE
Raise up to the shoulder bridge position with control, then inhale and bring one leg up off the mat, bringing your hip to 90 degrees and keeping the knee bent.

### STAGE TWO
Exhale to return this leg back down to the mat and repeat on the opposite leg. Continue to alternate for up to 6 repetitions on each side.

# LEG EXTENSIONS

The extended leg further challenges your core and gluteal strength as you aim to keep your trunk neutral and steady while you reach the leg away. To assist, you could try placing a cushion between the knees and squeezing it for more activation.

### PREPARATORY STAGE
Start in the neutral position with your knees and feet hip-distance apart and arms by your sides. Lift yourself up into the shoulder bridge position vertebra by vertebra.

### STAGE ONE
Inhale as you raise one foot off the floor and extend the leg outwards so that the thighs are parallel and the knee is straight. Keep the knee on the static leg bent, and your foot on the mat.

### STAGE TWO
Exhale as you bend the knee of your extended leg and return it back to the mat. Repeat on the other leg. Continue alternating legs for up to 6 repetitions.

87

# SWIMMING

**This exercise works into spine extension**, promoting full body symmetry and coordination of the upper and lower body through opposition and spinal stability. It opens the chest and hips and strengthens the upper back and gluteal muscles. Its posterior chain strengthening and pelvic stability benefits make it ideal for all.

## THE **BIG PICTURE**

Elongate your spine by lengthening the crown of your head away from your tailbone. Aim to lengthen the arms and legs away from each other when you lift them for further elongation. Focus on keeping your pelvis neutral and avoid leaning to the side for better pelvic stability. Swimming is a great counter exercise to the more flexion-based Pilates exercises, such as One Leg Stretch (see p.60) and Roll Up (see p.122). Perform Swimming after completing any of these, for balance.

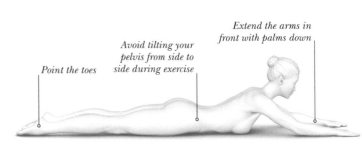

*Extend the arms in front with palms down*

*Avoid tilting your pelvis from side to side during exercise*

*Point the toes*

**PREPARATORY STAGE**
Lie on your front with your legs extended hip-distance apart and both arms stretching out in front of you shoulder-width apart, palms downwards and on the mat. Your head and chest are raised slightly and your gaze is outwards, with length in the neck.

**Lower** body
Your **hip extensors** lift your thighs; your **hip flexors** lengthen. Your **quadriceps** extend the knees. Your **gastrocnemius** and **soleus** bend your ankles; the **tibialis anterior** and **ankle dorsiflexors** stretch.

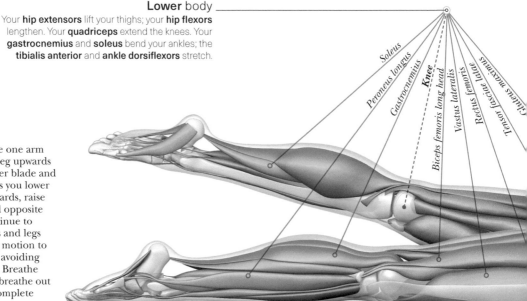

Soleus

Peroneus longus

Gastrocnemius

*Knee*

Biceps femoris long head

Vastus lateralis

Rectus femoris

Tensor fasciae latae

Gluteus maximus

**STAGE ONE**
Exhale as you raise one arm and the opposite leg upwards using your shoulder blade and gluteal muscles. As you lower these back downwards, raise the other arm and opposite leg upwards. Continue to alternate the arms and legs in a fast fluttering motion to mimic swimming, avoiding touching the mat. Breathe in for 5 beats and breathe out for 5 beats, and complete 8–10 repetitions.

*Almost all everyday **activities will** **benefit** from performing *the* Swimming* **exercise**.*

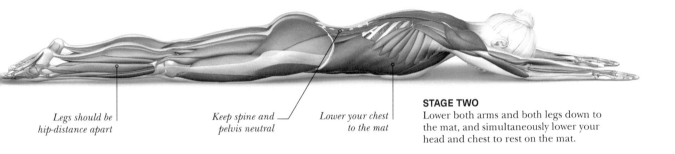

Legs should be
hip-distance apart

Keep spine and
pelvis neutral

Lower your chest
to the mat

### STAGE TWO
Lower both arms and both legs down to
the mat, and simultaneously lower your
head and chest to rest on the mat.

### Upper body
Your **cervical extensors** and **cervical flexors**
hold the head upwards. Your **middle** and **lower**
**trapezius** and **rhomboids** retract the scapulae.
Your **spinal extensors** and **latissimus dorsi**
engage, and your **abdominals** lengthen.

### ! Caution
Be careful with Swimming if you have
shoulder joint instability or lower back
problems. Placing a block under the
pelvis can help if your hip flexors are
tight, or if you have lordosis (curvature
of the lower spine).

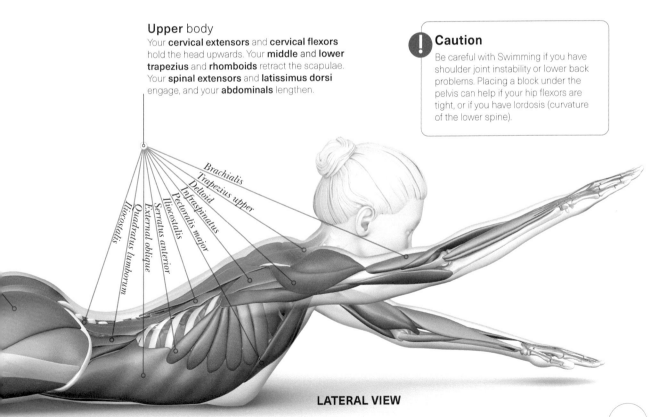

Brachialis
Trapezius upper
Deltoid
Infraspinatus
Pectoralis major
Serratus anterior
External oblique
Quadratus lumborum
Iliocostalis

**LATERAL VIEW**

# » VARIATIONS

Lying on your front while exercising can be uncomfortable for some people. Place a small cushion under your pelvis if you have any pubic bone pain. For both exercises, lengthen the arms and legs away from each other as you lift and draw your core upwards to stabilize your spine.

**KEY**
- ● Primary target muscle
- ● Secondary target muscle

## SLOWER OPTION (HEAD DOWN)

The movement here is the same as the main Swimming one, however you rest your head on a cushion to reduce neck strain. In addition, the limbs move much slower with a pause in between changing sides to allow control of the trunk.

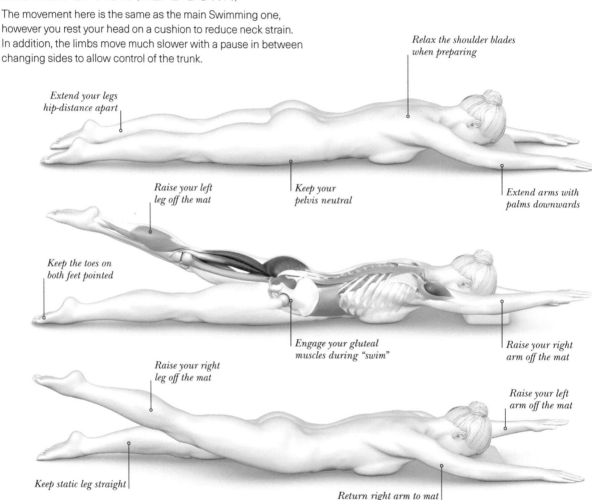

*Relax the shoulder blades when preparing*

*Extend your legs hip-distance apart*

*Raise your left leg off the mat*

*Keep your pelvis neutral*

*Extend arms with palms downwards*

*Keep the toes on both feet pointed*

*Engage your gluteal muscles during "swim"*

*Raise your right arm off the mat*

*Raise your right leg off the mat*

*Raise your left arm off the mat*

*Keep static leg straight*

*Return right arm to mat*

**PREPARATORY STAGE**
Lie on your front with your legs extended and hip-distance apart. Stretch both arms out in front of you shoulder-width apart with palms facing downwards on the mat. Rest your forehead on a small cushion with your neck long and your shoulder blades relaxed.

**STAGE ONE**
Exhale as you raise one arm and your opposite leg upwards off the mat using your shoulder blade and gluteal muscles. Keep your core engaged underneath. Inhale to return the arm and leg back downwards onto the mat.

**STAGE TWO**
Repeat on the opposite side and continue alternating opposite legs and arms for 8–10 repetitions.

## FOUR POINT KNEELING

This exercise has a much smaller base of support and requires more balance as you raise the arm and opposite leg. Ensure you maintain height through your chest by pressing away from the mat and keep your back neutral throughout.

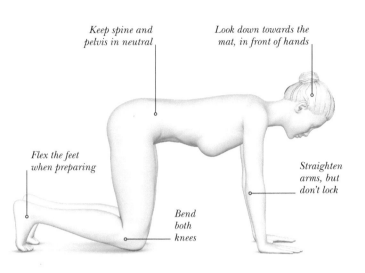

*Keep spine and pelvis in neutral*

*Look down towards the mat, in front of hands*

*Flex the feet when preparing*

*Straighten arms, but don't lock*

*Bend both knees*

### PREPARATORY STAGE
Come into the four point kneeling position with equal weight between the hands and knees. Make sure the spine and pelvis are in neutral and the neck is long with your eye gaze downwards, just slightly in front of your hands. Inhale to prepare.

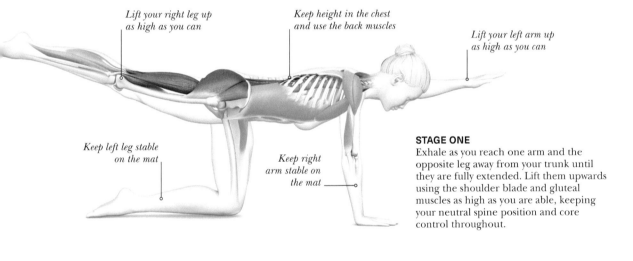

*Lift your right leg up as high as you can*

*Keep height in the chest and use the back muscles*

*Lift your left arm up as high as you can*

*Keep left leg stable on the mat*

*Keep right arm stable on the mat*

### STAGE ONE
Exhale as you reach one arm and the opposite leg away from your trunk until they are fully extended. Lift them upwards using the shoulder blade and gluteal muscles as high as you are able, keeping your neutral spine position and core control throughout.

*Try to lift the left leg up as high as you can*

*Raise the right arm up as high as you can*

*Maintain stability in the static leg*

*Keep your left arm stable on the mat*

### STAGE TWO
Inhale to return both the arm and leg back to the mat, then simultaneously lengthen and lift the opposite arm and leg. Continue to alternate sides for 8–10 repetitions.

91

# SEAL

**Seal challenges spinal stability** in a rolling motion and mobilizes the spine in flexion. It develops a strong core support to maintain the integrity of the C-curve formed while rolling, and promotes the symmetry to do so.

## THE **BIG PICTURE**

Once you have formed the preparatory position, there are no further adjustments needed other than the curving of the spine as you roll into flexion. Focus on forming a rigid shape for the whole body, and on your core engagement. The speed should be equal for rolling in both directions, with a pause at the top to balance on your sitting bones. Clap the feet together, keeping your trunk upright.

**KEY**

●-- *Joints*

○— *Muscles*

● Shortening with tension

● Lengthening with tension

● Lengthening without tension

● Held muscles without motion

**LATERAL VIEW**

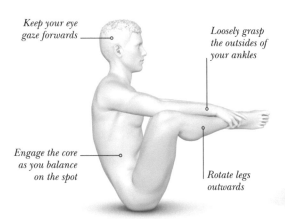

*Keep your eye gaze forwards*

*Loosely grasp the outsides of your ankles*

*Engage the core as you balance on the spot*

*Rotate legs outwards*

**PREPARATORY STAGE**
Sit upright with your pelvis underneath you, just slightly tilted backwards. Flex your legs at the hips and knees, raise them upwards and rotate outwards from the hips. Place the soles of your feet together, and stretch your arms forward.

**STAGE ONE**
Exhale as you c-curve your spine and gently roll backwards, rolling your pelvis and spine and letting your legs follow. Keep the integrity of your C-curve intact until you are resting on your upper body, your elbows tucked behind your knees.

## Legs

Your **hip flexors** engage throughout, while your **small hip rotators** externally rotate the hip to part the knees. Your **quadriceps** stretch, while your **hamstrings** and **calves** engage to maintain the knee flexion angle.

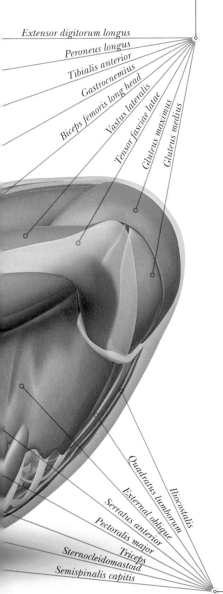

Extensor digitorum longus
Peroneus longus
Tibialis anterior
Gastrocnemius
Biceps femoris long head
Vastus lateralis
Tensor fasciae latae
Gluteus maximus
Gluteus medius

Quadratus lumborum
Iliocostalis
External oblique
Serratus anterior
Pectoralis major
Triceps
Sternocleidomastoid
Semispinalis capitis

### ! Caution

Due to the pressure applied to the vertebrae in the rolling motions, this exercise is not suitable if you have neck and lumbar instability or osteoporosis.

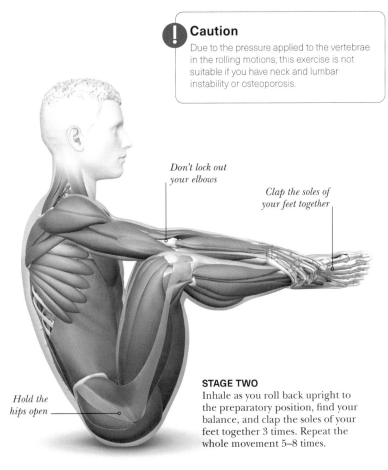

*Don't lock out your elbows*

*Clap the soles of your feet together*

*Hold the hips open*

**STAGE TWO**
Inhale as you roll back upright to the preparatory position, find your balance, and clap the soles of your feet together 3 times. Repeat the whole movement 5–8 times.

*It is important to **maintain** space between your trunk and legs **throughout** the exercise.*

### Trunk and neck

Your **spinal extensors** stretch. Your **cervical extensors** also stretch, while your **cervical flexors** are engaged to prevent the head being thrown backwards as you roll back. Your **pectoralis major** engages as your arms adduct to reach for the ankles.

# ROTATORY
# EXERCISES

**The exercises in this section stabilize the joints through rotation** and improve their function by targeting often smaller and more specific muscle groups. They increase the range of motion for the joint region, while also strengthening the associated muscles. Rotatory strength is especially important for the pelvis and hips – an area from which our entire lower limb function operates, and which underpins our lateral stability, as well as transferring energy to and from the trunk.

# ONE LEG CIRCLE

**This exercise is both a multi-directional and endurance challenge** for core and pelvic stability, giving it a unique place in the Pilates repertoire. It also stretches the hamstrings at the back and works the hip flexors at the front. It can make an excellent rehabilitation exercise for adductor injuries or for return to sports where direction changes are required.

## THE **BIG PICTURE**

Begin forming small circles and gradually expand to bigger circles when you are able to control your trunk and keep it still. Use your arms to press down into the mat to increase stability, and activate your back and core muscles for extra support. As you circle the leg out to the side, visualize engaging the opposite hip and core further to anchor the pelvis down and prevent the trunk deviating to follow the leg.

**KEY**

- - - *Joints*

○— *Muscles*

● Shortening with tension

● Lengthening with tension

● Lengthening without tension

● Held muscles without motion

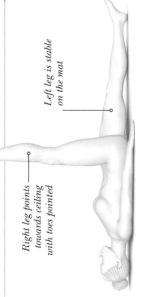

*Right leg points towards ceiling with toes pointed*

*Left leg is stable on the mat*

### PREPARATORY STAGE

Lie on your back with both legs extended and hip-distance apart, and your spine and pelvis in neutral. Rest both arms down by your sides with palms facing downwards. Extend one leg directly upwards towards the ceiling, with your toes pointed.

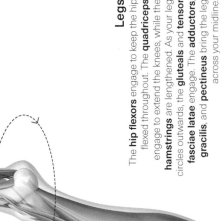

### Legs

The **hip flexors** engage to keep the hip flexed throughout. The **quadriceps** engage to extend the knees, while the **hamstrings** are lengthened. As your leg circles outwards, the **gluteals** and **tensor fasciae latae** engage. The **adductors**, **gracilis**, and **pectineus** bring the leg across your midline.

❝❝

*The abdominal muscles work* **hard** *to keep the torso stable when circling the leg.*

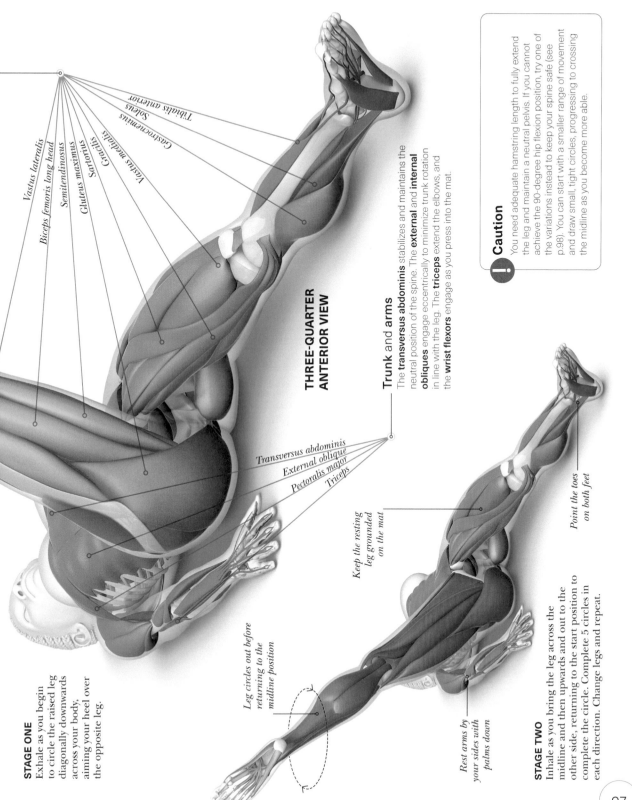

**STAGE ONE**
Exhale as you begin to circle the raised leg diagonally downwards across your body, aiming your heel over the opposite leg.

Vastus lateralis
Biceps femoris long head
Semitendinosus
Gluteus maximus
Sartorius
Gracilis
Vastus medialis
Gastrocnemius
Soleus
Tibialis anterior

**THREE-QUARTER ANTERIOR VIEW**

**Trunk and arms**
The **transversus abdominis** stabilizes and maintains the neutral position of the spine. The **external** and **internal obliques** engage eccentrically to minimize trunk rotation in line with the leg. The **triceps** extend the elbows, and the **wrist flexors** engage as you press into the mat.

Transversus abdominis
External oblique
Pectoralis major
Triceps

Keep the resting leg grounded on the mat

Leg circles out before returning to the midline position

Rest arms by your sides with palms down

Point the toes on both feet

**STAGE TWO**
Inhale as you bring the leg across the midline and then upwards and out to the other side, returning to the start position to complete the circle. Complete 5 circles in each direction. Change legs and repeat.

**Caution**

You need adequate hamstring length to fully extend the leg and maintain a neutral pelvis. If you cannot achieve the 90-degree hip flexion position, try one of the variations instead to keep your spine safe (see p.98). You can start with a smaller range of movement and draw small, tight circles, progressing to crossing the midline as you become more able.

# ≫ VARIATIONS

These variations all have the supporting leg bent with the foot on the mat for extra pelvic stability. Press this leg down to further stabilize as your leg moves out to the side. Learn to keep your pelvis stable in each of these before progressing to the main One Leg Circle.

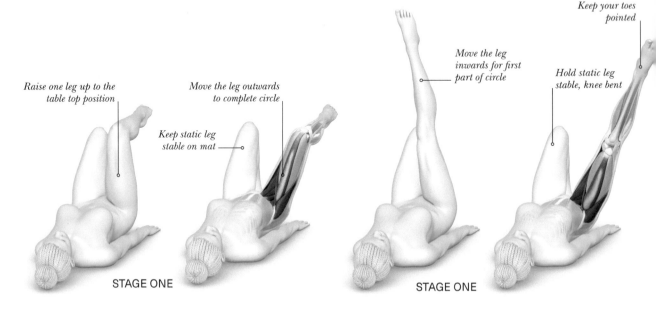

*Raise one leg up to the table top position*

*Move the leg outwards to complete circle*

*Keep static leg stable on mat*

STAGE ONE

*Keep your toes pointed*

*Move the leg inwards for first part of circle*

*Hold static leg stable, knee bent*

STAGE ONE

## LEGS BENT

This variation has a short leg lever to really focus on stabilizing the pelvis and engaging the core as your leg rotates. The rotation movement comes from your hip joint and the knee, and the lower leg follows.

### PREPARATORY STAGE
Lie on your back with your legs hip-distance apart and flexed at your hips and knees, your feet flat on the mat. Keep your spine and pelvis in neutral and rest your arms by your sides with palms facing downwards. Make sure your head and neck are also in neutral.

### STAGE ONE
Raise one leg up to the table top position and begin circling the leg, moving from the hip joint. Exhale as you move the leg inwards for the first part of the circle and inhale as it returns outwards to complete the circle. Repeat 5–8 times in each direction.

### STAGE TWO
Switch legs and complete the circle sequence on the other leg.

## ONE LEG EXTENDED

In this variation, you lengthen your leg away from you to fully extend it. Start with small, neat circles near the top and progress to wider and lower circles as you become more confident and able to maintain a stable pelvis.

### PREPARATORY STAGE
Lie on your back with your legs hip-distance apart, flexed at your hips and knees, and your feet flat on the mat. Keep your spine and pelvis in neutral and rest your arms by your sides with palms facing downwards. Keep your head and neck in neutral.

### STAGE ONE
Extend one leg straight upwards towards the ceiling with your toes pointed and begin circling the leg, moving from the hip joint. Exhale as you move the leg inwards for the first part of the circle and inhale as it returns outwards to complete the circle. Repeat 5–8 times in each direction.

### STAGE TWO
Switch legs and complete the circle sequence on the other leg.

# **WITH** BAND SUPPORT

The use of the band here allows you to explore a greater range of movement by forming bigger circles. Keep your elbows resting on the mat for support and let the leg move as far as you are able with the band.

**KEY**

● Primary target muscle    ● Secondary target muscle

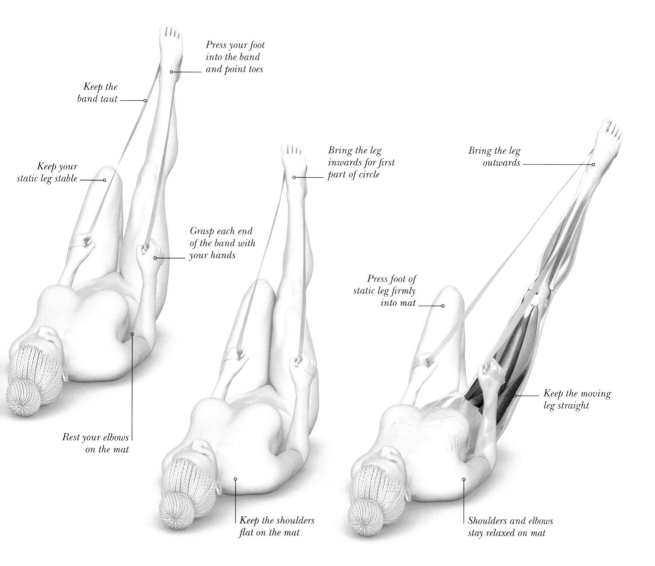

*Press your foot into the band and point toes*

*Keep the band taut*

*Keep your static leg stable*

*Grasp each end of the band with your hands*

*Rest your elbows on the mat*

*Bring the leg inwards for first part of circle*

*Press foot of static leg firmly into mat*

*Keep the shoulders flat on the mat*

*Bring the leg outwards*

*Keep the moving leg straight*

*Shoulders and elbows stay relaxed on mat*

**PREPARATORY STAGE**
Lie on your back with your legs hip-distance apart, flexed at your hips and knees, and your feet flat on the mat. Loop a band around one foot and extend this leg upwards towards the ceiling with your toes pointed.

**STAGE ONE**
Begin circling the leg, moving from the hip joint. Exhale as you move the leg inwards for the first part of the circle and inhale as you return it outwards to complete the circle. Repeat 5–8 times in each direction.

**STAGE TWO**
Switch sides and repeat the circle sequence on the other leg.

# SIDE KICK

**This is a great exercise to promote rotational stability of the pelvis** with a large focus on gluteal strength and endurance. It also trains balance in side lying, and strengthens the oblique abdominal muscles as they resist the trunk mobility with the leg movements.

*Flex the foot and lead with the heel*

## THE **BIG PICTURE**

Side Kick challenges you to keep the top leg at hip height throughout to encourage proper alignment and muscle activation. On the forward kick, lengthen the foot away from you for greater reach. On the return, flex the ankle and lengthen the heel away to stretch the hamstrings. Reduce the leg range initially and increase as you become accustomed to the movement.

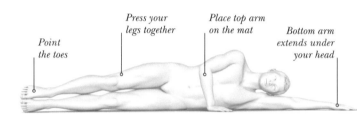

*Point the toes*

*Press your legs together*

*Place top arm on the mat*

*Bottom arm extends under your head*

### PREPARATORY STAGE

Lie on one side with your spine and pelvis in neutral, legs lengthened away from you and flexed forwards slightly at the hips. Stack your shoulders, hips, and ankles on top of each other. Lengthen your bottom arm and rest your bottom ear on the top of your shoulder. Bend your top arm and position your hand lightly on the mat.

### **Lower** body

On the bottom leg, your **adductors** stabilize along with the **gluteals** and **hamstrings**. Your **hip flexors** bring the top leg forwards; the **gluteals** and **hamstrings** bring it back on the return. The **quadriceps** engage bilaterally.

### STAGE ONE

Exhale as you lift the top leg up to hip height parallel with your bottom leg, keeping toes pointed. Glide it forwards as far as able. Keep trunk and pelvis stable.

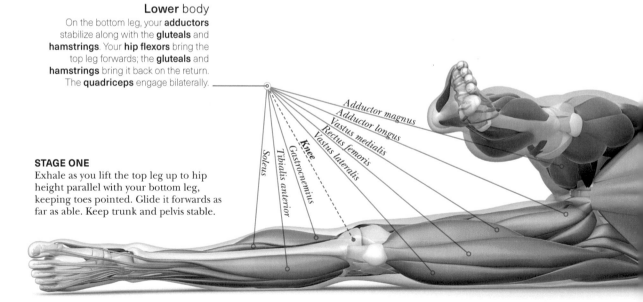

*Adductor magnus*
*Adductor longus*
*Vastus medialis*
*Rectus femoris*
*Vastus lateralis*
*Knee*
*Gastrocnemius*
*Tibialis anterior*
*Soleus*

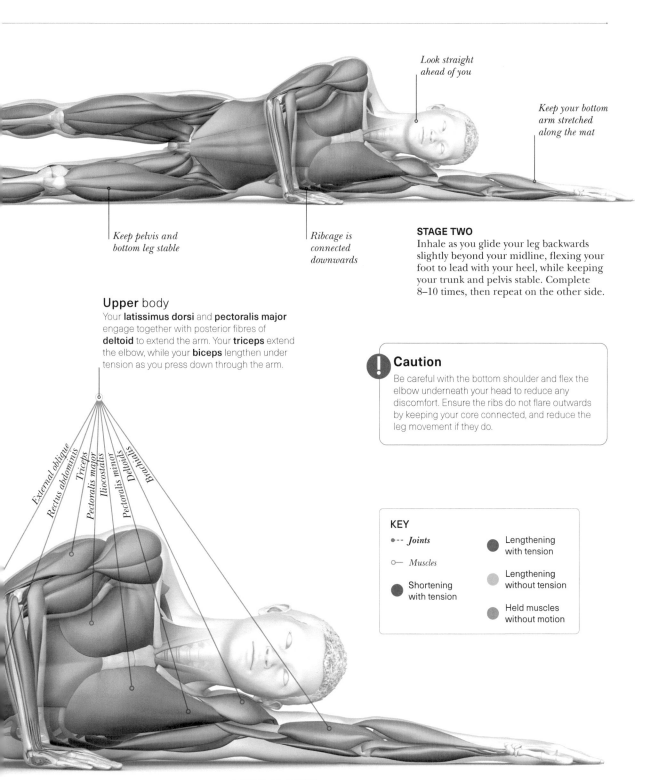

*Look straight ahead of you*

*Keep your bottom arm stretched along the mat*

*Keep pelvis and bottom leg stable*

*Ribcage is connected downwards*

## STAGE TWO
Inhale as you glide your leg backwards slightly beyond your midline, flexing your foot to lead with your heel, while keeping your trunk and pelvis stable. Complete 8–10 times, then repeat on the other side.

## Upper body
Your **latissimus dorsi** and **pectoralis major** engage together with posterior fibres of **deltoid** to extend the arm. Your **triceps** extend the elbow, while your **biceps** lengthen under tension as you press down through the arm.

## Caution
Be careful with the bottom shoulder and flex the elbow underneath your head to reduce any discomfort. Ensure the ribs do not flare outwards by keeping your core connected, and reduce the leg movement if they do.

External oblique
Rectus abdominis
Triceps
Pectoralis major
Iliocostalis
Pectoralis minor
Deltoids
Brachialis

## KEY
- ●-- *Joints*
- ○— *Muscles*
- ● Shortening with tension
- ● Lengthening with tension
- ● Lengthening without tension
- ● Held muscles without motion

**LATERAL VIEW**

# » VARIATIONS

Side Kick represents an everyday leg movement of hip flexion and extension that we do even when walking. These variations allow both the beginner (With Knees Flexed) and the more experienced (other two exercises) to strengthen their obliques and gluteals further. The final variation is advanced, adding an upper body challenge too.

## **WITH** KNEES FLEXED

Build endurance more easily in this shortened lever variation. Try to keep the whole leg at the same height as you move it back and forth. Place a Pilates soft ball behind your knee for further gluteal and hamstring activation.

**KEY**

● Primary target muscle

● Secondary target muscle

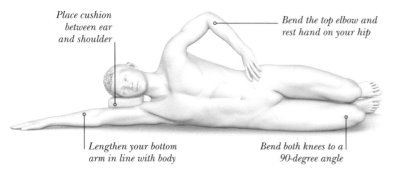

*Place cushion between ear and shoulder*

*Bend the top elbow and rest hand on your hip*

*Lengthen your bottom arm in line with body*

*Bend both knees to a 90-degree angle*

### PREPARATORY STAGE
Lie on one side with your spine and pelvis in neutral, your hips bent slightly and your knees bent to approximately 90 degrees. Stack your shoulders, hips, and ankles on top of each other. Lengthen your bottom arm in line with your body and place a small cushion between your ear and your shoulder.

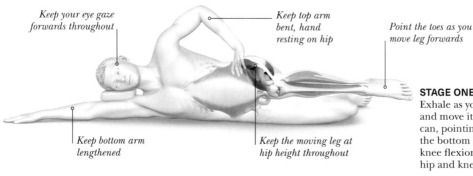

*Keep your eye gaze forwards throughout*

*Keep top arm bent, hand resting on hip*

*Point the toes as you move leg forwards*

*Keep bottom arm lengthened*

*Keep the moving leg at hip height throughout*

### STAGE ONE
Exhale as you raise your top leg and move it forwards as far as you can, pointing the toes and keeping the bottom leg still. Maintain the knee flexion angle and keep your hip and knee level.

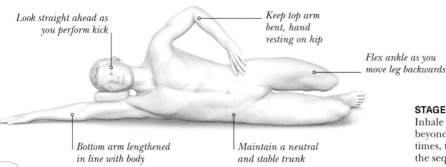

*Look straight ahead as you perform kick*

*Keep top arm bent, hand resting on hip*

*Flex ankle as you move leg backwards*

*Bottom arm lengthened in line with body*

*Maintain a neutral and stable trunk*

### STAGE TWO
Inhale to move the leg backwards just beyond your midline. Repeat 5–8 times, then switch sides and complete the sequence on the other leg.

# BOTH LEGS ELEVATED

This continues the Side Kick motion while adding the additional demand of balancing on one side with no support from the legs on the mat. It requires increased oblique and gluteal strength to support you. Ensure you have no lateral hip pain when performing this variation.

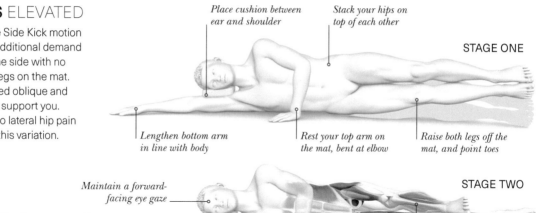

*Place cushion between ear and shoulder*

*Stack your hips on top of each other*

**STAGE ONE**

*Lengthen bottom arm in line with body*

*Rest your top arm on the mat, bent at elbow*

*Raise both legs off the mat, and point toes*

*Maintain a forward-facing eye gaze*

*Keep bottom arm stable and extended*

**STAGE TWO**

*Keep pelvis stable as you move top leg*

### PREPARATORY STAGE
Lie on one side with your spine and pelvis in neutral, legs lengthened away from you and flexed forwards just slightly at the hips. Stack your shoulders, hips, and ankles on top of each other. Lengthen your bottom arm in line with your body.

### STAGE ONE
Lift your top leg up to hip height and lift your bottom leg up to meet it so that they are connected in mid air. Both legs will stay in mid air for the whole exercise.

### STAGE TWO
Exhale as you glide your top leg forwards as far as able, leading with the heel. Inhale and glide your leg backwards. Repeat 5–8 times, then complete the sequence on the other side.

# ON ELBOWS WITH
## BOTH LEGS ELEVATED

This requires good shoulder stability. Gently draw your shoulder blades back to engage your scapular muscles and maintain lift away from your underneath shoulder. Relax your neck.

### PREPARATORY STAGE
Lie on one side with your spine and pelvis in neutral, legs lengthened away from you and flexed forwards just slightly at the hips. Stack your hips and ankles on top of each other. Rest your bottom forearm on the mat with your elbow underneath your shoulder and lift through your lower waist to lengthen your trunk. Rest your top hand on your hip throughout the exercise.

### STAGE ONE
Exhale as you lift your top leg up to hip height, and lift your bottom leg up to meet it so that they are connected in mid air.

### STAGE TWO
Exhale as you glide your top leg forwards as far as able, keeping your trunk and pelvis stable. Inhale as you glide your leg backwards slightly beyond your midline, flexing your foot to lead with your heel. Repeat 8–10 times, then complete the sequence on the other side.

*Rest your top arm on your hip*

*Keep both legs lifted throughout exercise*

**STAGE ONE**

*Rest bottom forearm on the mat, elbow beneath shoulder*

*Point the toes but flex at heel when moving*

*Bend your top arm at the elbow*

*Bring the leg forwards as far as you can*

**STAGE TWO**

# HIP TWIST

**This advanced exercise develops rotational control of the pelvis**, as well as oblique abdominal muscle strength to control the legs, and mobility of the spine in the variations (see p.106). It is a combination of various elements of Teaser (see p.136) and Corkscrew (see p.128).

## THE **BIG PICTURE**

Your weight rests in the hands with your chest open and lifted and ribcage drawn down. Keep your core engaged and maintain length in both sides of your waist for a rigid trunk. The leg movements should originate from the hips and should be controlled through your core, yet at a dynamic pace to match your breath. If you require more support, try bending your elbows to rest on your forearms or practise the variations first.

> ❗ **Caution**
> Take caution with the pubic symphysis joint, sacroiliac joint, or adductor muscle pain, as the rotational movements may irritate these conditions.

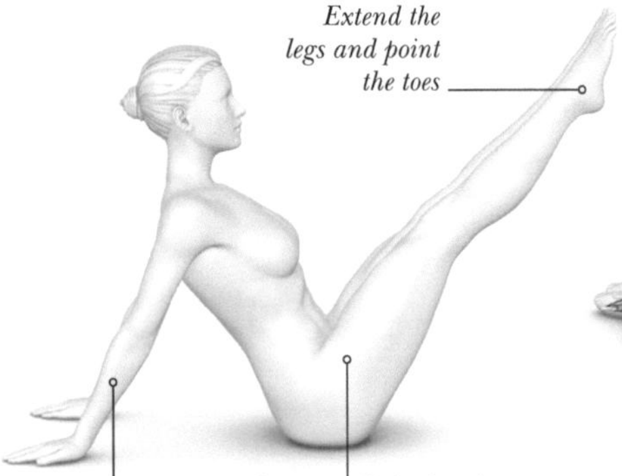

*Extend the legs and point the toes*

*Straighten the arms behind you*

*Raise legs into a diagonal line*

**PREPARATORY STAGE**
Sit upright with both legs stretched out in front of you, legs connected together. Place your arms behind you, with palms facing downwards. Exhale as you raise both legs upwards, forming a V-shape.

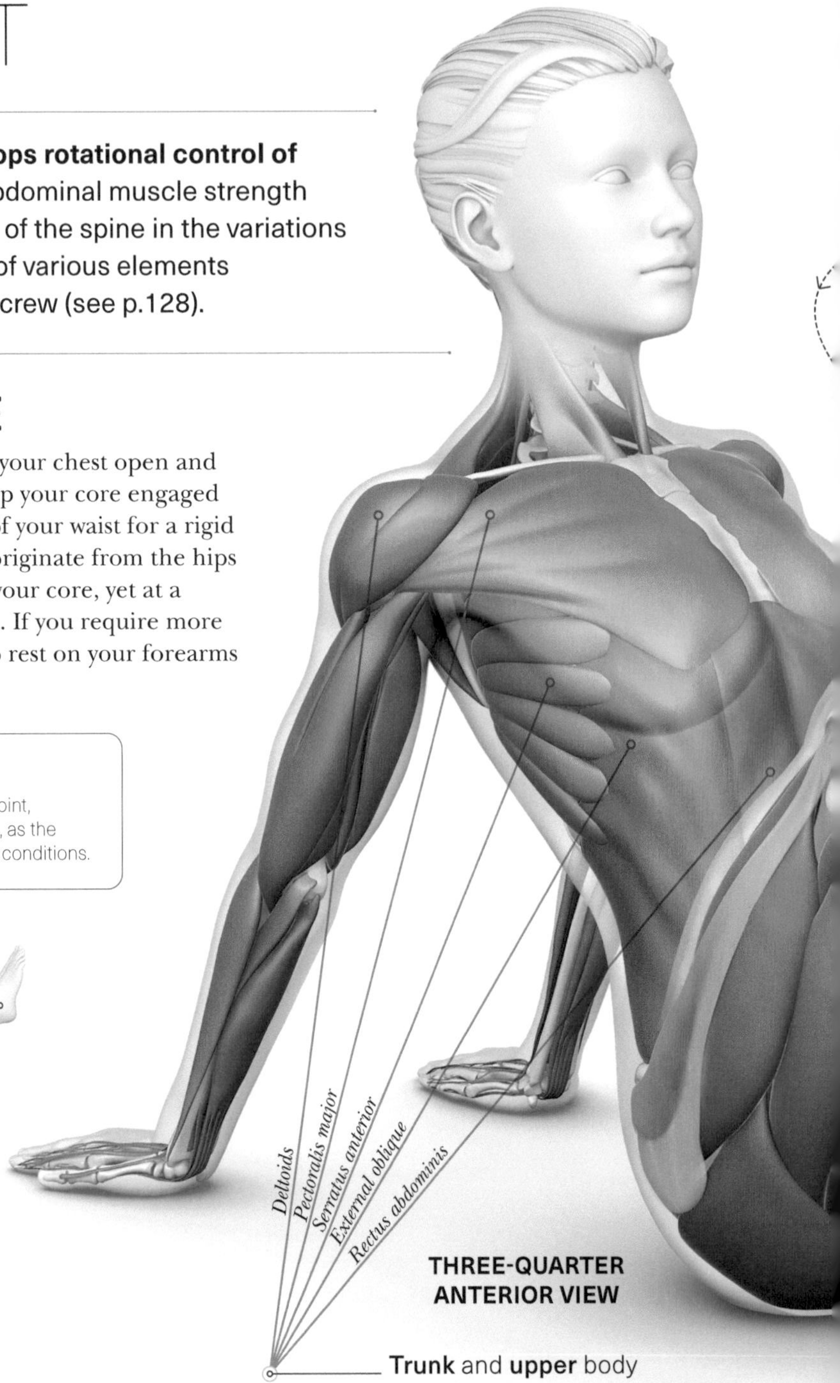

Deltoids
Pectoralis major
Serratus anterior
External oblique
Rectus abdominis

**THREE-QUARTER ANTERIOR VIEW**

**Trunk** and **upper** body
Your **wrist extensors** engage, and your **biceps** and **triceps** contract as you push your trunk up from the mat. Your **pectoralis major** stretches to open the chest. Your **abdominals** and **obliques** control the trunk.

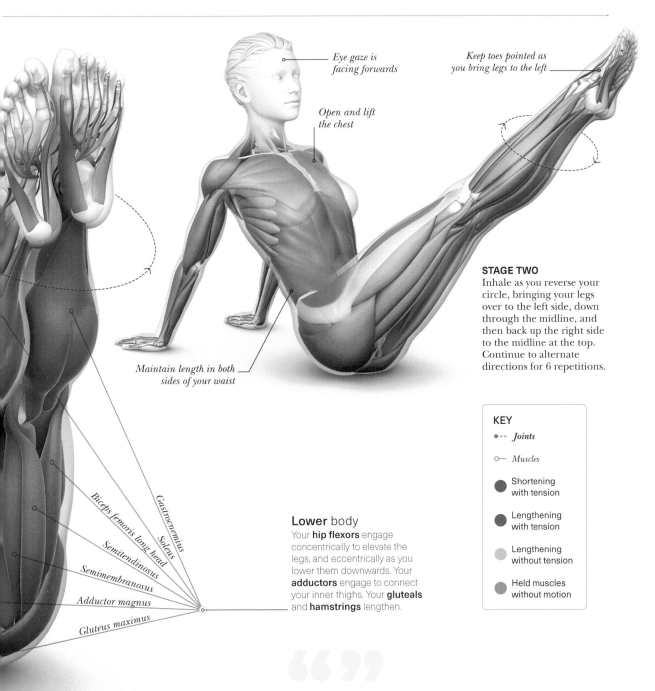

Eye gaze is
facing forwards

Keep toes pointed as
you bring legs to the left

Open and lift
the chest

**STAGE TWO**
Inhale as you reverse your
circle, bringing your legs
over to the left side, down
through the midline, and
then back up the right side
to the midline at the top.
Continue to alternate
directions for 6 repetitions.

Maintain length in both
sides of your waist

Gastrocnemius

Biceps femoris long head

Soleus

Semitendinosus

Semimembranosus

Adductor magnus

Gluteus maximus

**Lower** body
Your **hip flexors** engage
concentrically to elevate the
legs, and eccentrically as you
lower them downwards. Your
**adductors** engage to connect
your inner thighs. Your **gluteals**
and **hamstrings** lengthen.

**KEY**

•-- *Joints*

○- *Muscles*

⬤ Shortening
with tension

⬤ Lengthening
with tension

⬤ Lengthening
without tension

⬤ Held muscles
without motion

**STAGE ONE**
Exhale as you bring your legs over to your right
side, allowing your pelvis to roll with you and
keeping your trunk still. Continue forming a
circle, lowering your legs as they reach the
midline, and then circling up to the left side
and upwards to the midline at the top, as per
the preparatory stage.

*The* **hip twist** *movements
should be* **equal in size** *and
speed* in both *directions.*

## » VARIATIONS

These options all remove the need to balance on the elbows in the way that you do in the main Hip Twist. This allows you to focus on your pelvic stability and leg. The variations also have both knees flexed rather than extended, reducing core load and the risk of irritation on the lower back.

### SINGLE LEG

Pelvic stability is challenged throughout this exercise. The lateral gluteals and obliques engage as you move the leg outwards stretching the adductors, while the adductors engage to return the leg to the start position. Relax your top half throughout.

*Keep your **shoulders** relaxed, chest open, and hands light to avoid using your **upper body** and neck.*

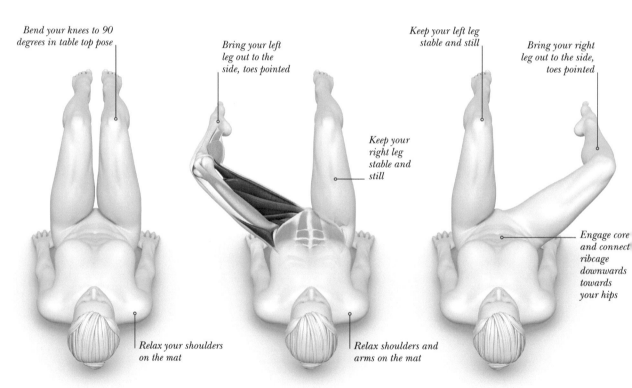

Bend your knees to 90 degrees in table top pose

Relax your shoulders on the mat

Bring your left leg out to the side, toes pointed

Keep your right leg stable and still

Relax shoulders and arms on the mat

Keep your left leg stable and still

Bring your right leg out to the side, toes pointed

Engage core and connect ribcage downwards towards your hips

**PREPARATORY STAGE**
Lie on your back with your spine and pelvis in neutral, and your hips and knees bent to 90 degrees in the table top position. Stretch your arms out by your sides with palms facing downwards.

**STAGE ONE**
Exhale as you move your left leg out to your left side as far as able, while keeping your spine neutral and pelvis stable. Inhale as you return the left leg to the starting position.

**STAGE TWO**
Exhale and bring your right leg out to the side as far as able. Complete 6 repetitions on each side, alternating sides.

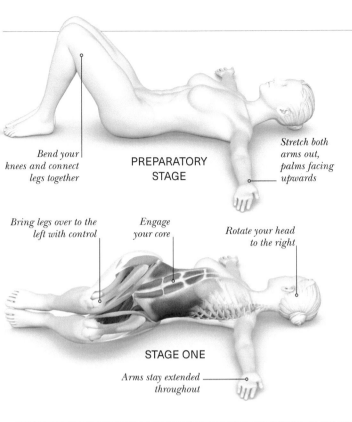

Bend your knees and connect legs together

PREPARATORY STAGE

*Stretch both arms out, palms facing upwards*

*Bring legs over to the left with control*

*Engage your core*

*Rotate your head to the right*

STAGE ONE

*Arms stay extended throughout*

## LEGS ON MAT

This is often used more as a relaxing exercise or for spinal mobility, but it does equally challenge pelvic stability and the obliques. Move in sequence and keep your inner thighs, knees, and ankles connected tightly together throughout.

### PREPARATORY STAGE
Lie on your back with your spine and pelvis in neutral and your hips and knees bent, with feet flat on the floor. Stretch your arms out either side of you at shoulder height. Connect your legs together and engage your core.

### STAGE ONE
Exhale as you roll your legs over to your left, allowing your pelvis and spine to roll with you, and simultaneously rotate your head to the right. Inhale to pause, and exhale to return to the starting postion, initiating from your lower back, pelvis, and then legs.

### STAGE TWO
Repeat to the right this time, and rotate your head to the left. Continue to alternate sides and complete for a total of 6 repetitions. Return to the preparatory position to finish.

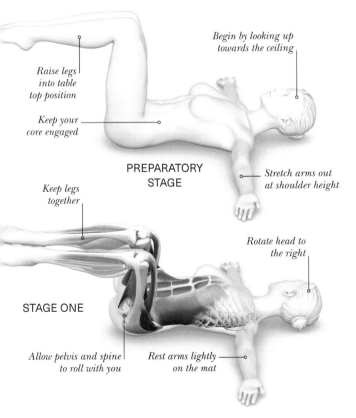

*Raise legs into table top position*

*Begin by looking up towards the ceiling*

*Keep your core engaged*

PREPARATORY STAGE

*Stretch arms out at shoulder height*

*Keep legs together*

*Rotate head to the right*

STAGE ONE

*Allow pelvis and spine to roll with you*

*Rest arms lightly on the mat*

## BOTH LEGS MOVE

This is a more advanced version of Legs on Mat. It provides the same benefits but adds the greater challenge of having no base of support for the legs. This requires greater abdominal strength to control and support the legs.

### PREPARATORY STAGE
Lie on your back with your spine and pelvis in neutral and your hips and knees bent up to the 90-degree table top position. Stretch your arms out at shoulder height with palms facing upwards. Connect your legs together.

### STAGE ONE
Exhale as you roll the legs over to your left side as far as you can, allowing your pelvis and spine to roll with you, and simultaneously rotate your head to the right. Inhale to pause, and exhale to return to the preparatory position, rolling from the spine, pelvis, and finally from the legs. Complete 6 repetitions.

### STAGE TWO
Switch sides, bringing your legs over to the right this time, and rotating your head to the left. Complete 6 repetitions, then return to the preparatory position.

# SIDE KICK IN KNEELING

**Strengthening the gluteal and oblique muscles** while working with a small base of support, this advanced version of Side Kick (see p.100) requires good shoulder stability as your foundation. It also challenges your trunk against the long lever of your leg moving forwards and backwards.

## THE BIG PICTURE

This exercise requires isolation of the top hip movements. The trunk should remain still and avoid rotating towards the floor. Keep your chest open and shoulders and hips stacked to help with this. You can place a block under the supporting hand to help maintain the hip position, or lower the leg initially for ease, progressing to perpendicular to the floor when able. Increase the challenge by pulsing or circling the top leg.

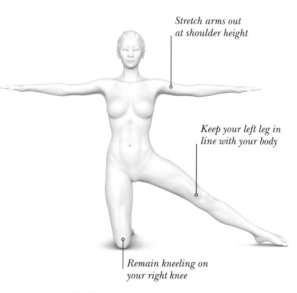

*Stretch arms out at shoulder height*

*Keep your left leg in line with your body*

*Remain kneeling on your right knee*

**PREPARATORY STAGE**
Kneel upright on both knees and raise your arms out to your sides at shoulder height with your palms facing downwards. Extend your left leg out to your side with toes pointed.

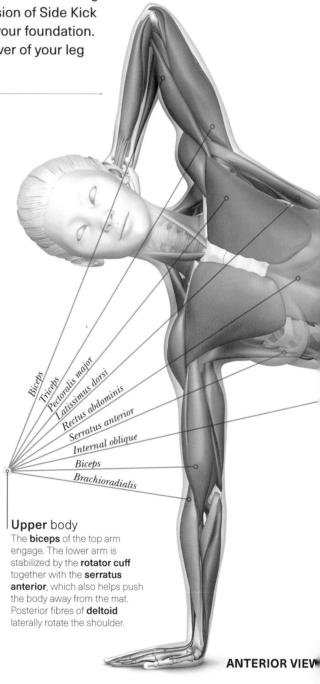

Biceps
Triceps
Pectoralis major
Latissimus dorsi
Rectus abdominis
Serratus anterior
Internal oblique
Biceps
Brachioradialis

**Upper** body
The **biceps** of the top arm engage. The lower arm is stabilized by the **rotator cuff** together with the **serratus anterior**, which also helps push the body away from the mat. Posterior fibres of **deltoid** laterally rotate the shoulder.

**ANTERIOR VIEW**

108

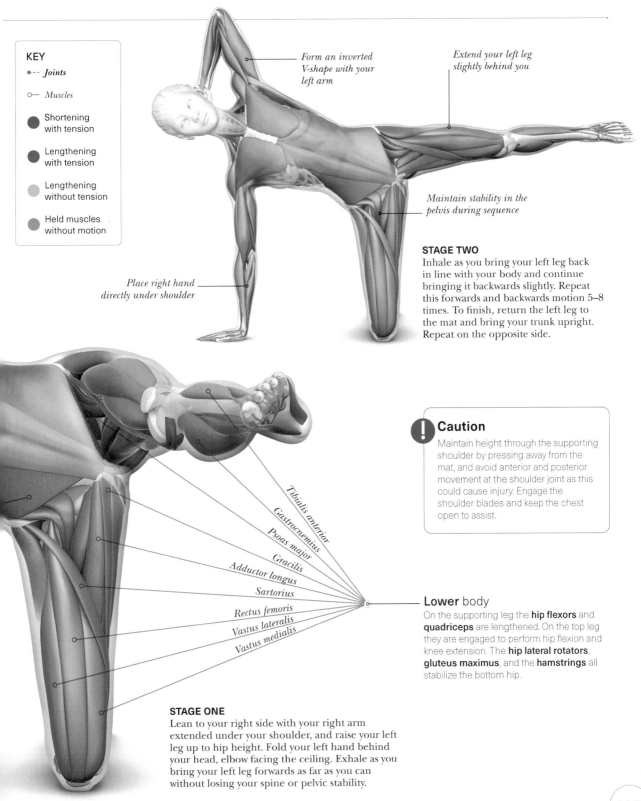

## KEY

●-- *Joints*

○— *Muscles*

● Shortening with tension

● Lengthening with tension

○ Lengthening without tension

● Held muscles without motion

*Form an inverted V-shape with your left arm*

*Extend your left leg slightly behind you*

*Maintain stability in the pelvis during sequence*

*Place right hand directly under shoulder*

**STAGE TWO**
Inhale as you bring your left leg back in line with your body and continue bringing it backwards slightly. Repeat this forwards and backwards motion 5–8 times. To finish, return the left leg to the mat and bring your trunk upright. Repeat on the opposite side.

*Tibialis anterior*
*Gastrocnemius*
*Psoas major*
*Gracilis*
*Adductor longus*
*Sartorius*
*Rectus femoris*
*Vastus lateralis*
*Vastus medialis*

### ! Caution
Maintain height through the supporting shoulder by pressing away from the mat, and avoid anterior and posterior movement at the shoulder joint as this could cause injury. Engage the shoulder blades and keep the chest open to assist.

### Lower body
On the supporting leg the **hip flexors** and **quadriceps** are lengthened. On the top leg they are engaged to perform hip flexion and knee extension. The **hip lateral rotators**, **gluteus maximus**, and the **hamstrings** all stabilize the bottom hip.

**STAGE ONE**
Lean to your right side with your right arm extended under your shoulder, and raise your left leg up to hip height. Fold your left hand behind your head, elbow facing the ceiling. Exhale as you bring your left leg forwards as far as you can without losing your spine or pelvic stability.

# SIDE BEND

**This advanced exercise** develops balance and coordination, as well as strengthening the oblique muscles. The top obliques and latissimus dorsi are also stretched. It is a challenging exercise for the upper body and requires good shoulder stability. It calls for a strong focus on technique, good muscular endurance, and body awareness.

## THE BIG PICTURE

Initiate the movement from the hips and spine rather than the upper arm, and keep the shoulder blades set lightly backwards. Pay particular attention to keeping the lower shoulder joint stable. Avoid locking the elbow or knee joints. Beginners can modify this exercise by bringing the left knee down to meet the right one from the preparatory position, then raising upwards with bent knees.

Complete 3 reps on one side, then switch sides and perform starting on your left hip.

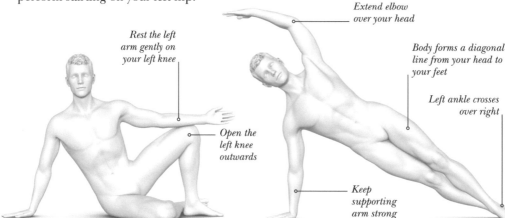

*Rest the left arm gently on your left knee*

*Open the left knee outwards*

*Extend elbow over your head*

*Body forms a diagonal line from your head to your feet*

*Left ankle crosses over right*

*Keep supporting arm strong*

**PREPARATORY STAGE ONE**
Sit on your right hip with your right leg bent underneath you and your shoulders and pelvis facing forwards. Cross the left ankle over the right leg, keeping your left foot flat on the mat. Support yourself on the right arm. Inhale and engage your core and gluteal muscles.

**PREPARATORY STAGE TWO**
Exhale as you press through your feet to lift the pelvis upwards. Extend the legs and connect the inner thighs to drive the body up horizontally, bringing your right shoulder over your wrist. Float your top arm overhead. Inhale to hold this position.

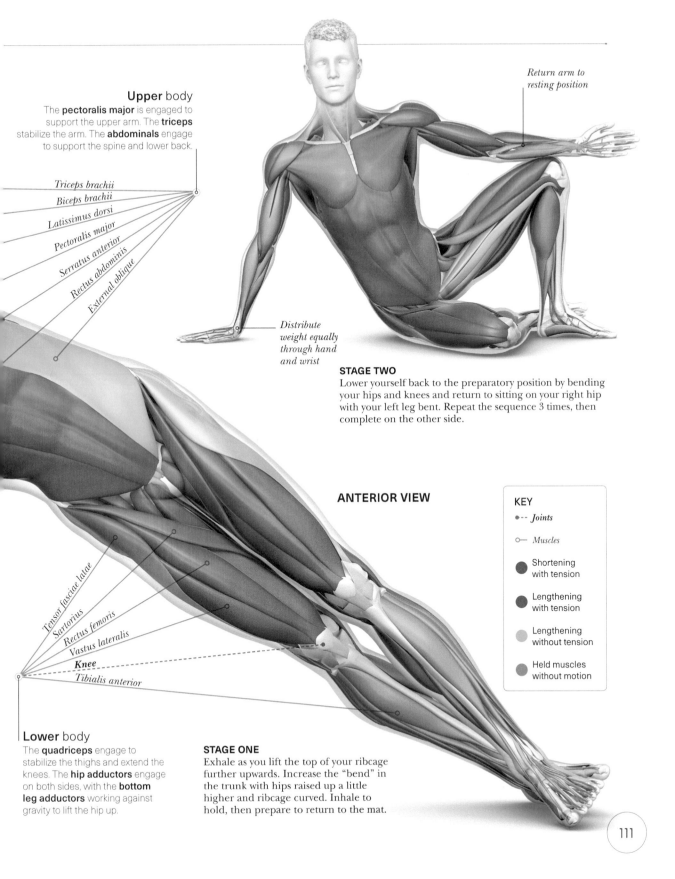

## Upper body

The **pectoralis major** is engaged to support the upper arm. The **triceps** stabilize the arm. The **abdominals** engage to support the spine and lower back.

*Triceps brachii*
*Biceps brachii*
*Latissimus dorsi*
*Pectoralis major*
*Serratus anterior*
*Rectus abdominis*
*External oblique*

*Return arm to resting position*

*Distribute weight equally through hand and wrist*

**STAGE TWO**
Lower yourself back to the preparatory position by bending your hips and knees and return to sitting on your right hip with your left leg bent. Repeat the sequence 3 times, then complete on the other side.

**ANTERIOR VIEW**

**KEY**
●--- *Joints*
○— *Muscles*
● Shortening with tension
● Lengthening with tension
● Lengthening without tension
● Held muscles without motion

*Tensor fasciae latae*
*Sartorius*
*Rectus femoris*
*Vastus lateralis*
***Knee***
*Tibialis anterior*

## Lower body

The **quadriceps** engage to stabilize the thighs and extend the knees. The **hip adductors** engage on both sides, with the **bottom leg adductors** working against gravity to lift the hip up.

**STAGE ONE**
Exhale as you lift the top of your ribcage further upwards. Increase the "bend" in the trunk with hips raised up a little higher and ribcage curved. Inhale to hold, then prepare to return to the mat.

# » VARIATIONS

In contrast to the main Side Bend, these variations reduce the upper body challenge to allow shoulder and core strength to develop. The last variation develops core and gluteal endurance, as you hold the position and work harder through the core with the addition of the arm and leg levers.

**KEY**
● Primary target muscle   ● Secondary target muscle

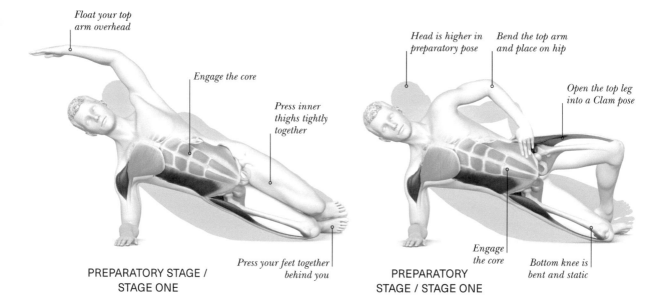

*Float your top arm overhead*

*Engage the core*

*Press inner thighs tightly together*

*Press your feet together behind you*

PREPARATORY STAGE / STAGE ONE

*Head is higher in preparatory pose*

*Bend the top arm and place on hip*

*Open the top leg into a Clam pose*

*Engage the core*

*Bottom knee is bent and static*

PREPARATORY STAGE / STAGE ONE

## HALF SIDE BEND

Keep your inner thighs and feet connected and focus on the ribcage connection to your core. Your pubic bone should press forwards and your gluteals should engage behind you. Reach your upper body away from your lower shoulder.

**PREPARATORY STAGE**
Begin sitting on your right hip, then rest your right forearm on the floor with your shoulder stacked above your elbow and palm facing downwards. Bend the knees and press the legs together.

**STAGE ONE**
Exhale as you raise your side up off of the mat, lifting the hips upwards to form a diagonal line from your head to your knees. At the same time, float the top arm overhead. Inhale to increase the bend by reaching the top ribcage further upwards.

**STAGE TWO**
Exhale to return back down to the mat. Repeat 4–6 times, then change sides.

## HALF SIDE BEND WITH CLAM

The addition of the Clam exercise (see p.116) further challenges your pelvic stability while strengthening the top gluteals. It is a great way to combine these two exercises for more intensity. Progress further by holding the position and pulsing the top leg.

**PREPARATORY STAGE**
Begin sitting on your right hip, then rest your right forearm on the floor with your shoulder stacked above your elbow and palm facing downwards. Bend the knees and press the legs together. Place your top hand on your hip.

**STAGE ONE**
Raise your side up off the mat and exhale to gently thrust the hips upwards to form a diagonal line from your head to your knees. Open your top hip and knee into a Clam pose.

**STAGE TWO**
Inhale to return back down to the mat. Repeat 4–6 times, then change sides.

# HALF SIDE BEND WITH
## ELBOW TO KNEE

Keep your spine neutral and trunk lifted as you reach your top arm and leg away. Feel the length in both sides of your waist and try to maintain this as you bring the elbow to touch the knee.

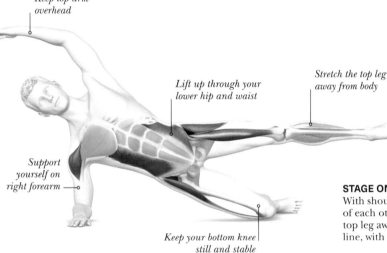

*Float your top arm overhead*

*Body forms a diagonal line from neck to knees*

*Rest your right forearm on the floor*

*Bend the knees and press the legs together*

### PREPARATORY STAGE

Begin sitting on your right hip, resting your right forearm on the floor. Bend the knees and press the legs together. Exhale as you raise your side off the mat, lifting your hips and floating the top arm overhead.

*Keep top arm overhead*

*Lift up through your lower hip and waist*

*Stretch the top leg away from body*

*Support yourself on right forearm*

*Keep your bottom knee still and stable*

### STAGE ONE

With shoulders and hips stacked on top of each other, inhale as you extend your top leg away from your body in a straight line, with your toes pointed.

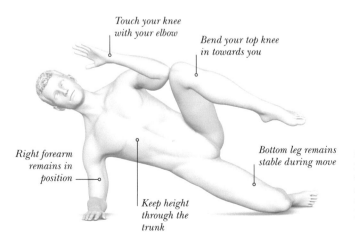

*Touch your knee with your elbow*

*Bend your top knee in towards you*

*Right forearm remains in position*

*Bottom leg remains stable during move*

*Keep height through the trunk*

### STAGE TWO

Exhale and bend your knee in towards you while bending your elbow and bringing it down to touch the knee. Inhale to return the arm overhead and extend the leg again. Repeat 4–6 times, then change sides.

# SIDE TWIST

**A challenging progression of the Side Bend** (see p.110), the Side Twist mobilizes the spine through rotation, while demanding a high level of pelvic stability, core strength, and shoulder strength. It is an exercise to work up to for most and is especially useful for creative sports such as gymnastics and martial arts, which require this advanced level of rotation and control.

## THE **BIG PICTURE**

From the preparatory stage 2 position, initiate the movement from your pelvis by lifting it upwards and rotating round using your core. Your top arm should follow with your spine to thread under your trunk, maintaining control so that the arm does not drop down. Keep pressing yourself away from the supporting arm for shoulder stability and height, and keep your legs connected together throughout for a smooth transition.

### STAGE ONE

Exhale as you lift your pelvis upwards and rotate your trunk towards the mat, threading your top arm underneath your trunk, while your other arm continues to support you. Inhale to return to the

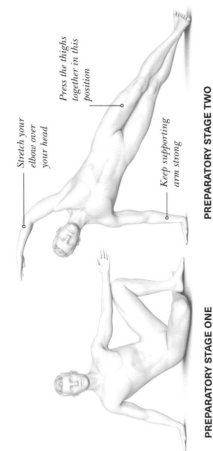

*Stretch your elbow over your head*

*Press the thighs together in this position*

*Keep supporting arm strong*

### PREPARATORY STAGE ONE
Sit on your right hip with your right leg bent and shoulders and pelvis facing forwards. Cross the left ankle over the right leg, and support yourself on your right arm. Inhale and engage the core.

### PREPARATORY STAGE TWO
Exhale and lift the pelvis upwards. Extend the legs and connect the inner thighs to drive the body up horizontally, forming a diagonal line with your body. Float your top arm overhead and inhale.

**Lower** body
Your **hip flexors** engage to bend at the hips. Your **quadriceps** engage to extend the knees and your **adductors** stabilize the hips and legs. Your **gluteals**, **hamstrings**, and **calves** lengthen.

*Gluteus maximus*

*Gluteus medius*

*Tensor fasciae latae*

*Biceps femoris long head*

*Vastus lateralis*

*Rectus femoris*

*Soleus*

*Tibialis anterior*

*Peroneus longus*

*Gastrocnemius*

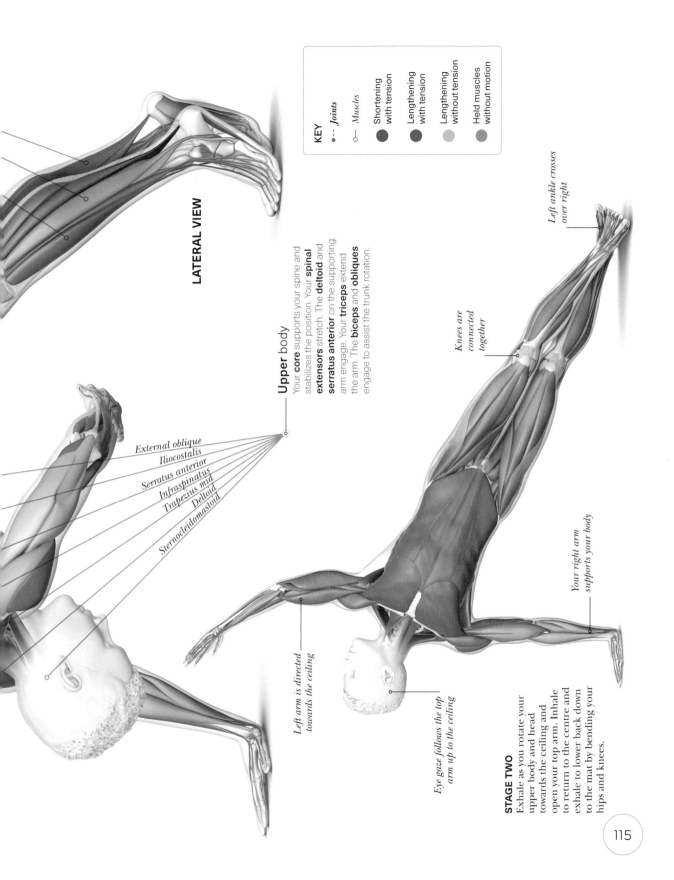

**LATERAL VIEW**

**KEY**

●--- *Joints*

○— *Muscles*

● Shortening with tension

● Lengthening with tension

● Lengthening without tension

● Held muscles without motion

External oblique
Iliocostalis
Serratus anterior
Infraspinatus
Trapezius mid
Deltoid
Sternocleidomastoid

**Upper** body

Your **core** supports your spine and stabilizes the position. Your **spinal extensors** stretch. The **deltoid** and **serratus anterior** on the supporting arm engage. Your **triceps** extend the arm. The **biceps** and **obliques** engage to assist the trunk rotation.

*Left ankle crosses over right*

*Knees are connected together*

*Your right arm supports your body*

*Left arm is directed towards the ceiling*

*Eye gaze follows the top arm up to the ceiling*

**STAGE TWO**

Exhale as you rotate your upper body and head towards the ceiling and open your top arm. Inhale to return to the centre and exhale to lower back down to the mat by bending your hips and knees.

115

# CLAM

This exercise activates and strengthens the gluteal muscles, and provides core stability through hip rotation. You can choose to hold the end position, or add in pulses at this end range to additionally develop gluteal endurance. This combination of muscle strength and endurance creates support to promote hip strength.

**Caution**

This exercise may not be suitable for any lateral hip pathologies as the pressure of lying on the hip may be too uncomfortable. It should also be avoided if you have pain in your piriformis muscle (located in the buttock). If pain limits your hip range, try an isometric Clam by placing a tight band around both knees to prevent movement and press your top knee up into the band for 5 seconds each time.

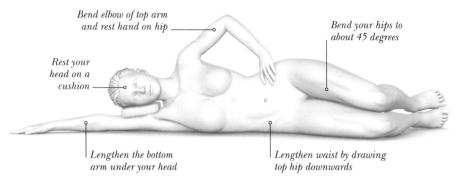

Bend elbow of top arm and rest hand on hip

Rest your head on a cushion

Bend your hips to about 45 degrees

Lengthen the bottom arm under your head

Lengthen waist by drawing top hip downwards

**PREPARATORY STAGE**
Lie on your side with your hips and shoulders stacked on top of each other and your spine and pelvis in neutral. Bend your knees so that your feet are in line with your spine and lengthen your bottom arm under your head. Place a cushion between your ear and shoulder. Rest your top hand on your top hip and set your shoulder blades in neutral.

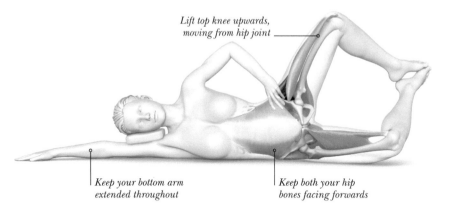

Lift top knee upwards, moving from hip joint

Keep your bottom arm extended throughout

Keep both your hip bones facing forwards

**STAGE ONE**
Bring both feet up to hip height, keeping them connected and your trunk neutral. Inhale to lengthen the body. Exhale as you lift your top knee upwards, moving from the hip joint. Lift as far as you can, keeping your pelvis and spine neutral.

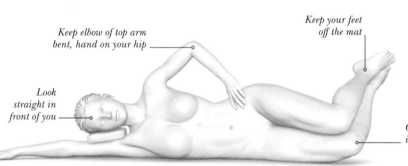

Keep elbow of top arm bent, hand on your hip

Look straight in front of you

Keep your feet off the mat

Connect knees and inner thighs together

**STAGE TWO**
Inhale to return the knee back to the starting position, connecting the knees and inner thighs together and keeping your feet off the mat. Complete 8–10 repetitions, then repeat the sequence on the other side.

# LEG **LIFT** AND **LOWER**

This simple hip exercise strengthens the gluteal muscles and stabilizes the hip through rotatory movements. It is an ideal starting exercise for any hip programme to develop balance and side-lying stability, and can be used as a precursor to Side Kick (see p.100), and Double Leg Lift (see p.118).

**KEY**

● Primary target muscle    ● Secondary target muscle

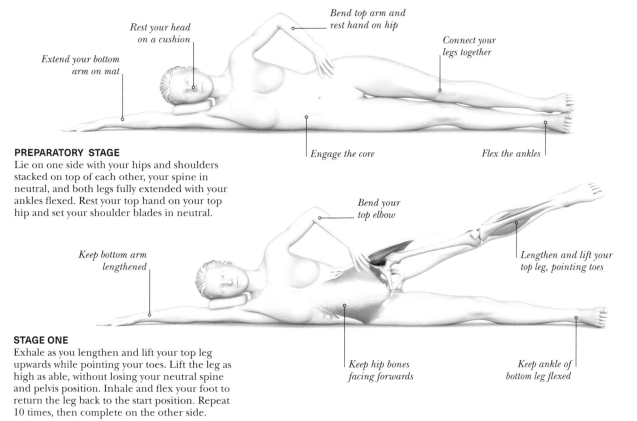

*Rest your head on a cushion*

*Extend your bottom arm on mat*

*Bend top arm and rest hand on hip*

*Connect your legs together*

*Engage the core*

*Flex the ankles*

*Keep bottom arm lengthened*

*Bend your top elbow*

*Lengthen and lift your top leg, pointing toes*

*Keep hip bones facing forwards*

*Keep ankle of bottom leg flexed*

**PREPARATORY STAGE**

Lie on one side with your hips and shoulders stacked on top of each other, your spine in neutral, and both legs fully extended with your ankles flexed. Rest your top hand on your top hip and set your shoulder blades in neutral.

**STAGE ONE**

Exhale as you lengthen and lift your top leg upwards while pointing your toes. Lift the leg as high as able, without losing your neutral spine and pelvis position. Inhale and flex your foot to return the leg back to the start position. Repeat 10 times, then complete on the other side.

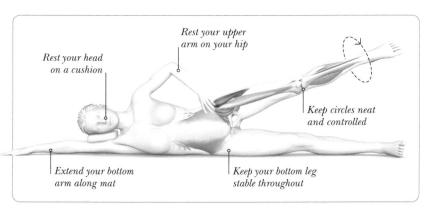

*Rest your head on a cushion*

*Rest your upper arm on your hip*

*Keep circles neat and controlled*

*Extend your bottom arm along mat*

*Keep your bottom leg stable throughout*

**VARIATION**

Starting in the preparatory position, raise your top leg to hip height, keeping the leg parallel to your bottom leg, and point your toes. Inhale to lengthen your leg and trunk. Exhale as you move your leg round in a circle, moving it forwards, upwards, backwards, and downwards. Inhale on the next circle and continue alternating your breath with each circle. Repeat 10 times before changing direction to draw your circle another 10 times. Switch sides and repeat sequence on the other leg.

# DOUBLE LEG LIFT

This is a challenging side-lying exercise that strengthens the gluteal muscles, develops rotatory hip stability, while also developing side-lying balance and coordination. It is useful to master prior to attempting Side Kick (see p.100), and can be used as a good foundational exercise for adductor and groin muscle activation and rehabilitation. You could perform this exercise with both knees flexed to reduce the load on your core and adductor muscles, as a precursor to stage 1.

**Caution**

Keep length in the trunk to avoid collapsing into the lower back. If pain presents, or acute back pain exists, this is best avoided as the weight of both legs must be properly supported by the core.

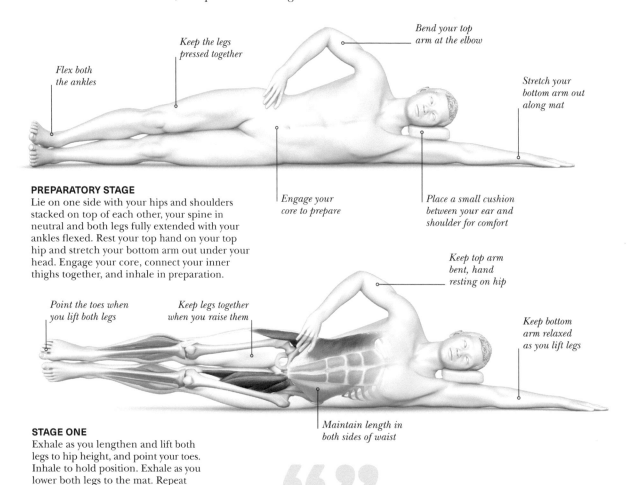

Flex both the ankles

Keep the legs pressed together

Bend your top arm at the elbow

Stretch your bottom arm out along mat

Engage your core to prepare

Place a small cushion between your ear and shoulder for comfort

**PREPARATORY STAGE**
Lie on one side with your hips and shoulders stacked on top of each other, your spine in neutral and both legs fully extended with your ankles flexed. Rest your top hand on your top hip and stretch your bottom arm out under your head. Engage your core, connect your inner thighs together, and inhale in preparation.

Point the toes when you lift both legs

Keep legs together when you raise them

Keep top arm bent, hand resting on hip

Keep bottom arm relaxed as you lift legs

**STAGE ONE**
Exhale as you lengthen and lift both legs to hip height, and point your toes. Inhale to hold position. Exhale as you lower both legs to the mat. Repeat up to 10 times then change sides

Maintain length in both sides of waist

**KEY**
● Primary target muscle
● Secondary target muscle

*Hold **both legs** raised for a longer duration to further **challenge** gluteal and oblique endurance.*

# ONE LEG LIFTED

This exercise can be used as a precursor to Double Leg Lift as it allows you to practise side balance with a staged approach of lifting the legs. It also increases endurance and control.

*Bend the top arm at the elbow*

*Keep your eye gaze forwards*

*Stretch out your bottom arm*

*Flex feet at the ankles*

*Engage your core to prepare*

### PREPARATORY STAGE
Assume the Double Leg Lift preparatory position, lying on one side with your hips and shoulders stacked, your spine in neutral, and both legs fully extended. Rest your head on a small cushion.

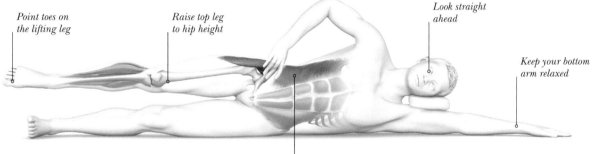

*Point toes on the lifting leg*

*Raise top leg to hip height*

*Look straight ahead*

*Keep your bottom arm relaxed*

*Maintain length in both sides of waist*

### STAGE ONE
Exhale as you raise your top leg up to hip height and point your toes, lengthening both legs away from the trunk.

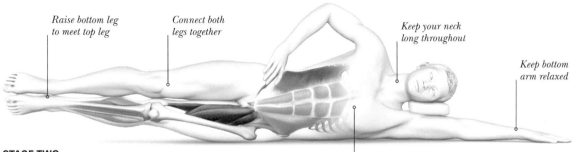

*Raise bottom leg to meet top leg*

*Connect both legs together*

*Keep your neck long throughout*

*Keep bottom arm relaxed*

*Keep ribcage neutral, drawing down to hips*

### STAGE TWO
Inhale to bring your bottom leg up to join the top leg and connect your legs together. Exhale to hold this position. Inhale, lower both legs back to the mat together. Repeat up to 10 times, then change sides.

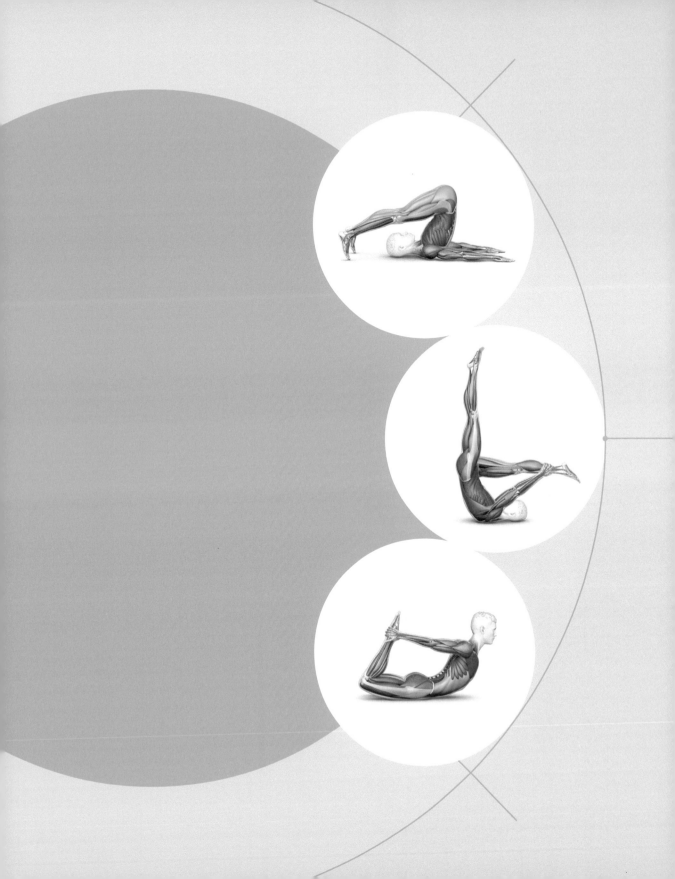

# STRENGTH
# EXERCISES

**The exercises in this section build upon the stability exercises**, utilizing our global musculature, and more external layers, to enhance movement and provide a base for everyday activities and performance. Strength exercises are focussed on generating additional strength through recruiting more or larger muscle groups, and they provide an additional challenge for the body to overcome.

# ROLL UP

**Perfecting the Roll Up provides a masterclass** in mobilizing the spine and strengthening the abdominal muscles with the utmost control of movement. It teaches coordination between the spine, pelvis, and ribcage and requires a foundation of strength and control, to prevent yourself falling back on the descent.

## THE **BIG PICTURE**

Use your breath to guide this movement by inhaling as you raise the arms upwards followed by your head, and exhaling as you continue to roll up and forwards, engaging your core to support and lengthen your spine. Press your legs firmly down into the mat and squeeze them together to anchor your body and isolate the movement to the core. Maintain adequate lift through your spine and chest to prevent collapsing through your upper body.

*Stretch arms up above your head, palms up*

*Draw ribcage down to connect your core*

*Press feet together and flex them upwards*

### PREPARATORY STAGE

Lie on your back with both legs extended and connected together. Your spine is neutral and feet are flexed upwards. Your arms begin overhead flat on the floor.

### ⓘ Caution

The Roll Up is not suitable for those with acute back pain as the large range of spinal mobility and load placed upon the spine may aggravate the condition.

### STAGE ONE

Inhale to raise both arms up to above shoulder height with palms facing forwards and curl upwards along with your head, neck, and upper body, bringing your chin towards your chest. Exhale slowly as you continue to roll upwards one vertebra at a time, curving your spine forwards and reaching your arms towards your toes. Maintain height in your pelvis as you form a C-curve.

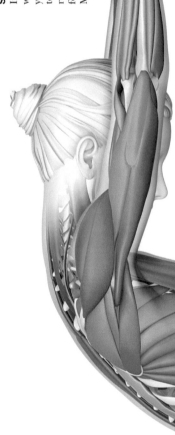

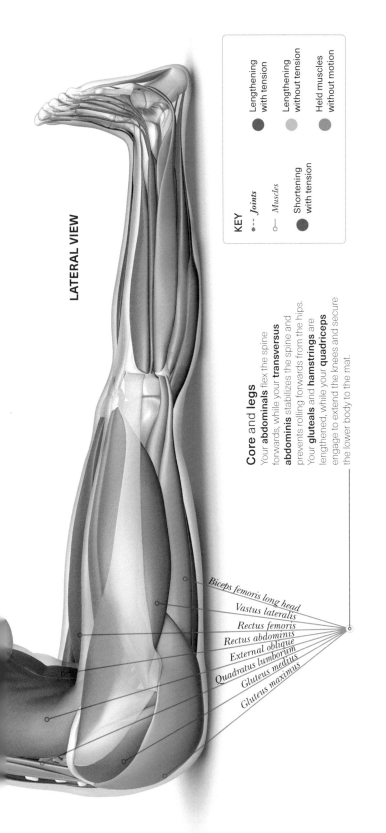

**LATERAL VIEW**

### KEY

● - - *Joints*

○ — *Muscles*

● Shortening
with tension

● Lengthening
with tension

● Lengthening
without tension

● Held muscles
without motion

### Core and legs

Your **abdominals** flex the spine forwards, while your **transversus abdominis** stabilizes the spine and prevents rolling forwards from the hips. Your **gluteals** and **hamstrings** are lengthened, while your **quadriceps** engage to extend the knees and secure the lower body to the mat.

Biceps femoris long head
Vastus lateralis
Rectus femoris
Rectus abdominis
External oblique
Quadratus lumborum
Gluteus medius
Gluteus maximus

## Articulate *through each spinal segment* in order **as you** *roll up and down.*

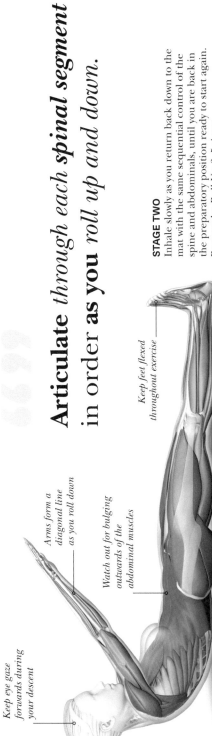

**STAGE TWO**
Inhale slowly as you return back down to the mat with the same sequential control of the spine and abdominals, until you are back in the preparatory position ready to start again. Repeat the Roll Up 3–5 times.

*Keep feet flexed throughout exercise*

*Arms form a diagonal line as you roll down*

*Watch out for bulging outwards of the abdominal muscles*

*Keep eye gaze forwards during your descent*

## » VARIATIONS

These variations are considerably different from the main Roll Up, but they develop the same abdominal strength and control through movement. You can integrate these options into your everyday life (On a Chair), as matwork transitions (On a Mat), or with the use of Pilates equipment (With Band Support).

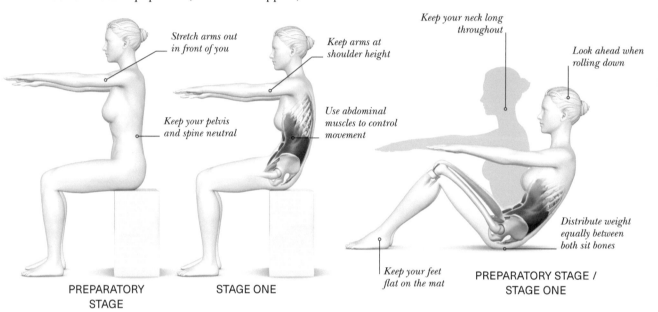

*Stretch arms out in front of you*

*Keep your pelvis and spine neutral*

*Keep arms at shoulder height*

*Use abdominal muscles to control movement*

*Keep your neck long throughout*

*Look ahead when rolling down*

*Distribute weight equally between both sit bones*

*Keep your feet flat on the mat*

PREPARATORY STAGE

STAGE ONE

PREPARATORY STAGE / STAGE ONE

## ON A CHAIR

Sit on the edge of a chair and keep both feet flat on the floor. Be careful not to collapse your upper body as you roll back. Thinking of continued length in your waist and spine will help you with this.

### PREPARATORY STAGE
Sit upright on a chair with equal weight between both sitting bones, your pelvis and spine in neutral, and your neck long. Raise both arms in front of you to shoulder height with palms facing downwards.

### STAGE ONE
Exhale as you roll your pelvis backwards and articulate your spine backwards into a C-curve, vertebra by vertebra.

### STAGE TWO
Inhale to return back to upright sitting, bringing your upper body forwards slightly, followed by your mid-back, and then your lower back and pelvis. Repeat 8–10 times.

## ON A MAT

This exercise can be useful for beginners to practise the Roll Up motion and grade the distance they roll to. Ensure you can roll up with ease for each distance you attempt. Keep your abdominals engaged throughout, and avoid them doming outwards.

### PREPARATORY STAGE
Sit on a mat with your hips and knees flexed and your feet flat on the floor, and your pelvis and spine in neutral. Raise arms to shoulder height, palms facing down.

### STAGE ONE
Exhale as you roll your pelvis backwards and articulate your spine into a C-curve bone by bone.

### STAGE TWO
Inhale to return back to upright sitting, bringing your upper body forwards slightly, followed by your mid-back, and then your lower back and pelvis. Repeat 8–10 times, increasing how far back you roll gradually, until you can roll to the mat and back up.

*Using the **band** builds **confidence** in your ability to* move back *further, allowing gentle **progression**, which may give faster* results.

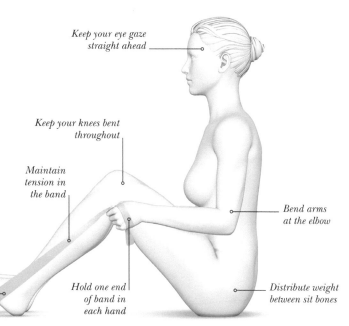

Keep your eye gaze
straight ahead

Keep your knees bent
throughout

Maintain
tension in
the band

Bend arms
at the elbow

Loop resistance
band around soles

Hold one end
of band in
each hand

Distribute weight
between sit bones

PREPARATORY STAGE

## WITH BAND SUPPORT

The resistance band is a useful asset to facilitate the curving of the spine and the control required. The tighter your band, the greater the level of support. Ensure your shoulders and arms remain relaxed to fully target your abdominal muscles, and keep your breastbone lifted.

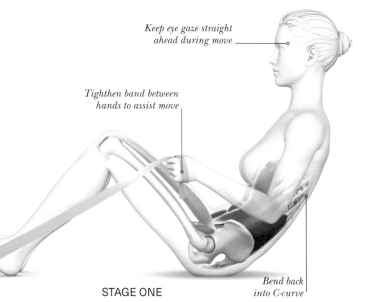

Keep eye gaze straight
ahead during move

Tighthen band between
hands to assist move

Use tension in band to
control movement

Bend back
into C-curve

STAGE ONE

**PREPARATORY STAGE**
Sit upright on a mat. Place your feet flat on the floor, flexed at the ankles, with your pelvis and spine neutral and your neck long. Loop a resistance band around both feet.

**STAGE ONE**
Relax your shoulders downwards, then exhale as you roll your pelvis back, articulating your spine into a C-curve bone by bone. Control the move with your abdominal muscles.

**STAGE TWO**
Inhale to gradually return back to upright sitting, bringing your upper body forwards. Repeat 8–10 times, increasing how far back you roll, loosening the band to reduce support.

# ROLL OVER

**The Roll Over is an advanced exercise** that is the reverse of the Roll Up (see p.122). It focusses on abdominal strength and spinal control through a large range of movement, while going into an inverted (upside-down) position.

## THE **BIG PICTURE**

Ensure your spine is warmed up and mobile prior to trying Roll Over (see p.46). Initiate the movement from your core and keep enough length in your spine by reaching your feet away from you, and maintaining the distance between your feet and your tailbone. Keep your chest open, shoulders wide, and neck long. You can bend your knees initially to make Roll Over easier but avoid bringing them in towards your chest. Complete 3–6 repetitions of the Roll Over.

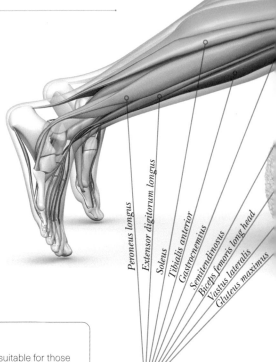

Peroneus longus
Extensor digitorum longus
Soleus
Tibialis anterior
Gastrocnemius
Semitendinosus
Biceps femoris long head
Vastus lateralis
Gluteus maximus

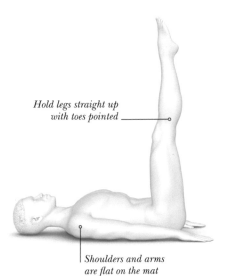

*Hold legs straight up
with toes pointed*

*Shoulders and arms
are flat on the mat*

**PREPARATORY STAGE**
Lie flat on the mat with both legs extended outwards, toes pointed, and inner thighs connected. Inhale and extend both legs upwards towards the ceiling to form a 90-degree angle at the hips.

> **❗ Caution**
> The Roll Over is not suitable for those with neck injuries as it can overload the neck, aggravating it further. People who experience lower back pain should also avoid this exercise because of the significant spinal flexion and strength required.

**Legs**
Your **hamstrings** lengthen and engage to keep the reach upwards. Your **quadriceps** engage to maintain knee extension and prevent the legs collapsing towards your trunk. Your **calves** lengthen as the **ankle dorsiflexors** engage.

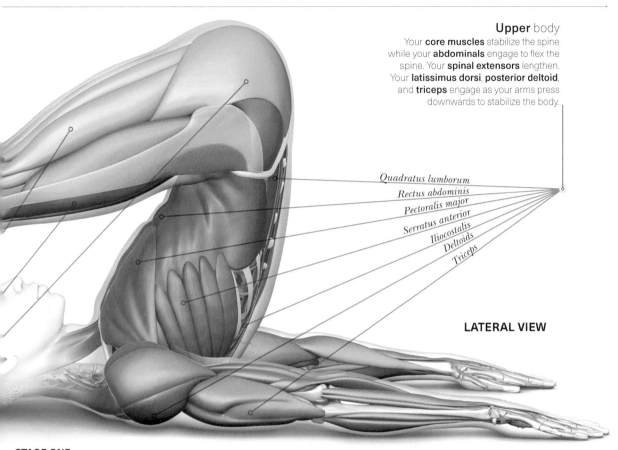

Your **core muscles** stabilize the spine while your **abdominals** engage to flex the spine. Your **spinal extensors** lengthen. Your **latissimus dorsi**, **posterior deltoid**, and **triceps** engage as your arms press downwards to stabilize the body.

*Quadratus lumborum*
*Rectus abdominis*
*Pectoralis major*
*Serratus anterior*
*Iliocostalis*
*Deltoids*
*Triceps*

**LATERAL VIEW**

## STAGE ONE

Exhale as you lift up through your pelvis and spine sequentially and float your legs overhead until they are parallel with the mat. Inhale as you part your legs to shoulder-width apart, flex your feet, and aim to lower your feet further towards the mat. The spine does not move as the feet lower further to the mat.

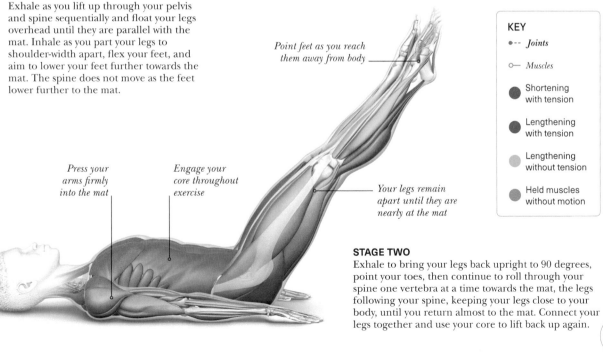

*Point feet as you reach them away from body*

*Your legs remain apart until they are nearly at the mat*

*Press your arms firmly into the mat*

*Engage your core throughout exercise*

### KEY

- ●--  *Joints*
- ○—  *Muscles*
- ● Shortening with tension
- ● Lengthening with tension
- ● Lengthening without tension
- ● Held muscles without motion

## STAGE TWO

Exhale to bring your legs back upright to 90 degrees, point your toes, then continue to roll through your spine one vertebra at a time towards the mat, the legs following your spine, keeping your legs close to your body, until you return almost to the mat. Connect your legs together and use your core to lift back up again.

# CORKSCREW

**This advanced exercise challenges abdominal strength** and spinal and pelvic stability, as well as massaging your internal organs. It builds greatly upon skills learned in the preceding exercises. It would be useful to master the Rocker with Open Legs (see p.68) and Roll Over (see p.126) prior to attempting Corkscrew.

## THE BIG PICTURE

Allow length in your spine throughout this exercise to avoid compression. As your legs come overhead, imagine pressing the ceiling away to activate the legs while keeping your hips and feet in line. Your legs rotate to the side without shifting your pelvis, and this is controlled through core activation and body awareness of your movements, and the ability to isolate the pelvis from the lower back.

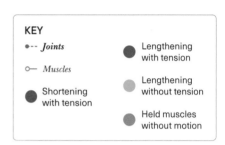

**KEY**

•-- *Joints*

o— *Muscles*

● Shortening with tension

● Lengthening with tension

● Lengthening without tension

● Held muscles without motion

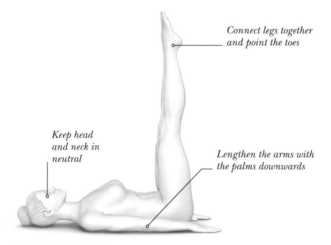

*Connect legs together and point the toes*

*Keep head and neck in neutral*

*Lengthen the arms with the palms downwards*

**PREPARATORY STAGE**
Begin lying flat on your back with your legs extended and connected together and your arms lengthened by your sides. Engage your core and inhale as you lift your legs upwards to 90 degrees with your toes pointed.

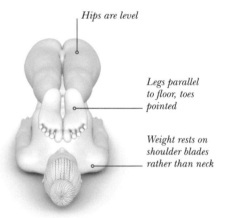

*Hips are level*

*Legs parallel to floor, toes pointed*

*Weight rests on shoulder blades rather than neck*

**STAGE ONE**
Exhale as you lift your hips upwards to roll your legs overhead until they are parallel to the floor, toes pointed and spine lengthened.

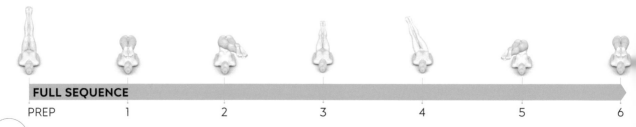

**FULL SEQUENCE**

PREP        1        2        3        4        5        6

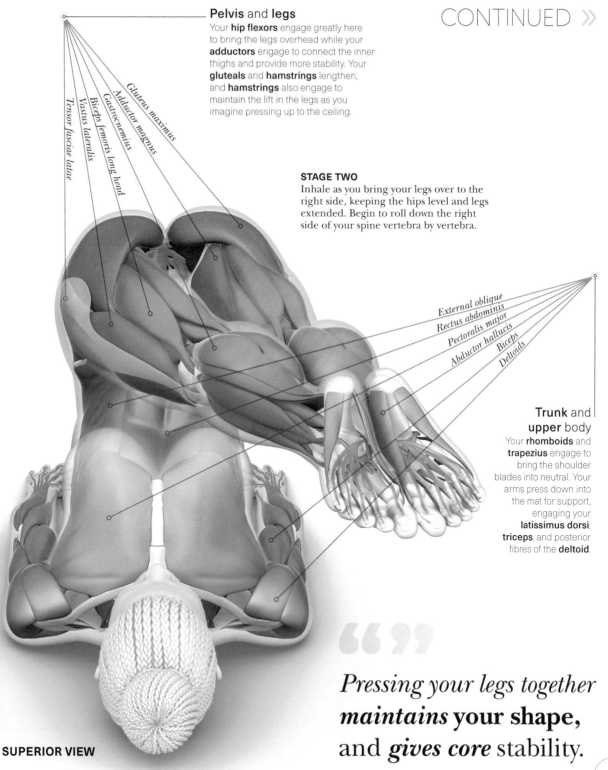

### Pelvis and legs

Your **hip flexors** engage greatly here to bring the legs overhead while your **adductors** engage to connect the inner thighs and provide more stability. Your **gluteals** and **hamstrings** lengthen, and **hamstrings** also engage to maintain the lift in the legs as you imagine pressing up to the ceiling.

Gluteus maximus
Adductor magnus
Gastrocnemius
Biceps femoris long head
Vastus lateralis
Tensor fasciae latae

### STAGE TWO

Inhale as you bring your legs over to the right side, keeping the hips level and legs extended. Begin to roll down the right side of your spine vertebra by vertebra.

External oblique
Rectus abdominis
Pectoralis major
Abductor hallucis
Biceps
Deltoids

### Trunk and upper body

Your **rhomboids** and **trapezius** engage to bring the shoulder blades into neutral. Your arms press down into the mat for support, engaging your **latissimus dorsi**, **triceps**, and posterior fibres of the **deltoid**.

**SUPERIOR VIEW**

“”

*Pressing your legs together* **maintains** *your shape,* and *gives core* stability.

# »CORKSCREW (FOLLOW-ON)

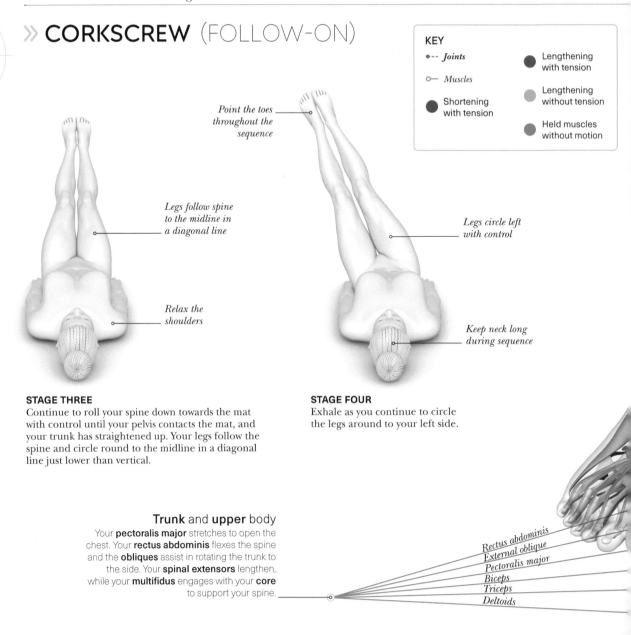

**KEY**

•--- *Joints*

o— *Muscles*

● Shortening with tension

● Lengthening with tension

● Lengthening without tension

● Held muscles without motion

*Point the toes throughout the sequence*

*Legs follow spine to the midline in a diagonal line*

*Relax the shoulders*

*Legs circle left with control*

*Keep neck long during sequence*

**STAGE THREE**
Continue to roll your spine down towards the mat with control until your pelvis contacts the mat, and your trunk has straightened up. Your legs follow the spine and circle round to the midline in a diagonal line just lower than vertical.

**STAGE FOUR**
Exhale as you continue to circle the legs around to your left side.

**Trunk** and **upper** body
Your **pectoralis major** stretches to open the chest. Your **rectus abdominis** flexes the spine and the **obliques** assist in rotating the trunk to the side. Your **spinal extensors** lengthen, while your **multifidus** engages with your **core** to support your spine.

*Rectus abdominis*
*External oblique*
*Pectoralis major*
*Biceps*
*Triceps*
*Deltoids*

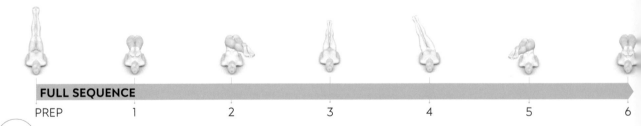

**FULL SEQUENCE**

PREP          1          2          3          4          5          6

### Pelvis and legs

The **hip lateral rotators** stabilize the hip joints while the **gluteus medius** and **minimus**, along with the **tensor fasciae latae**, maintain the level of the pelvis when performing the exercise. Your **quadriceps** engage to extend the knees. Your **calves** engage to plantarflex the ankles.

Gluteus maximus
Gastrocnemius
Biceps femoris long head
Vastus lateralis
Semitendinosus
Tensor fasciae latae

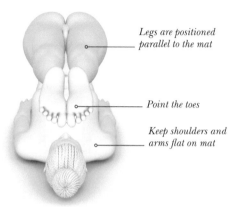

*Legs are positioned parallel to the mat*

*Point the toes*

*Keep shoulders and arms flat on mat*

### STAGE SIX

Bring your legs fully overhead and parallel to the mat, your spine rolling up until you are resting on your shoulder blades. Repeat the full sequence again by swinging your legs to the left side to begin this time. Repeat 3 times in total to each side. To exit the position, bend both knees in towards your chest, keeping the legs connected, and carefully lower your legs, along with your spine, down to the mat.

*Use your core muscles, **not** **momentum,** to move your legs around in the Corkscrew exercise.*

### STAGE FIVE

Your legs continue overhead as you roll up the left side of your spine to be partially resting on your shoulders as in stage 1, but this time the legs go to the left.

**SUPERIOR VIEW**

# NECK PULL

**This exercise consists of one continuous movement** requiring sequential mobilization of the spine and advanced abdominal strength. It also provides a deep stretch for the back of the body – the hamstrings, back extensors, and neck extensors. You should master the Roll Up (see p.122) before trying the Neck Pull.

## THE **BIG PICTURE**

Maintain shape throughout your upper body by keeping the head and neck long, chest lifted, and elbows wide to prevent excessive flexion. Imagine a coat hanger is holding your chest open and elbows outwards so that the movement comes from your core rather than from force through the arms. Glide the shoulder blades down your back to avoid hitching the shoulders up to the ears. Repeat 3–5 times.

**Caution**

The Neck Pull is not suitable for those with neck injuries, acute back pain, or neural tension such as sciatic nerve irritations.

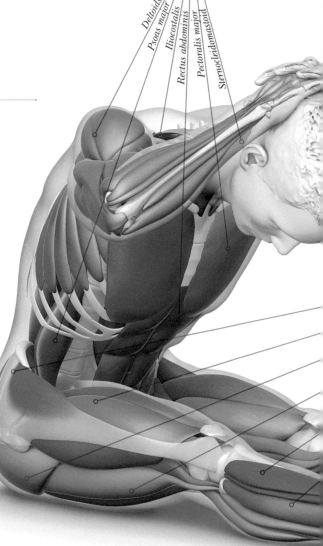

*Deltoids*
*Psoas major*
*Iliocostalis*
*Rectus abdominis*
*Pectoralis major*
*Sternocleidomastoid*

*Keep your elbows wide*

*Engage the core to prepare*

*Position legs hip-distance apart, and flex the feet*

**PREPARATORY STAGE**
Lie on your back with your spine and pelvis in neutral, your legs hip-distance apart, and your feet flexed. Clasp your hands together behind your head with your elbows wide and your chest open. Engage your core.

**STAGE ONE**
Inhale as you lengthen your neck and lift your head and neck upwards. Continue by lifting one vertebra at a time off the mat to curl your upper body upwards. Exhale as you keep curling forwards and bring your trunk over the legs. Press your heels away from you to further lengthen the legs outwards.

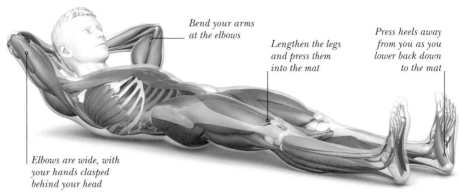

Bend your arms at the elbows

Lengthen the legs and press them into the mat

Press heels away from you as you lower back down to the mat

### Upper body

Your **rhomboids** and **middle** and **lower trapezius** maintain the neutral scapular position. Your **deltoid** and **supraspinatus** abduct the arms. Your **neck extensors** engage as you lightly press your head into your hands.

*Elbows are wide, with your hands clasped behind your head*

**STAGE TWO**

Inhale as you roll your spine back to upright sitting. Lengthen the neck and press it backwards into the palms of your hands. Exhale as you then tilt your pelvis backwards and use your abdominal muscles to control rolling sequentially back down to the mat, lowering from the pelvis, the lower back, mid-back, upper back, and finally your head and neck until you are back in the preparatory position.

### Lower body

Your **quadriceps** extend your knees and anchor the legs down. Your **abdominal muscles** flex the trunk with assistance from your **hip flexors** and **psoas major**. Your **ankle dorsiflexors** pull the toes upwards and allow you to lengthen your heels away from you.

Tensor fasciae latae
Vastus lateralis
Gluteus maximus
Biceps femoris long head
Tibialis anterior
Peroneus longus
Soleus

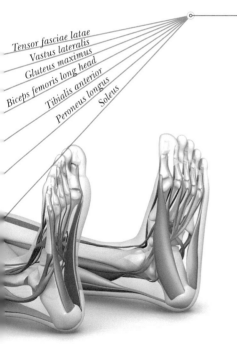

**THREE-QUARTER LATERAL VIEW**

| KEY | |
|---|---|
| ●--- | *Joints* |
| ○— | *Muscles* |
| ● | Shortening with tension |
| ● | Lengthening with tension |
| ● | Lengthening without tension |
| ● | Held muscles without motion |

*The name "Neck Pull" is **misleading, as** you actually hold your hands **behind your head**, and **avoid** pulling on the neck.*

# JACK KNIFE

## This classic Pilates exercise

creates length and strength in the trunk and spine while using leg and gluteal strength for support. It requires a lot of control, with long leg levers through spinal flexion, and also being in the inverted position.

## THE **BIG PICTURE**

Begin by connecting your inner thighs together, engaging your quadriceps and gluteals, and connecting your core to create the elevation. Lengthen your legs and pelvis away from your trunk and think about elongating your waist to avoid spine compression. Avoid flexing your chin towards your chest. If new to this exercise, place your hands on your lower back to support you during stage 1, and to facilitate transitioning to stage 2.

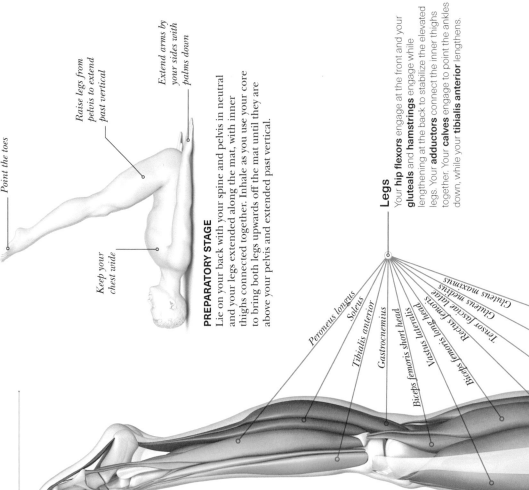

*Point the toes*

*Raise legs from pelvis to extend past vertical*

*Extend arms by your sides with palms down*

*Keep your chest wide*

### PREPARATORY STAGE

Lie on your back with your spine and pelvis in neutral and your legs extended along the mat, with inner thighs connected together. Inhale as you use your core to bring both legs upwards off the mat until they are above your pelvis and extended past vertical.

### Legs

Your **hip flexors** engage at the front and your **gluteals** and **hamstrings** engage while lengthening at the back to stabilize the elevated legs. Your **adductors** connect the inner thighs together. Your **calves** engage to point the ankles down, while your **tibialis anterior** lengthens.

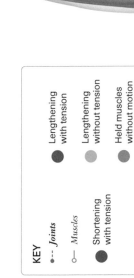

*Peroneus longus*
*Soleus*
*Tibialis anterior*
*Gastrocnemius*
*Biceps femoris short head*
*Vastus lateralis*
*Rectus femoris long head*
*Tensor fasciae latae*
*Gluteus medius*
*Gluteus maximus*

### KEY

- - - **Joints**

—○— **Muscles**

● Shortening with tension

● Lengthening with tension

● Lengthening without tension

● Held muscles without motion

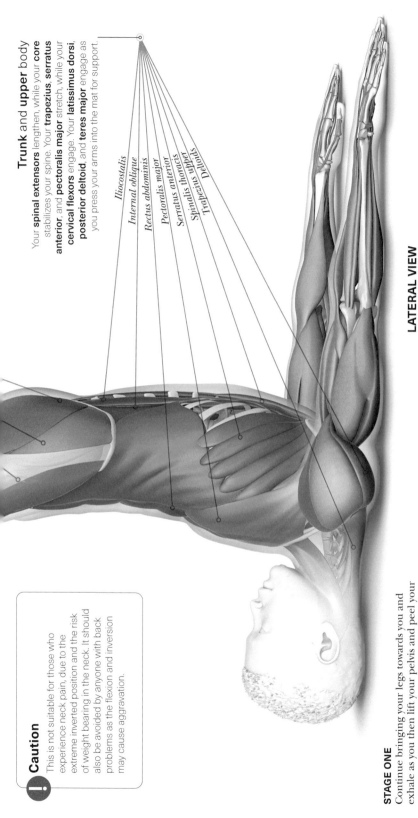

## Trunk and upper body

Your **spinal extensors** lengthen, while your **core** stabilizes your spine. Your **trapezius**, **serratus anterior**, and **pectoralis major** stretch, while your **cervical flexors** engage. Your **latissimus dorsi**, **posterior deltoid**, and **teres major** engage as you press your arms into the mat for support.

*Iliocostalis*
*Internal oblique*
*Rectus abdominis*
*Pectoralis major*
*Serratus anterior*
*Spinalis thoracis*
*Trapezius upper*
*Deltoids*

**LATERAL VIEW**

### STAGE ONE
Continue bringing your legs towards you and exhale as you then lift your pelvis and peel your spine up off the mat vertically until you are resting on your shoulder blades. Align your legs directly upwards with toes pointed.

### STAGE TWO
Inhale as you slowly control the roll down of your spine, vertebra by vertebra, back down to the mat. Follow this with your pelvis and legs until your legs are flat on the mat. Repeat up to 5 times.

*Connect legs together and point the toes*

*Arms remain stretched by your sides*

*Core is strongly active to control descent*

135

# TEASER

**A fun, advanced exercise,** Teaser is often thought of as the accumulation of all that is Pilates. It requires extensive abdominal strength, control through movement, and the use of long arm and leg levers.

## THE **BIG PICTURE**

In Teaser, keep your legs connected, long, and reaching away from you. The legs remain loose, not gripping, as you use your core to drive the movement. Roll smoothly and sequentially through your spine in both directions. Keep the space between the shoulders and ears consistent. When you reach the upright position, lengthen your arms and legs away from you, lift your chest, and engage your core further to balance before commencing the descent.

**THREE-QUARTER LATERAL VIEW**

Gastrocnemius
Soleus
Tibialis anterior
Peroneus longus
Biceps femoris short head
Semitendinosus
Rectus femoris
Vastus lateralis
Biceps femoris long head
Tensor fasciae latae
Gluteus maximus

### Legs
Your **hip flexors** bring the legs into the raised position and then contract isometrically to hold them there, together with the **quadriceps**, which extend the knees. Your **adductors** connect the inner thighs together and your **hamstrings** are lengthened. If tightness prevents you fully extending the knees, you can bend them slightly.

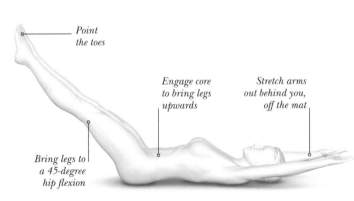

Point the toes

Engage core to bring legs upwards

Stretch arms out behind you, off the mat

Bring legs to a 45-degree hip flexion

### PREPARATORY STAGE
Begin lying on your back with your legs connected together and toes pointed. Bring your arms behind you and use your core to bring your legs up off the mat to a high diagonal line.

### STAGE ONE
Inhale as you use your core to curl your head, neck, upper body, and spine up off the mat while lengthening your legs and arms away from you, until you form the V-shaped Teaser position with your trunk and legs.

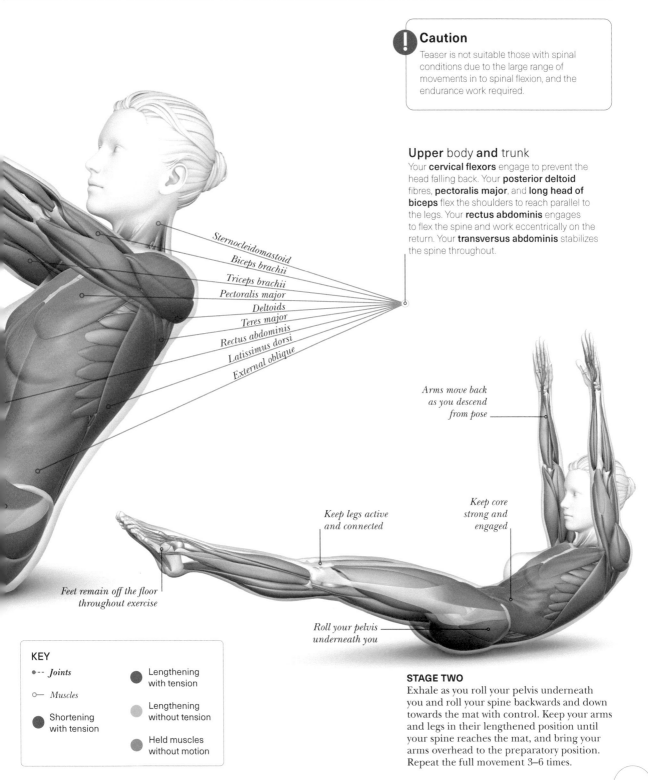

## Upper body **and** trunk

Your **cervical flexors** engage to prevent the head falling back. Your **posterior deltoid** fibres, **pectoralis major**, and **long head of biceps** flex the shoulders to reach parallel to the legs. Your **rectus abdominis** engages to flex the spine and work eccentrically on the return. Your **transversus abdominis** stabilizes the spine throughout.

*Sternocleidomastoid*
*Biceps brachii*
*Triceps brachii*
*Pectoralis major*
*Deltoids*
*Teres major*
*Rectus abdominis*
*Latissimus dorsi*
*External oblique*

*Arms move back as you descend from pose*

*Keep core strong and engaged*

*Keep legs active and connected*

*Feet remain off the floor throughout exercise*

*Roll your pelvis underneath you*

**KEY**

•-- *Joints*

o— *Muscles*

● Shortening with tension

● Lengthening with tension

● Lengthening without tension

● Held muscles without motion

**STAGE TWO**

Exhale as you roll your pelvis underneath you and roll your spine backwards and down towards the mat with control. Keep your arms and legs in their lengthened position until your spine reaches the mat, and bring your arms overhead to the preparatory position. Repeat the full movement 3–6 times.

137

# » VARIATIONS

The main Teaser is a very demanding exercise and these variations offer much less strenuous options for beginners. While they still allow you to experience the Teaser position, they add support of either a single leg or hand and work well as energizing stand-alone exercises.

## SINGLE LEG TEASER

This option combines a Roll Up with a single extended leg to introduce the Teaser concepts. Squeeze the inner thighs together for additional support as you move between the two positions.

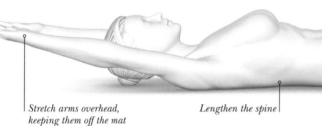

*Point the toes on the raised leg*

*Raise one leg on the diagonal*

*Stretch arms overhead, keeping them off the mat*

*Lengthen the spine*

**PREPARATORY STAGE**

*Keep static leg bent, foot flat on mat*

### PREPARATORY STAGE
Begin lying on your back with your hips and knees bent and your arms extended overhead. Extend one leg upwards on a diagonal line.

### STAGE ONE
Inhale as you roll your spine upwards into the V-shaped Teaser position, bringing your arms forward until they are parallel with the raised leg.

### STAGE TWO
Exhale to sequentially roll your spine back down to the mat and bring your arms overhead, as per the preparatory position. Repeat up to 5 times as able, then switch the legs over.

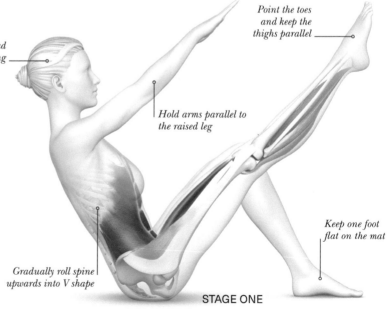

*Look straight ahead and keep neck long*

*Point the toes and keep the thighs parallel*

*Hold arms parallel to the raised leg*

*Keep one foot flat on the mat*

*Gradually roll spine upwards into V shape*

**STAGE ONE**

KEY
● Primary target muscle
● Secondary target muscle

*Practise* sitting *up on your* **sitting bones** *in the Teaser* **V-shaped position** *before trying the full* dynamic *exercise.*

## TEASER WITH SUPPORT

Use your arms for assistance with the trunk flexion. Pause at the top of the position to ensure your core is engaged, and keep your arms lightly grasping your outer legs for additional support as you roll down.

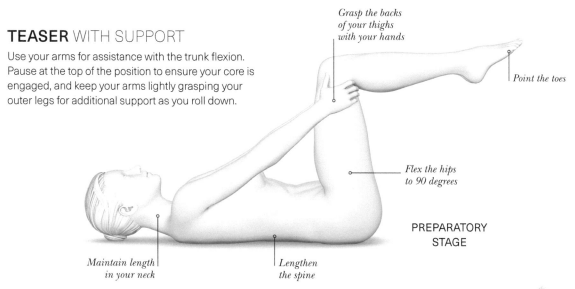

*Grasp the backs of your thighs with your hands*

*Point the toes*

*Flex the hips to 90 degrees*

PREPARATORY STAGE

*Maintain length in your neck*

*Lengthen the spine*

**PREPARATORY STAGE**
Begin lying on your back with your hips and knees bent into the table top position and inner thighs connected together, and arms extended overhead. Reach your arms to grasp the backs of your thighs.

**STAGE ONE**
Inhale as you roll your spine upwards while simultaneously extending your legs out on to the high diagonal to form the V-shaped Teaser position.

**STAGE TWO**
Exhale to sequentially roll your spine back down to the mat, and bring your arms back overhead. Float the arms forwards to reach for the legs and repeat 5 times.

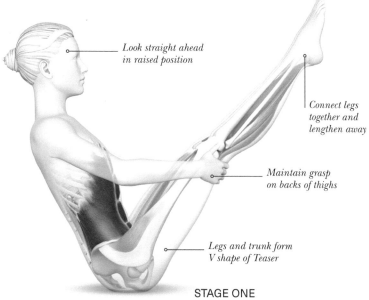

*Look straight ahead in raised position*

*Connect legs together and lengthen away*

*Maintain grasp on backs of thighs*

*Legs and trunk form V shape of Teaser*

STAGE ONE

# LEG PULL FRONT

**Challenging controlled strength** and endurance of the abdominals and shoulder girdle, this exercise resembles a prone plank position. It is a great way to combine both shoulder and pelvic stability, and is aimed at intermediate to advanced participants.

**Lower** body
Your **glutes**, together with your **hamstrings** perform hip extension to raise the leg. Your **quadriceps** engage to maintain knee extension. Your **calves** engage as the toes point and your **ankle dorsiflexors** stretch.

## THE BIG PICTURE

Leg Pull Front is all about focussing on maintaining stability throughout your trunk, upper body, and lower body. Keep your core engaged and spine neutral to control the centre. Maintain height through your chest, and keep your legs active. You can vary the exercise by pulsing the leg multiple times on the lift, bringing your knee to touch your elbow, or adding a Push Up (see p.158) in between each leg lift.

> **! Caution**
> Avoid this if you have shoulder instability or if you cannot weight bear comfortably through both wrists. You could try weight bearing on your knuckles to relieve the wrists, or try the variations to reduce the upper-body load (see p.142).

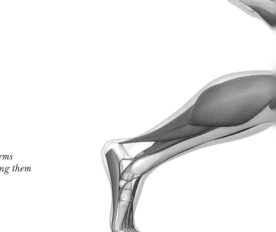

Gluteus maximus
Gluteus medius
Tensor fasciae latae
Rectus femoris
Vastus medialis
Gastrocnemius
Soleus
Peroneus longus

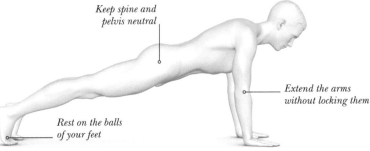

*Keep spine and pelvis neutral*

*Extend the arms without locking them*

*Rest on the balls of your feet*

**PREPARATORY STAGE**
Form a plank position with your shoulders above your wrists and the arms extended. Your legs and feet are hip-distance apart, legs fully extended and resting on the balls of your feet. Your spine and pelvis are neutral and your neck is long, eyes downwards. Engage the core.

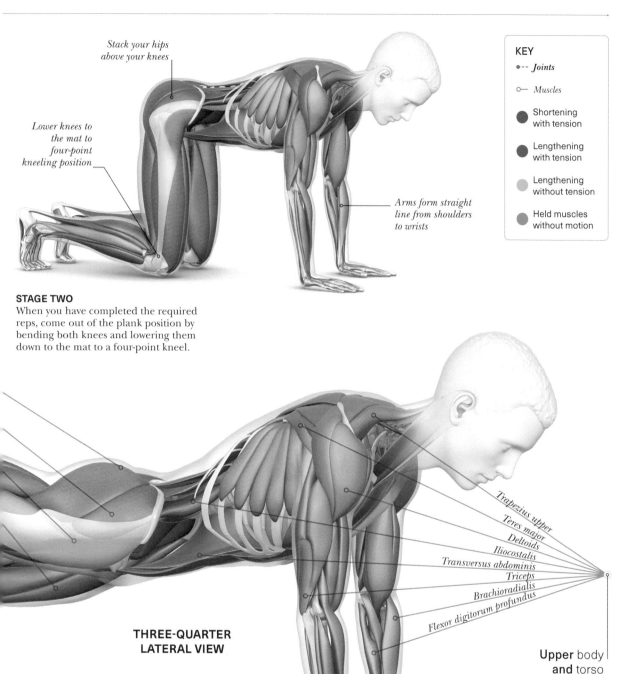

**Stack your hips above your knees**

**Lower knees to the mat to four-point kneeling position**

**Arms form straight line from shoulders to wrists**

## STAGE TWO

When you have completed the required reps, come out of the plank position by bending both knees and lowering them down to the mat to a four-point kneel.

Trapezius upper
Teres major
Deltoids
Iliocostalis
Transversus abdominis
Triceps
Brachioradialis
Flexor digitorum profundus

## THREE-QUARTER LATERAL VIEW

## STAGE ONE

Inhale to begin, and exhale to lengthen one leg away from your body, lifting it up to hip height and pointing your toes. Inhale to return the raised leg back to the mat. Exhale as you lengthen and lift the opposite leg upwards. Repeat the sequence 3 times on each leg, alternating each time.

**Upper** body **and** torso
Your **neck extensors** and **flexors** support the head and prevent it flexing down. The **trapezius** and **rhomboids** keep the scapulae neutral. The **deltoids** support the shoulder joint.

141

## » VARIATIONS

These variations can be used to create a Leg Pull Front routine, as each offers a separate focus. Try performing one of each in a circuit and repeat the circuit 3–5 times. Alternatively, you can repeat each exercise 5 times to build your core and upper body endurance in this position.

**KEY**
● Primary target muscle      ● Secondary target muscle

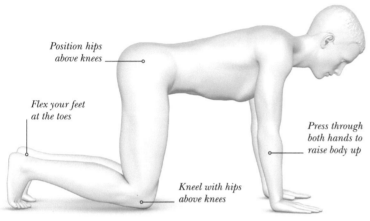

*Position hips above knees*

*Flex your feet at the toes*

*Press through both hands to raise body up*

*Kneel with hips above knees*

PREPARATORY STAGE

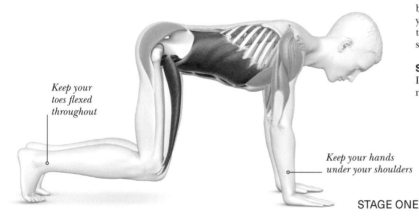

*Keep your toes flexed throughout*

*Keep your hands under your shoulders*

STAGE ONE

### HOVER

This is a simple exercise that requires you to move only the trunk upwards and back down, however it requires good abdominal control and upper body stability. Try squeezing a soft ball between the knees for increased core activation.

**PREPARATORY STAGE**
Begin in a four-point kneeling position with your shoulders above your wrists and your hips above your knees, legs just less than hip-distance apart. Hold your spine and pelvis in neutral and engage your core. Inhale.

**STAGE ONE**
Exhale as you press through both hands and both feet to raise your body upwards so that your knees are "hovering" just slightly above the mat. Your toes and hands remain in the same position on the mat as you hover.

**STAGE TWO**
Inhale to hold this position, then exhale to return to the mat. Repeat the sequence 5 times.

*Hovers are **excellent** for teaching **abdominal control** against gravity, and can also be used safely in pre- or postnatal workouts.*

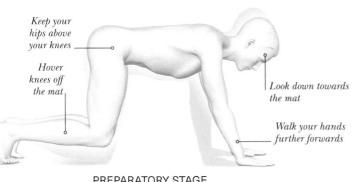

*Keep your hips above your knees*

*Hover knees off the mat*

*Look down towards the mat*

*Walk your hands further forwards*

PREPARATORY STAGE
/ STAGE ONE

## HOVER TO HIGH PLANK

Move smoothly between the hover and high plank position and back again, keeping your spine neutral at each stage. Your chest remains high throughout the exercise. Your hips should stay in line with your spine, or elevate higher for more ease.

### PREPARATORY STAGE
Begin in a four-point kneeling position with your shoulders above your wrists, your hips above the knees, legs hip-distance apart. Hold your spine and pelvis in neutral, and engage your core. Inhale to prepare.

### STAGE ONE
Walk your hands further forwards than your shoulders. Exhale and come up into the hover position by raising the knees upwards from the mat.

### STAGE TWO
Continue moving to bring your body forwards, aligning the shoulders over the wrists and lengthening your legs until you are in a high plank position, resting on your hands and toes. Complete the whole sequence 5 times.

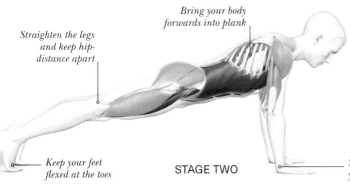

*Bring your body forwards into plank*

*Straighten the legs and keep hip-distance apart*

*Keep your feet flexed at the toes*

STAGE TWO

*Support your weight on your hands and toes*

## LEG ABDUCTIONS

This variation provides core endurance as you hold the position and abduct the legs. It is an excellent way to target the lateral hip muscles and can be combined with Leg Pull Front for a multi-direction hip strengthening routine.

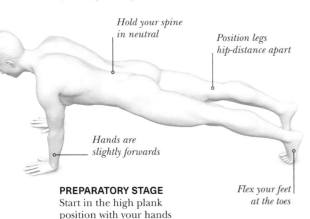

*Hold your spine in neutral*

*Position legs hip-distance apart*

*Hands are slightly forwards*

*Flex your feet at the toes*

### PREPARATORY STAGE
Start in the high plank position with your hands slightly forwards and your feet flexed at the toes.

*Hold your trunk stable throughout exercise*

*Bring one leg out to the side, then back in*

*Support your weight between hands and toes*

### STAGE ONE
Holding the trunk stable, exhale to bring one leg out to the side, inhale to return it to the start. Repeat on the other side, and complete 5 repetitions on each side.

# LEG PULL BACK

**This is the reverse of Leg Pull Front**, but the supine position makes the challenge much more upper body focussed, while maintaining a stable trunk as you move the hips. It is an intermediate to advanced level exercise for those who want to achieve a high level of upper body strength and core control.

## THE BIG PICTURE

Focus on your core throughout this movement to stabilize the spine and remain static through the trunk. Use your hips to lift your body up into the position and then flex the hip joint to lift the leg upwards, independent of your pelvis and spine. Be careful not to lock the elbow joints, and maintain lift and openness through the chest. Keep your neck long and your eye gaze forwards.

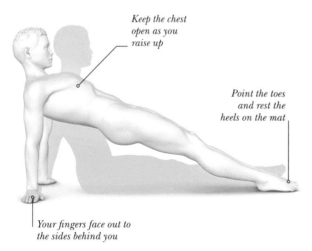

*Keep the chest open as you raise up*

*Point the toes and rest the heels on the mat*

*Your fingers face out to the sides behind you*

**PREPARATORY STAGE**
Sit upright with your legs extended out in front of you and connected together with your toes pointed. Extend your arms behind you with palms flat on the mat and fingers facing out to the sides. Press up through your hands to raise your pelvis upwards until your body forms a diagonal line from your trunk to your feet.

**Trunk** and **upper** body
Your **pectoralis major** and **serratus anterior** stretch. Your **posterior deltoid** and **teres minor** externally rotate the shoulders, while your **rhomboids** and **middle** and **lower trapezius** stabilize your scapulae. Your **wrist extensors** engage to support your body weight; their **flexors** lengthen.

*Brachioradialis*
*Biceps brachii*
*Deltoids*
*Pectoralis major*
*Serratus anterior*
*Latissimus dorsi*
*Rectus abdominis*
*External oblique*

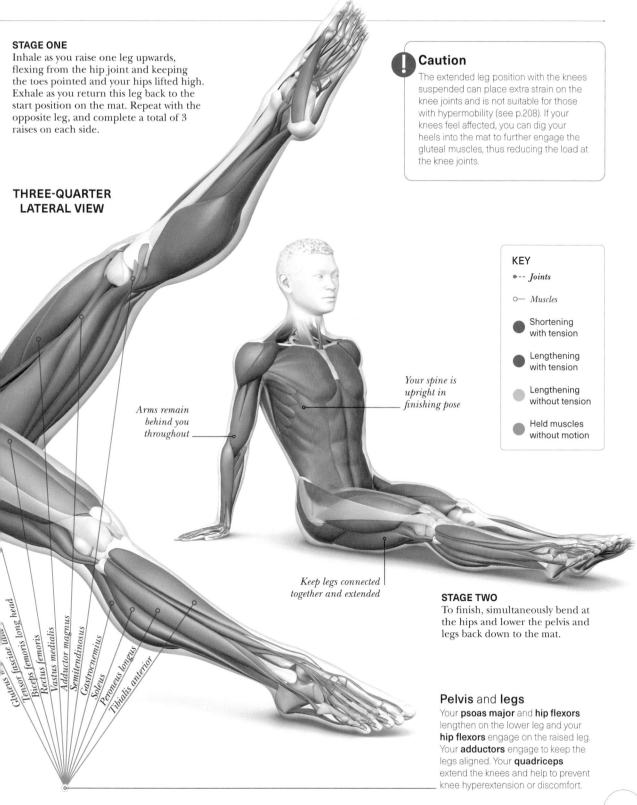

**STAGE ONE**
Inhale as you raise one leg upwards, flexing from the hip joint and keeping the toes pointed and your hips lifted high. Exhale as you return this leg back to the start position on the mat. Repeat with the opposite leg, and complete a total of 3 raises on each side.

**THREE-QUARTER LATERAL VIEW**

**! Caution**
The extended leg position with the knees suspended can place extra strain on the knee joints and is not suitable for those with hypermobility (see p.208). If your knees feel affected, you can dig your heels into the mat to further engage the gluteal muscles, thus reducing the load at the knee joints.

**KEY**
- ●--- *Joints*
- ○— *Muscles*
- ● Shortening with tension
- ● Lengthening with tension
- ● Lengthening without tension
- ● Held muscles without motion

*Your spine is upright in finishing pose*

*Arms remain behind you throughout*

*Keep legs connected together and extended*

Gluteus "
Tensor fasciae latae
Biceps femoris long head
Rectus femoris
Vastus medialis
Adductor magnus
Semitendinosus
Gastrocnemius
Soleus
Peroneus longus
Tibialis anterior

**STAGE TWO**
To finish, simultaneously bend at the hips and lower the pelvis and legs back down to the mat.

**Pelvis and legs**
Your **psoas major** and **hip flexors** lengthen on the lower leg and your **hip flexors** engage on the raised leg. Your **adductors** engage to keep the legs aligned. Your **quadriceps** extend the knees and help to prevent knee hyperextension or discomfort.

## » VARIATIONS

These variations break down the main exercise to focus on upper body stability while both feet remain on the mat for support. The first option bends the knees, while the final variation introduces the movement of one leg in preparation for the main Leg Pull Back.

**KEY**

● Primary target muscle    ● Secondary target muscle

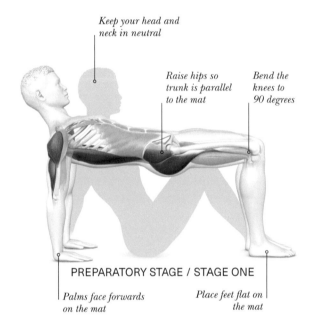

*Keep your head and neck in neutral*

*Raise hips so trunk is parallel to the mat*

*Bend the knees to 90 degrees*

PREPARATORY STAGE / STAGE ONE

*Palms face forwards on the mat*

*Place feet flat on the mat*

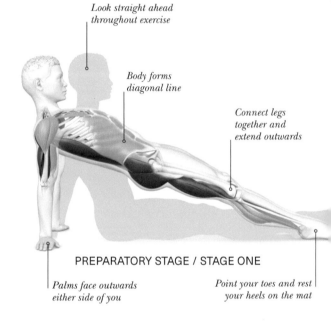

*Look straight ahead throughout exercise*

*Body forms diagonal line*

*Connect legs together and extend outwards*

PREPARATORY STAGE / STAGE ONE

*Palms face outwards either side of you*

*Point your toes and rest your heels on the mat*

### REVERSE TABLE TOP

Open your chest and gently roll your shoulders back to engage your shoulder blades. Keep your eye gaze forwards and initiate the movement from your upper body, rather than thinking about a hip thrust style of movement.

**PREPARATORY STAGE**
Sit with your hips and knees bent and your feet flat on the floor, with your arms extended behind you, and palms on the floor facing forwards.

**STAGE ONE**
Exhale as you press through your hands and feet to raise your hips upwards until your trunk becomes parallel to the floor. Inhale to hold this position.

**STAGE TWO**
Exhale to lower the hips back down again. Complete up to 6 repetitions.

### LEG PULL BACK LIFTS

As you lift upwards, focus on keeping your core engaged and ribcage connected downwards to prevent flaring the ribs. Be careful not to lock your elbows or knees and use your gluteals to support you underneath.

**PREPARATORY STAGE**
Sit upright with your legs extended out in front of you and connected together with your toes pointed. Extend your arms behind you, with palms flat on the mat and fingers facing out to the sides.

**STAGE ONE**
Exhale as you press up through your hands to raise your pelvis upwards until your body forms a diagonal line from your trunk to your feet. Inhale to hold this position, and exhale to lower back down again. Complete up to 6 repetitions of this routine.

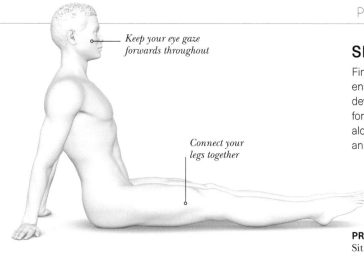

*Keep your eye gaze forwards throughout*

*Connect your legs together*

# SINGLE LEG SLIDES

Find your balance before sliding the leg inwards, to ensure your pelvis remains stationary and does not deviate to one side. Connect your gluteals together for extra support, and imagine sliding your toes along a line on the floor. Keep the hips, knees, and ankles in line throughout.

### PREPARATORY STAGE

Sit upright with your legs extended out in front of you and connected together with your toes pointed. Extend your arms behind you, with palms flat on the mat and fingers facing out to the sides.

*Keep your chest open when elevated*

*Slide one leg towards you, pointing the toes*

*Support your body with your arms*

### STAGE ONE

Exhale as you press up through your hands to raise your pelvis upwards until your body forms a diagonal line from your trunk to your feet. Inhale as you slide one foot inwards towards your body, flexing at the hip and knee joints, and keeping the toes pointed and your hips lifted high.

*Point the toes on the static foot*

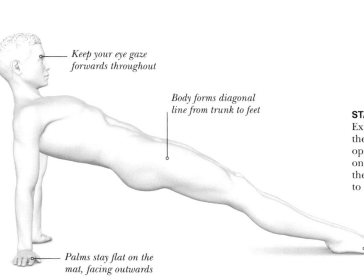

*Keep your eye gaze forwards throughout*

*Body forms diagonal line from trunk to feet*

### STAGE TWO

Exhale as you return this leg back to the extended position. Repeat with the opposite leg and complete 3 repetitions on each side. Bend at the hips and lower the legs down to the mat at the same time to return to the preparatory position.

*Palms stay flat on the mat, facing outwards*

*Connect legs together and point the toes*

# BOOMERANG

**This advanced Pilates exercise works your abdominal strength** by mobilizing and controlling your spine through varying tempos. It also incorporates hip stability and movement with long leg levers. Make sure you can perform Roll Over (see p.126) and Teaser (see p.136) before trying Boomerang, as they are key stages.

## THE BIG PICTURE

Lengthen your spine fully and reach both legs away from your pelvis, maintaining this throughout Boomerang to hold your shape. Flow through the first phase with a dynamic tempo and pause briefly in Teaser position to re-balance before flowing to stage 5. Elongate your spine along your legs and briefly pause here to deepen the stretch. Practise up to stage 3 initially before progressing to the full exercise.

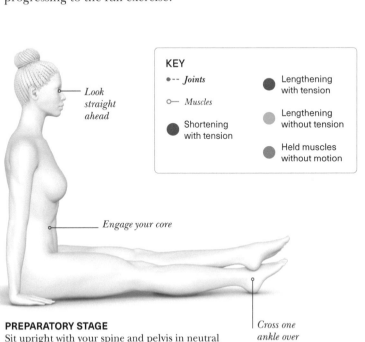

— Look straight ahead

**KEY**

•-- *Joints*

○- *Muscles*

● Shortening with tension

● Lengthening with tension

● Lengthening without tension

● Held muscles without motion

— Engage your core

*Peroneus longus*
*Extensor digitorum longus*
*Soleus*
*Gastrocnemius*
*Biceps femoris short head*
*Biceps femoris long head*
*Gluteus maximus*
*Gluteus medius*

**LATERAL VIEW**

### PREPARATORY STAGE

Sit upright with your spine and pelvis in neutral and your legs lengthened out in front of you, connected together. Cross your ankles and point your toes. Place your hands facing forwards on either side of your hips, with palms facing down.

Cross one ankle over the other

### Lower body

Your **gluteus maximus** and **hamstrings** stretch, while the hamstrings also engage as you imagine pressing the legs up to the ceiling to maintain leg height. Your **quadriceps** engage to keep the knees extended, and your **gluteus medius** and **minimus** stabilize the pelvis on both sides.

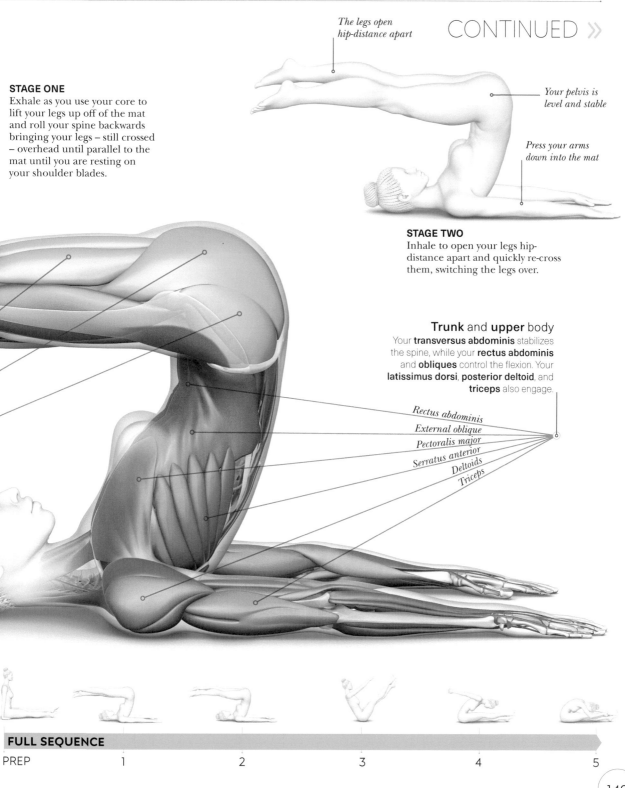

*The legs open
hip-distance apart*

*Your pelvis is
level and stable*

*Press your arms
down into the mat*

## STAGE ONE

Exhale as you use your core to
lift your legs up off of the mat
and roll your spine backwards
bringing your legs – still crossed
– overhead until parallel to the
mat until you are resting on
your shoulder blades.

## STAGE TWO

Inhale to open your legs hip-
distance apart and quickly re-cross
them, switching the legs over.

### Trunk and upper body

Your **transversus abdominis** stabilizes
the spine, while your **rectus abdominis**
and **obliques** control the flexion. Your
**latissimus dorsi**, **posterior deltoid**, and
**triceps** also engage.

*Rectus abdominis*
*External oblique*
*Pectoralis major*
*Serratus anterior*
*Deltoids*
*Triceps*

**FULL SEQUENCE**

PREP        1        2        3        4        5

# » BOOMERANG
## (FOLLOW-ON)

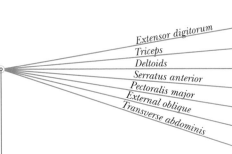

Extensor digitorum
Triceps
Deltoids
Serratus anterior
Pectoralis major
External oblique
Transverse abdominis

### Trunk and upper body
Your **spine flexors** bring your trunk forwards
and the elevation of your arms provides further
forward flexion. Your **spine extensors** stretch.
Your **rhomboids** and **trapezius** retract your
shoulder blades while your **lower trapezius**
depresses them as you reach away.

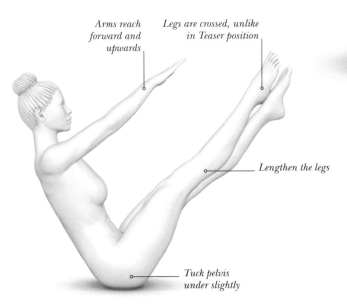

Arms reach
forward and
upwards

Legs are crossed, unlike
in Teaser position

Lengthen the legs

Tuck pelvis
under slightly

### STAGE THREE
Exhale as you roll your spine forwards and
lower your legs to form a high diagonal
position and reach your arms outwards,
forming the Teaser position (see p.136).

### STAGE FOUR
Lower your legs back to the starting
position, then inhale as you reach
your arms behind you and clasp your
hands together. Exhale to lengthen
and stretch your spine forwards,
bringing your chest towards your
knees and reaching your arms
backwards and upwards.

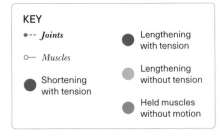

**KEY**

•-- *Joints*

o— *Muscles*

● Shortening
with tension

● Lengthening
with tension

● Lengthening
without tension

● Held muscles
without motion

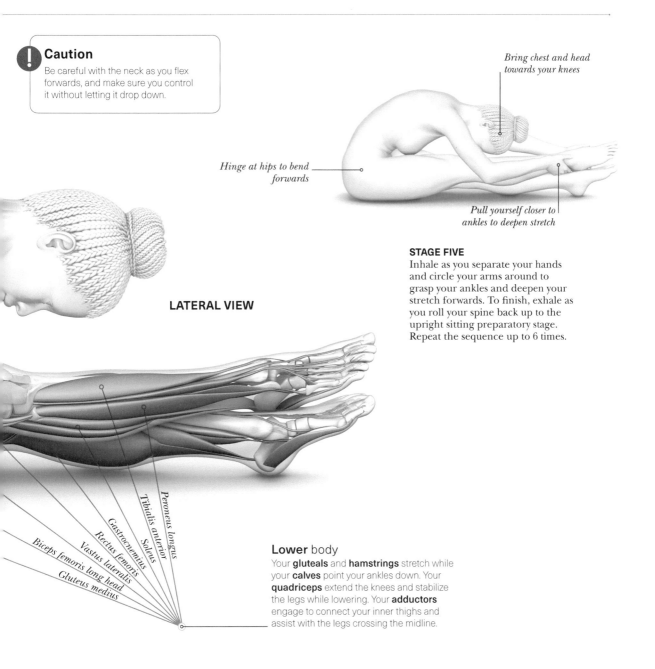

*Bring chest and head
towards your knees*

*Hinge at hips to bend
forwards*

*Pull yourself closer to
ankles to deepen stretch*

**LATERAL VIEW**

### STAGE FIVE
Inhale as you separate your hands
and circle your arms around to
grasp your ankles and deepen your
stretch forwards. To finish, exhale as
you roll your spine back up to the
upright sitting preparatory stage.
Repeat the sequence up to 6 times.

*Peroneus longus*
*Tibialis anterior*
*Soleus*
*Gastrocnemius*
*Rectus femoris*
*Vastus lateralis*
*Biceps femoris long head*
*Gluteus medius*

### Lower body
Your **gluteals** and **hamstrings** stretch while
your **calves** point your ankles down. Your
**quadriceps** extend the knees and stabilize
the legs while lowering. Your **adductors**
engage to connect your inner thighs and
assist with the legs crossing the midline.

**FULL SEQUENCE**

PREP      1      2      3      4      5

# ROCKING

**This advanced exercise develops spinal mobility** into extension, back strength, and gluteal and hamstring strength and is a step up from Swan Dive (see p.70). You need good core engagement and awareness to control the rocking movement – it's important to avoid using momentum for this.

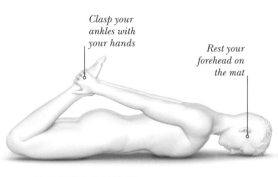

*Clasp your ankles with your hands*

*Rest your forehead on the mat*

**PREPARATORY STAGE**
Lie on your front with your forehead resting on the mat and your legs hip-distance apart. Bend both knees and bring your heels towards your pelvis as you reach your arms behind you to clasp your ankles.

## THE **BIG PICTURE**

The essence of Rocking is to maintain the shape between the legs and the spine throughout the exercise. As you rock forwards, focus on lifting the legs upwards, and as you rock backwards, press the feet back into your hands. Your arms remain extended and your spine should be lengthened at all times to avoid collapse, with your core gently engaged while lengthening.

### Legs
Your **hip flexors** and **quadriceps** lengthen while your **hamstrings** contract to flex the knees. Your quadriceps also engage under tension as you press the top of the feet into the hands to maintain space in the pose.

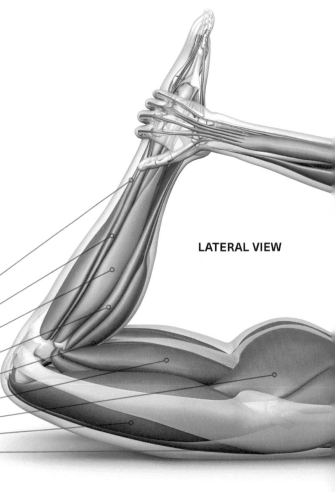

**LATERAL VIEW**

*Tibialis anterior*
*Extensor digitorum longus*
*Peroneus longus*
*Soleus*
*Gastrocnemius*
*Biceps femoris long head*
*Gluteus maximus*
*Vastus lateralis*
*Rectus femoris*

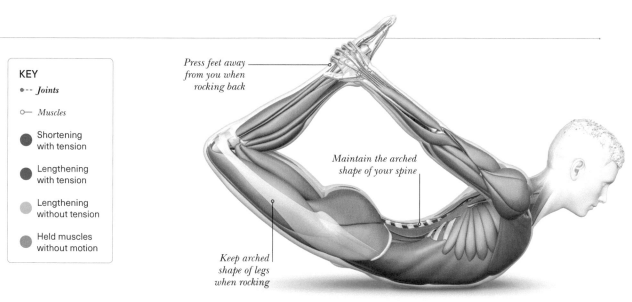

Press feet away
from you when
rocking back

Maintain the arched
shape of your spine

Keep arched
shape of legs
when rocking

## KEY

•--  *Joints*

○—  *Muscles*

● Shortening
with tension

● Lengthening
with tension

○ Lengthening
without tension

● Held muscles
without motion

### STAGE TWO
Exhale as you rock forwards on to your chest,
maintaining the arched shape of your spine and
legs, and inhale to press your feet in to your
hands and rock back again. Continue to rock
forwards and backwards for up to 6 repetitions.

### STAGE ONE
Inhale as you press your
pelvis into the mat and
your feet into your hands.
Immediately engage your
gluteal and hamstring
muscles to lift your upper
body and head upwards
until your ribcage peels
off the mat.

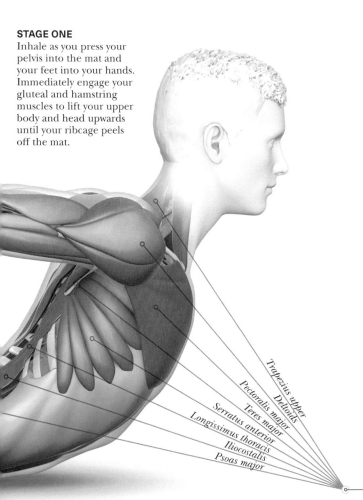

Trapezius upper

Deltoids

Pectoralis major

Teres major

Serratus anterior

Longissimus thoracis

Iliocostalis

Psoas major

66 99

## *Rocking promotes good posture and a strong, flexible back.*

### ! Caution
Omit this exercise if you have any back or
knee issues as the high back extension
or knee flexion positions may cause
compression and pain to the joints.

### Trunk
Your **spinal extensors** engage; your **abdominals**
and **psoas major** lengthen. The **serratus anterior**
and **pectoralis major** stretch to open the chest.
The **latissimus dorsi** and **deltoids** extend the
shoulder, and the **middle** and **lower trapezius**
retract the scapulae.

153

# BREASTSTROKE

This exercise mimics the swimming stroke, breaststroke, but in the Pilates exercise, you isolate the upper body and avoid extending through the lower spine. Keep your core engaged throughout to minimize any arching in the spine, and keep your eye gaze downwards.

**Caution**

Breaststroke may not be suitable if you have lower back, shoulder, or neck problems as all three are involved in the exercise. If this is the case, you could try the Swimming (Slower Option) variation instead (see p.90).

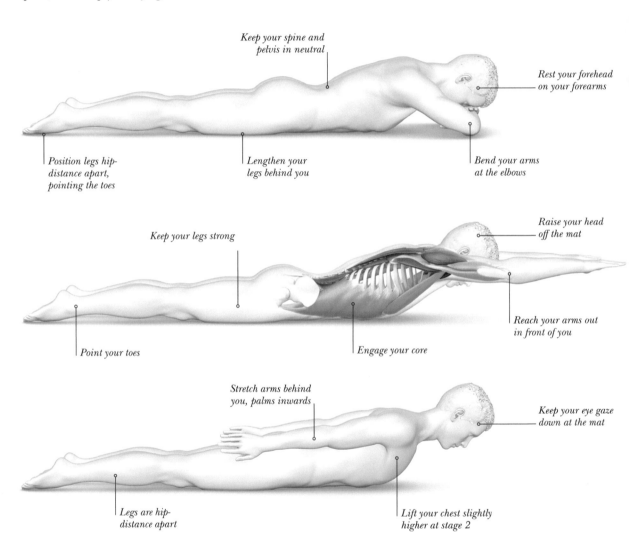

*Keep your spine and pelvis in neutral*

*Rest your forehead on your forearms*

*Position legs hip-distance apart, pointing the toes*

*Lengthen your legs behind you*

*Bend your arms at the elbows*

*Keep your legs strong*

*Raise your head off the mat*

*Point your toes*

*Engage your core*

*Reach your arms out in front of you*

*Stretch arms behind you, palms inwards*

*Keep your eye gaze down at the mat*

*Legs are hip-distance apart*

*Lift your chest slightly higher at stage 2*

**PREPARATORY STAGE**
Lie on your front with your spine and pelvis in neutral and legs lengthened behind you hip-distance apart. Bend your arms at the elbows and rest your forehead lightly on your forearms in front of you.

**STAGE ONE**
Exhale as you raise your head and upper body off the mat, then inhale to reach your arms out in front of you, palms facing downwards.

**STAGE TWO**
Exhale to circle your arms back to your sides and downwards towards your hips, while simultaneously raising your chest up slightly higher. Inhale to return to the mat and repeat sequence 8–10 times.

# CRISS CROSS

This is an endurance-based exercise that challenges coordinated abdominal strength, upper body rotation, and reciprocal leg movements. It requires a high level of precision and control.

**KEY**

● Primary target muscle    ● Secondary target muscle

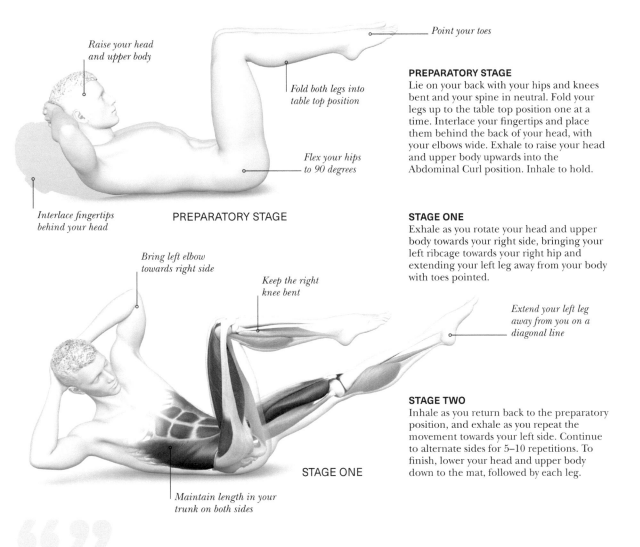

*Raise your head and upper body*

*Point your toes*

*Fold both legs into table top position*

*Flex your hips to 90 degrees*

*Interlace fingertips behind your head*

PREPARATORY STAGE

*Bring left elbow towards right side*

*Keep the right knee bent*

*Extend your left leg away from you on a diagonal line*

*Maintain length in your trunk on both sides*

STAGE ONE

### PREPARATORY STAGE
Lie on your back with your hips and knees bent and your spine in neutral. Fold your legs up to the table top position one at a time. Interlace your fingertips and place them behind the back of your head, with your elbows wide. Exhale to raise your head and upper body upwards into the Abdominal Curl position. Inhale to hold.

### STAGE ONE
Exhale as you rotate your head and upper body towards your right side, bringing your left ribcage towards your right hip and extending your left leg away from your body with toes pointed.

### STAGE TWO
Inhale as you return back to the preparatory position, and exhale as you repeat the movement towards your left side. Continue to alternate sides for 5–10 repetitions. To finish, lower your head and upper body down to the mat, followed by each leg.

*When performing Criss Cross, **rotate** with **control** from your obliques, rather than using **momentum** or speed to change **direction**.*

# CONTROL BALANCE

**This advanced exercise brings together everything** you have learned in the Pilates repertoire so far and requires excellent core and pelvic stability. Before attempting Control Balance, you need to master Jack Knife (see p.134), as well as Scissors (see p.78), and Rocker with Open Legs (see p.68).

## THE **BIG PICTURE**

Lengthen your legs and pelvis away from your trunk to elongate the spine and avoid compression. Continue to reach the legs away from you in both leg positions to create height and prevent collapsing through the trunk. The weight should rest upon the shoulder blades rather than the head and neck. This can be controlled by not rolling too far backwards and keeping your core engaged. Repeat up to 6 times.

**KEY**

- ●-- *Joints*
- ○- *Muscles*
- ● Shortening with tension
- ● Lengthening with tension
- ● Lengthening without tension
- ● Held muscles without motion

*Extend legs directly above pelvis and point the toes*

*Rest arms by your sides with palms downwards*

**PREPARATORY STAGE**
Lie on your back with a neutral spine and pelvis, connect your legs together and extend both legs up vertically towards the ceiling with toes pointed. Engage your core.

**Trunk** and **upper** body
Your **serratus anterior** shortens as you bring your arms forwards, and your **rhomboids** stretch as your arms adduct to reach for the lower leg. Your **gluteus medius** and **tensor fasciae latae** stabilize the hips laterally.

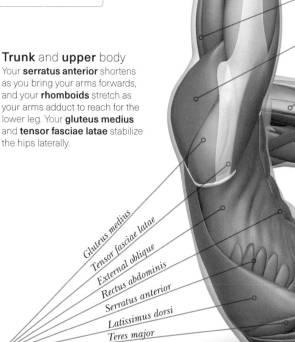

*Gluteus medius*
*Tensor fasciae latae*
*External oblique*
*Rectus abdominis*
*Serratus anterior*
*Latissimus dorsi*
*Teres major*
*Infraspinatus*

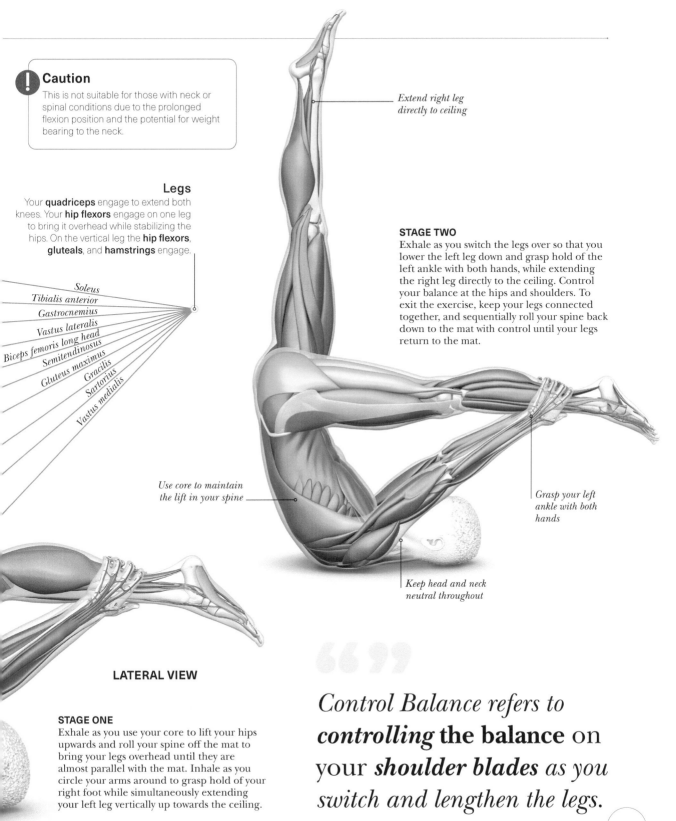

**Caution**

This is not suitable for those with neck or spinal conditions due to the prolonged flexion position and the potential for weight bearing to the neck.

### Legs

Your **quadriceps** engage to extend both knees. Your **hip flexors** engage on one leg to bring it overhead while stabilizing the hips. On the vertical leg the **hip flexors**, **gluteals**, and **hamstrings** engage.

Soleus
Tibialis anterior
Gastrocnemius
Vastus lateralis
Biceps femoris long head
Semitendinosus
Gluteus maximus
Gracilis
Sartorius
Vastus medialis

*Extend right leg directly to ceiling*

### STAGE TWO

Exhale as you switch the legs over so that you lower the left leg down and grasp hold of the left ankle with both hands, while extending the right leg directly to the ceiling. Control your balance at the hips and shoulders. To exit the exercise, keep your legs connected together, and sequentially roll your spine back down to the mat with control until your legs return to the mat.

*Use core to maintain the lift in your spine*

*Grasp your left ankle with both hands*

*Keep head and neck neutral throughout*

**LATERAL VIEW**

### STAGE ONE

Exhale as you use your core to lift your hips upwards and roll your spine off the mat to bring your legs overhead until they are almost parallel with the mat. Inhale as you circle your arms around to grasp hold of your right foot while simultaneously extending your left leg vertically up towards the ceiling.

*Control Balance refers to **controlling** the **balance** on your **shoulder blades** as you switch and lengthen the legs.*

157

# PUSH UP

**The Pilates Push Up promotes strength and stability** in the upper body. Rolling down to get into the push up position on the floor teaches mobilization, stability, and control of the spine, and this integration makes it a total body exercise.

## THE **BIG PICTURE**

Engage your core throughout the Push Up to maintain a straight line through your body from your heels to your head. Bending the elbows is the only movement you perform – the rest of the body moves as a whole to follow. Both the downward and upward movements should be controlled with a rigid posture to prevent the abdominals doming (descending) downwards or the spine collapsing.

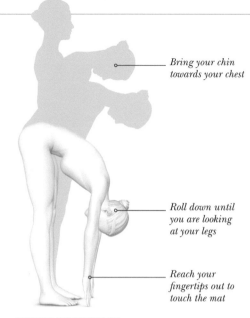

*Bring your chin towards your chest*

*Roll down until you are looking at your legs*

*Reach your fingertips out to touch the mat*

**PREPARATORY STAGE**
Stand upright with your legs hip-distance apart and your spine and pelvis in neutral with arms resting down by your sides. Bring your chin towards your chest and sequentially roll your spine forward and down towards the mat vertebra by vertebra, until your hands reach the mat.

**Lower** body
Your **core** works to hold tension in the trunk and stabilize your spine. Your **gluteus maximus** holds the hips in extension. The **gluteus medius** and **minimus**, the **hamstrings**, and the **adductors** also stabilize the hips. The **calf muscles** stabilize the lower leg.

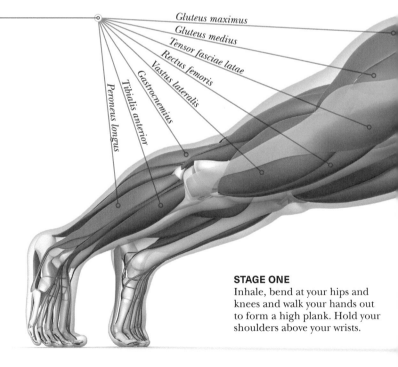

Gluteus maximus
Gluteus medius
Tensor fasciae latae
Rectus femoris
Vastus lateralis
Gastrocnemius
Tibialis anterior
Peroneus longus

> **(!) Caution**
> The roll down movement is not suitable for those with back problems, nerve tension, or difficulty in articulating the spine. Check that you can do a Push Up without the roll down prior to completing the full exercise. You can reduce the upper body load by trying the variations on pp.160–61, and/or omit the roll back up each time until your strength develops.

**STAGE ONE**
Inhale, bend at your hips and knees and walk your hands out to form a high plank. Hold your shoulders above your wrists.

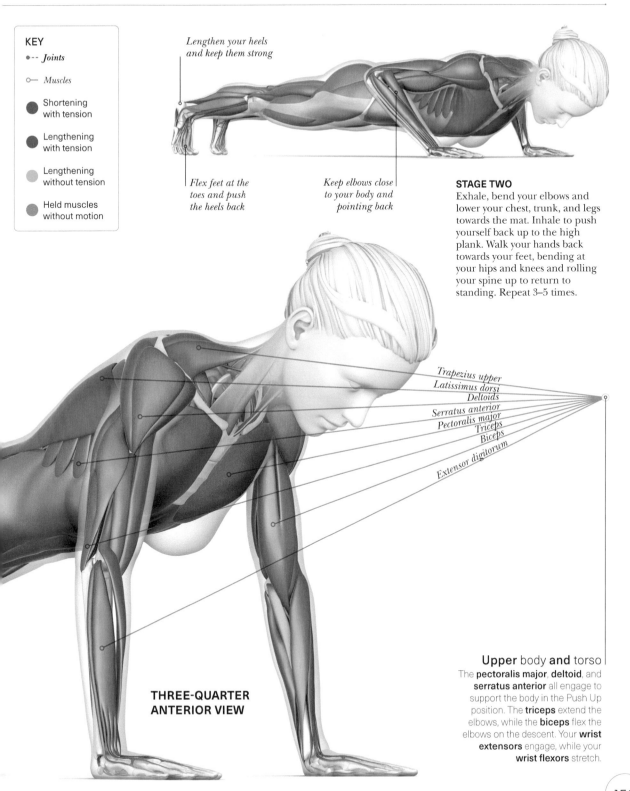

**KEY**

•-- *Joints*

○— *Muscles*

● Shortening
with tension

● Lengthening
with tension

○ Lengthening
without tension

● Held muscles
without motion

*Lengthen your heels
and keep them strong*

*Flex feet at the
toes and push
the heels back*

*Keep elbows close
to your body and
pointing back*

**STAGE TWO**
Exhale, bend your elbows and
lower your chest, trunk, and legs
towards the mat. Inhale to push
yourself back up to the high
plank. Walk your hands back
towards your feet, bending at
your hips and knees and rolling
your spine up to return to
standing. Repeat 3–5 times.

*Trapezius upper*
*Latissimus dorsi*
*Deltoids*
*Serratus anterior*
*Pectoralis major*
*Triceps*
*Biceps*
*Extensor digitorum*

**THREE-QUARTER
ANTERIOR VIEW**

**Upper** body **and** torso
The **pectoralis major**, **deltoid**, and
**serratus anterior** all engage to
support the body in the Push Up
position. The **triceps** extend the
elbows, while the **biceps** flex the
elbows on the descent. Your **wrist
extensors** engage, while your
**wrist flexors** stretch.

159

## » VARIATIONS

In both of these Push Up variations, you begin with the same roll down from standing. This can be omitted, however, until you are comfortable performing the Push Up on its own. Engage your core further as you walk your hands along the mat to the Push Up position, bending your knees as required.

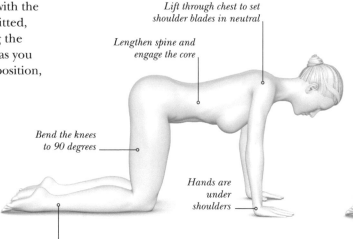

*Lift through chest to set shoulder blades in neutral*

*Lengthen spine and engage the core*

*Bend the knees to 90 degrees*

*Hands are under shoulders*

*Relax your feet hip-distance apart*

### BOX PUSH UP

The Box Push Up keeps the weight equal between the arms and the legs and allows you to gently take weight through the upper body without too much effort. Bend at the elbows and keep your hips raised up in the air.

**KEY**

● Primary target muscle

● Secondary target muscle

**PREPARATORY STAGE**
Roll down to the mat from upright standing following the illustration below. Bend the knees and assume the four-point kneeling position, shoulders over your wrists and back straight. Look down towards the mat.

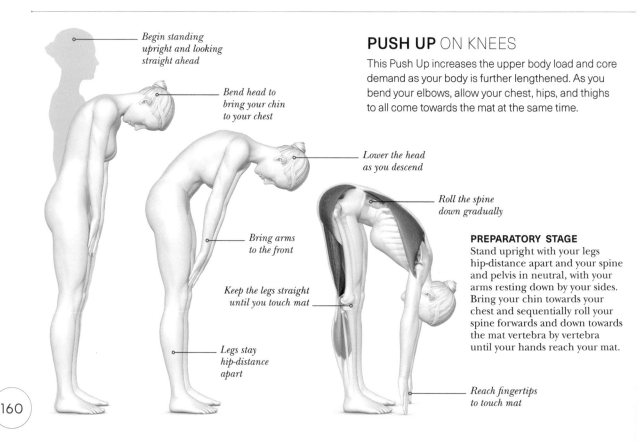

*Begin standing upright and looking straight ahead*

*Bend head to bring your chin to your chest*

*Bring arms to the front*

*Keep the legs straight until you touch mat*

*Legs stay hip-distance apart*

*Lower the head as you descend*

*Roll the spine down gradually*

*Reach fingertips to touch mat*

### PUSH UP ON KNEES

This Push Up increases the upper body load and core demand as your body is further lengthened. As you bend your elbows, allow your chest, hips, and thighs to all come towards the mat at the same time.

**PREPARATORY STAGE**
Stand upright with your legs hip-distance apart and your spine and pelvis in neutral, with your arms resting down by your sides. Bring your chin towards your chest and sequentially roll your spine forwards and down towards the mat vertebra by vertebra until your hands reach your mat.

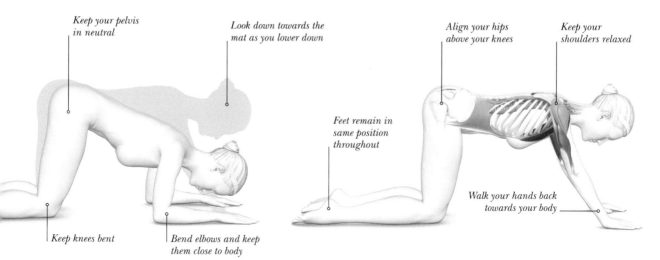

*Keep your pelvis in neutral*

*Look down towards the mat as you lower down*

*Align your hips above your knees*

*Keep your shoulders relaxed*

*Feet remain in same position throughout*

*Keep knees bent*

*Bend elbows and keep them close to body*

*Walk your hands back towards your body*

**STAGE ONE**
Walk your hands out to be slightly in front of you, then exhale to bend your elbows and lower your chest towards your mat. Keep your elbows close to your body throughout the movement.

**STAGE TWO**
Inhale to press back up and continue to walk your hands backwards towards your feet, rolling back up to standing. Repeat 3–6 times.

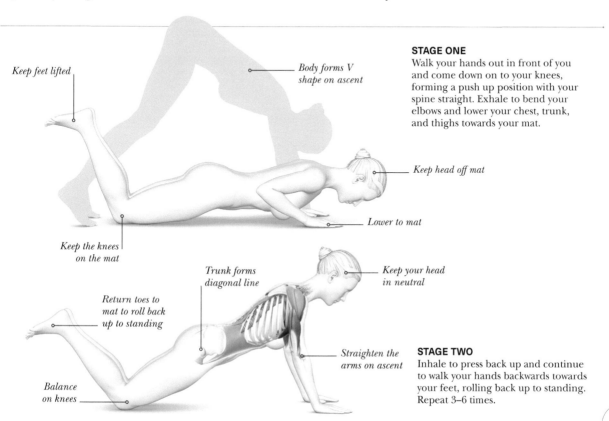

*Keep feet lifted*

*Body forms V shape on ascent*

*Keep head off mat*

*Keep the knees on the mat*

*Lower to mat*

**STAGE ONE**
Walk your hands out in front of you and come down on to your knees, forming a push up position with your spine straight. Exhale to bend your elbows and lower your chest, trunk, and thighs towards your mat.

*Return toes to mat to roll back up to standing*

*Trunk forms diagonal line*

*Keep your head in neutral*

*Balance on knees*

*Straighten the arms on ascent*

**STAGE TWO**
Inhale to press back up and continue to walk your hands backwards towards your feet, rolling back up to standing. Repeat 3–6 times.

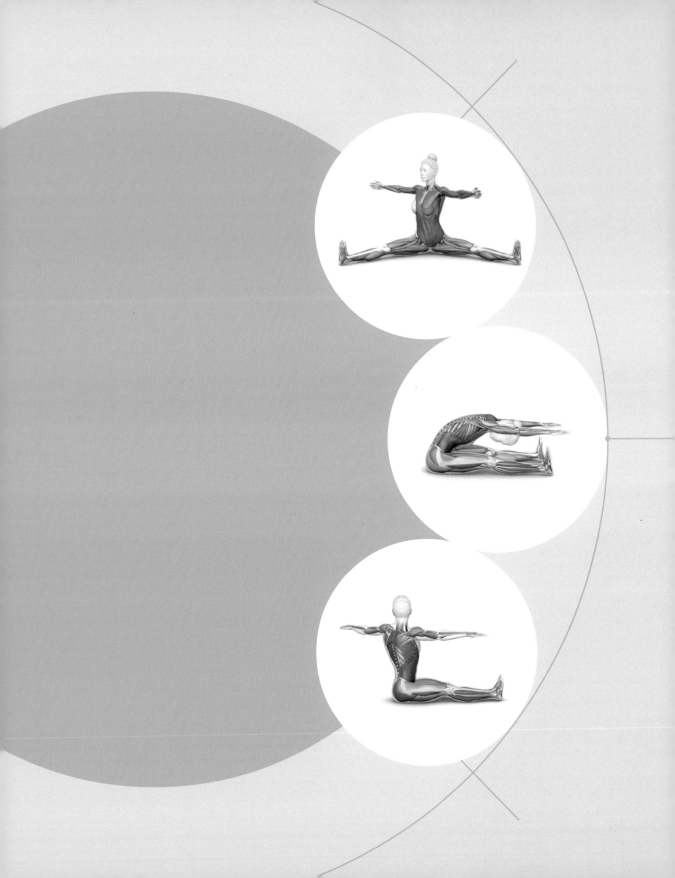

# MOBILITY
# EXERCISES

**The exercises in this section provide an intricate balance** of gentle strengthening through greater ranges of motion. They relieve joint stiffness and keep muscles long, and also have a naturally calming effect on the body and mind. Performing mobility exercises provides a perfect complement to your strength exercises, elevating your mobility for a well-balanced practice.

# SPINE STRETCH

**This beginner-level exercise mobilizes the spine into flexion.** Activating the core through this movement teaches proper control into flexion, as well as improving posture and flexibility of the spine and the hamstrings.

## THE **BIG PICTURE**

Ensure you have equal weight bearing through both sitting bones and maintain this contact with the mat throughout the exercise. As you roll forwards, roll directly through your centre to avoid deviating to one side. Notice the breathing pattern of exhaling on the stretch forwards, since this is important to empty the abdominal cavity and ensure you are not flexing against resistance. Repeat the Spine Stretch 3–6 times. If you struggle to reach over your legs, practise the Modified Spine Stretch first.

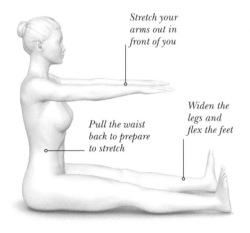

*Stretch your arms out in front of you*

*Widen the legs and flex the feet*

*Pull the waist back to prepare to stretch*

**PREPARATORY STAGE**
Sit upright with your pelvis and spine in neutral, legs just slightly wider than hip-distance apart, and ankles flexed upwards. Raise your arms up in front of you to shoulder height, keeping the shoulder blades relaxed and down. Inhale to lengthen your spine and neck.

### Trunk and lower body
Your **rectus abdominis** engages along with your **external** and **internal obliques** and **psoas major** and **minor** to flex your spine, while your **transversus abdominis** keeps the lift in your trunk. Your **spinal extensors** stretch. Your **hip flexors** engage throughout, and your **gluteals** and **hamstrings** are lengthened.

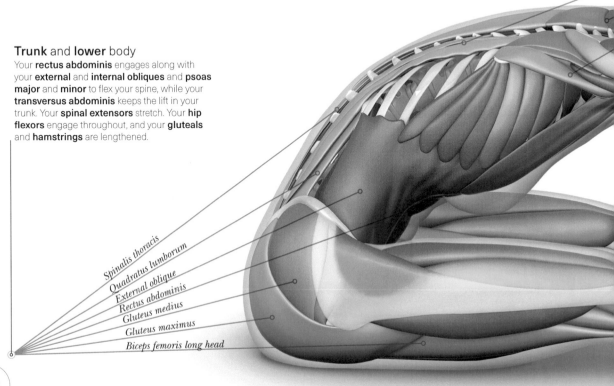

Spinalis thoracis
Quadratus lumborum
External oblique
Rectus abdominis
Gluteus medius
Gluteus maximus
Biceps femoris long head

## Caution

Don't collapse in the trunk by simply reaching forwards. Instead, focus on the articulation and segmental control of the spine, while engaging the core to create lift in the trunk. This technique will train the spine correctly and protect the back.

### Upper body

Your **spinal extensors** and **latissimus dorsi** stretch. Your **middle** and **lower trapezius** stabilize your scapulae, while your **deltoids** engage for shoulder flexion. Your **triceps** extend the elbows.

Longissimus thoracis
Trapezius upper
Teres major
Deltoids

Triceps
Brachioradialis
Extensor digitorum

**LATERAL VIEW**

# VARIATION: **MODIFIED SPINE** STRETCH

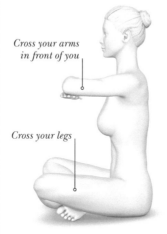

Cross your arms in front of you

Cross your legs

Curve forwards gradually, starting with the upper back

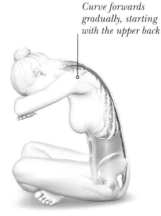

**PREPARATORY STAGE**
Sit upright with your legs crossed and forearms stacked on top of each other at shoulder height. Inhale as you lengthen the neck and spine.

**STAGE ONE**
Exhale as you roll the spine forwards from the upper back, mid-back, and lower back. Inhale to hold. Exhale as you stack the spine back upright in the same way.

### KEY

●-- *Joints*

○— *Muscles*

● Shortening with tension

● Lengthening with tension

● Lengthening without tension

● Held muscles without motion

**STAGE ONE**
Exhale as you roll your spine forwards, starting with your head and neck, then your upper back, mid-back, and lower back. Reach your arms out in front with palms facing downwards. Keep your pelvis neutral and your core engaged. Inhale to hold the stretch. Exhale as you reverse the movement one vertebra at a time, rolling back to the upright position. Return the arms back to their starting position, parallel to the legs.

# SAW

**Saw mobilizes the spine into rotation and flexion.** The rotational element strengthens the oblique muscles, while the flexion motion encourages hamstring lengthening. By mastering Saw, you will teach your trunk how to move properly when twisting and bending.

## THE **BIG PICTURE**

Your pelvis should remain grounded and neutral on your mat at all times, with particular attention on the opposite hip as you rotate to one side. Create the rotation from your centre and flex forwards in sequence from your lower to upper spine. Allow your arm reach to naturally follow your spinal movement rather than elevating your scapula in any way.

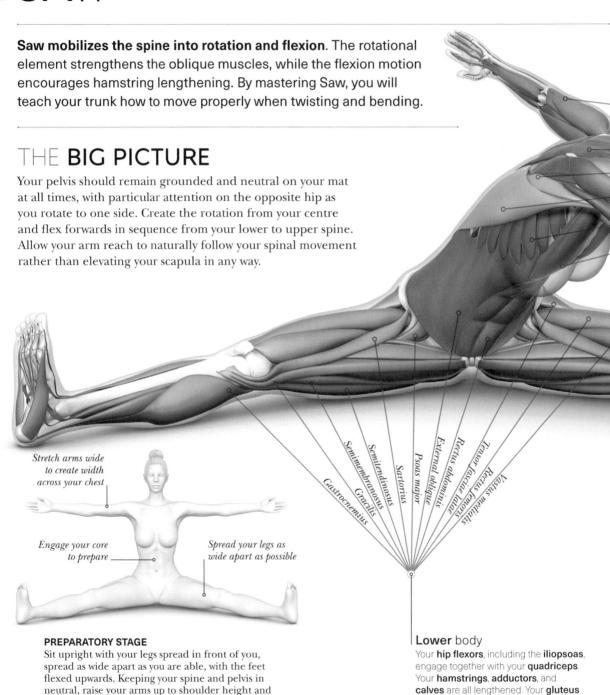

*Stretch arms wide to create width across your chest*

*Engage your core to prepare*

*Spread your legs as wide apart as possible*

Gastrocnemius
Gracilis
Semimembranosus
Semitendinosus
Sartorius
Psoas major
External oblique
Rectus abdominis
Tensor fasciae latae
Rectus femoris
Vastus medialis

**PREPARATORY STAGE**
Sit upright with your legs spread in front of you, spread as wide apart as you are able, with the feet flexed upwards. Keeping your spine and pelvis in neutral, raise your arms up to shoulder height and outwards with your palms facing outwards. Set your shoulder blades to neutral and engage your core.

**Lower** body
Your **hip flexors**, including the **iliopsoas**, engage together with your **quadriceps**. Your **hamstrings**, **adductors**, and **calves** are all lengthened. Your **gluteus medius** and **minimus** and **piriformis** all engage to stabilize the hip joints.

166

**STAGE ONE**

Inhale as you rotate your spine to the left, allowing your head, neck, and arms to follow. Exhale as you curl the spine forwards towards your left leg, reaching the right hand diagonally across to your left foot and the left arm behind you. Stretch your spine further by performing 3 pulses to bring yourself deeper into the position.

## **Upper** body **and** arms

Your **erector spinae** and **latissimus dorsi** stretch as you reach forwards. Your **pectoralis major** and anterior fibres of **deltoid** flex and adduct the **shoulder** as you reach forwards, while your **triceps** extend your elbow.

KEY

●-- *Joints*

○— *Muscles*

- Shortening with tension
- Lengthening with tension
- Lengthening without tension
- Held muscles without motion

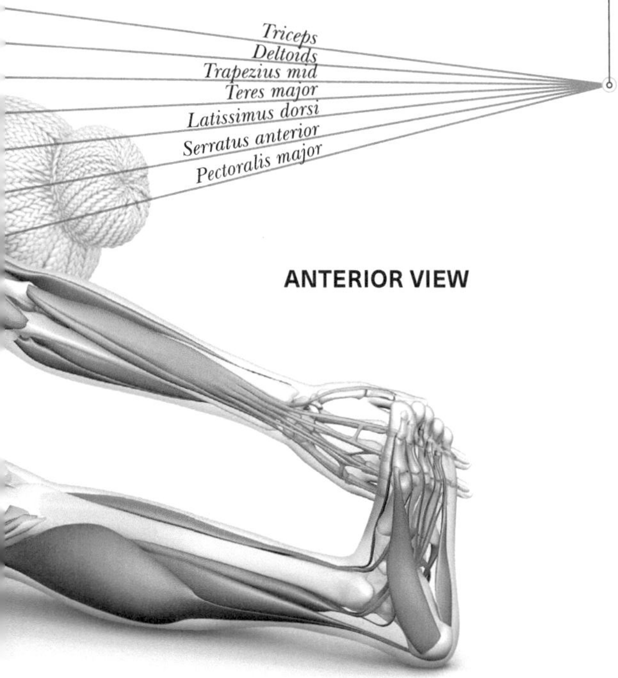

Triceps
Deltoids
Trapezius mid
Teres major
Latissimus dorsi
Serratus anterior
Pectoralis major


**ANTERIOR VIEW**

### Caution

If you have tightness in your hamstrings that prevents the legs fully extending, allow a small bend in the knees. This will ensure your pelvis can remain in neutral and maximize the benefits of the spinal mobility.

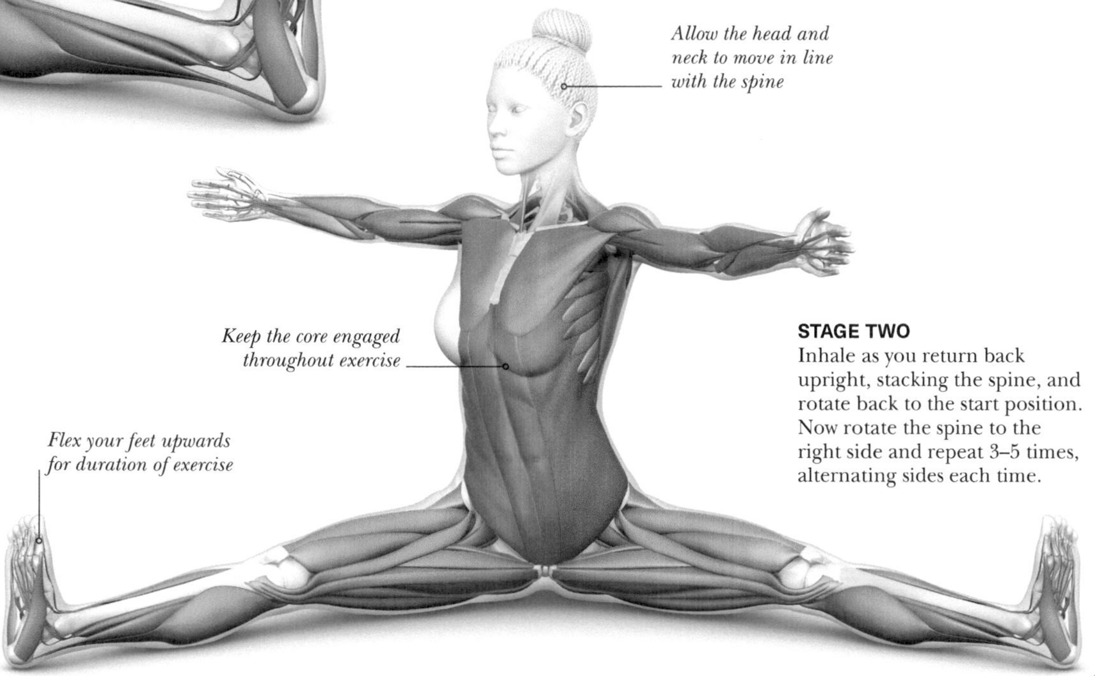

Allow the head and neck to move in line with the spine
Keep the core engaged throughout exercise
Flex your feet upwards for duration of exercise


**STAGE TWO**

Inhale as you return back upright, stacking the spine, and rotate back to the start position. Now rotate the spine to the right side and repeat 3–5 times, alternating sides each time.

# SPINE TWIST

**This beginner exercise mobilizes the spine through rotation.** It trains balance and good posture in sitting, while also lengthening the hamstrings. It is ideal for sedentary workers or those who experience mild back pain.

## THE **BIG** PICTURE

Initiate the Spine Twist from your core while keeping your pelvis still. Ensure you distribute your weight through both sides of your pelvis and maintain contact with the mat throughout. Lengthen your spine vertically and keep the length in both sides of your waist to prevent collapsing down to one side. Your head should move in line with your spine. Keep your scapulae (shoulder blades) in neutral to avoid over-rotating your upper body and arms. If you struggle with the extended arm twist practise the Modified Spine Twist, with arms folded, first.

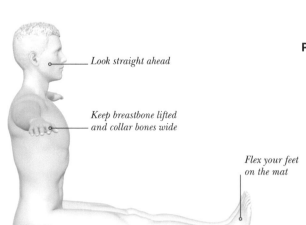

*Look straight ahead*

*Keep breastbone lifted and collar bones wide*

*Flex your feet on the mat*

**POSTERIOR-LATERAL VIEW**

**PREPARATORY STAGE**
Sit upright with your pelvis and spine in neutral. Lengthen your legs out in front of you with your inner thighs connected and feet flexed, heels down. Raise your arms on either side up to shoulder height with your palms facing downwards.

**STAGE ONE**
Inhale to prepare and lengthen your spine. Exhale as you rotate your trunk and arms to one side, allowing your head to follow in line with your spine. Bring your eye gaze over your shoulder. Pulse the trunk twice at the end range to increase your range further. Inhale to return to the preparatory position. Repeat on the other side, and complete the whole exercise 6–8 times.

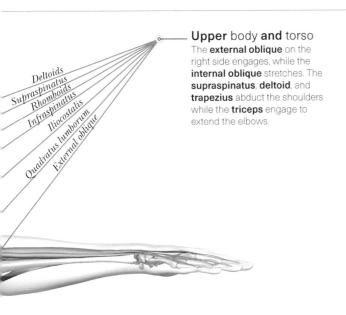

### Upper body and torso
The **external oblique** on the right side engages, while the **internal oblique** stretches. The **supraspinatus**, **deltoid**, and **trapezius** abduct the shoulders while the **triceps** engage to extend the elbows.

Deltoids
Supraspinatus
Rhomboids
Infraspinatus
Iliocostalis
Quadratus lumborum
External oblique

### Lower body
Your **spinal extensors** and **quadratus lumborum** engage on both sides. Your **gluteal muscles** are lengthened. Your **quadriceps** extend your knees and work to stabilize the legs, while your **hamstrings** lengthen. Your **calves** lengthen and your **tibialis anterior** and **ankle dorsiflexors** engage to flex the ankles.

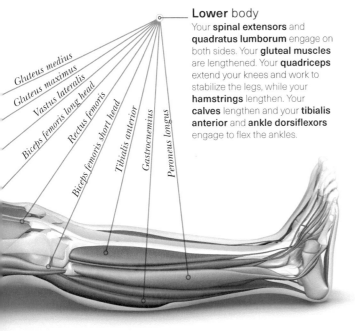

Gluteus medius
Gluteus maximus
Vastus lateralis
Biceps femoris long head
Rectus femoris
Biceps femoris short head
Tibialis anterior
Gastrocnemius
Peroneus longus

---

**KEY**

•-- *Joints*

o— *Muscles*

● Shortening with tension

● Lengthening with tension

● Lengthening without tension

● Held muscles without motion

---

# VARIATION: **MODIFIED** SPINE **TWIST**

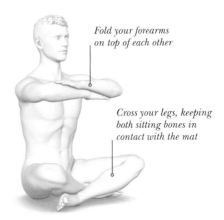

*Fold your forearms on top of each other*

*Cross your legs, keeping both sitting bones in contact with the mat*

**PREPARATORY STAGE**
Sit upright with your pelvis and spine in neutral. Cross your legs. Fold your forearms with one on top of the other and raise them to shoulder height.

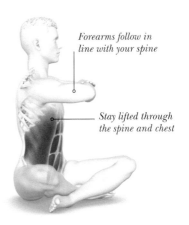

*Forearms follow in line with your spine*

*Stay lifted through the spine and chest*

**STAGE ONE**
Inhale to prepare and lengthen your spine. Exhale as you rotate your trunk to one side, allowing your forearms and head to follow in line with your spine. Repeat on the other side and complete sequence 3–5 times.

# COBRA

**This popular exercise sequentially mobilizes your spine** into extension. It strengthens the muscles down the back of your body and lengthens the muscles down the front of your body. Cobra is ideal to counteract strain from frequent everyday bending and can help treat lower back pain.

## THE BIG PICTURE

Relax your shoulders and use your arms to gently facilitate the move rather than pressing you upwards. Lengthen your head up towards the ceiling and follow with your chest, ribcage, lower abdominals, and front hip bones to create length in the spine. Move your arms further away from your body initially until you have comfort in full extension. Relax your buttocks, legs, and toes throughout. Try the Twisted Cobra variation to add an extra challenge.

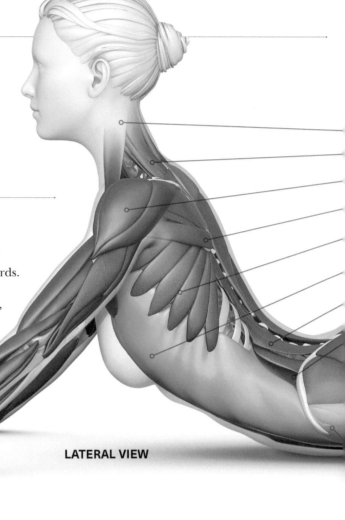

**LATERAL VIEW**

*Palms and forearms rest downwards*

*Tucking tailbone under brings pelvis into neutral*

**KEY**

●--- *Joints*

○— *Muscles*

● Shortening with tension

● Lengthening with tension

● Lengthening without tension

● Held muscles without motion

**PREPARATORY STAGE**
Lie flat on your front with your legs slightly wider than hip-distance apart. Rest your forehead on the mat with your neck lengthened and chin slightly tucked in. Place your arms out to the sides with your elbows flexed to 90 degrees. Inhale to lengthen your head away from your tailbone, and gently tuck your tailbone under.

*Rotate legs and feet outwards*

## Upper body

Your **neck extensors** keep the head lifted upright and your **spinal extensors** engage to extend your spine. Your **abdominal muscles** lengthen and your **rhomboids** engage to draw your scapulae together.

Sternocleidomastoid
Semispinalis capitis
Deltoids
Teres major
Serratus anterior
External oblique
Quadratus lumborum
Internal oblique

# VARIATION: **TWISTED** COBRA

*Head and chest both face right*

*Legs wider than hip-distance apart*

### STAGE ONE

Once you are raised up into your full Cobra position, gently walk both hands towards the right side, keeping the elbows extended. Maintain length in your trunk and avoid collapsing down on one side. Keep your chest lifted and collar bones wide. Inhale to hold the position and then exhale as you walk the hands over to the left side to repeat. Complete 3–5 times.

Biceps femoris long head
Biceps femoris short head
Vastus lateralis
Gastrocnemius
Rectus femoris
Peroneus longus
Gluteus maximus
Semitendinosus
Gluteus medius
Tensor fasciae latae

### STAGE ONE

Exhale as you glide your shoulder blades downwards away from your ears into neutral and rise up with your head, neck, and breastbone, followed by your ribcage and pelvis. Gradually extend your elbows at the same time, as far as you are able. Inhale to hold and lengthen. Exhale to return back to the mat – pelvis, then abdominals, ribcage, and breastbone, ending with your forehead back on the mat. Bend elbows to facilitate and control the lowering down of your body. Complete 3–6 times.

## Lower body

Your **gluteus maximus** and **hamstrings** engage to support your hips in extension, while your **hip flexors** lengthen. Your **gluteus medius** and **minimus** assist with stabilizing the hips in slight external rotation. Your **quadriceps** engage to support knee extension.

171

# ARM OPENINGS

This is a relaxing exercise that encourages spinal mobility through controlled rotation. It opens the chest and can help restore balance in postural conditions by mobilizing the back of the body and stretching the front.

**Caution**

If you have shoulder pain or instability, you may prefer to practise the Modified Arm Openings, which reduce the long lever length and circular motion of the uppermost arm.

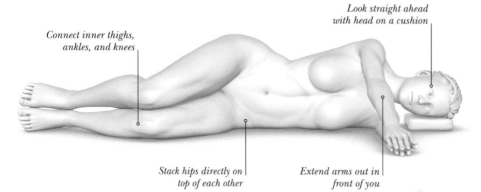

*Connect inner thighs, ankles, and knees*

*Look straight ahead with head on a cushion*

*Stack hips directly on top of each other*

*Extend arms out in front of you*

### PREPARATORY STAGE

Lie on one side with your hips and shoulders stacked on top of each other. Flex your hips to approximately 45 degrees and your knees to approximately 90 degrees. Rest your head on a cushion so that your head and neck are neutral. Stretch your arms out in front of you, on top of each other with palms touching.

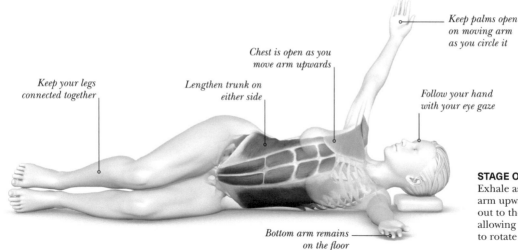

*Keep your legs connected together*

*Lengthen trunk on either side*

*Chest is open as you move arm upwards*

*Keep palms open on moving arm as you circle it*

*Follow your hand with your eye gaze*

*Bottom arm remains on the floor*

### STAGE ONE

Exhale as you reach your top arm upwards overhead, and out to the side, simultaneously allowing your spine and head to rotate with the arm.

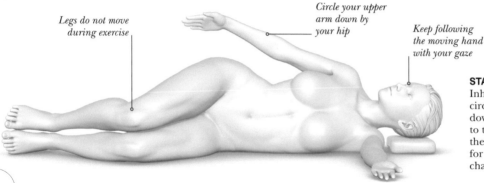

*Legs do not move during exercise*

*Circle your upper arm down by your hip*

*Keep following the moving hand with your gaze*

### STAGE TWO

Inhale as you continue the circle and bring your arm down by your hip, then back to the start position on top of the underneath arm. Repeat for 3–6 repetitions and then change sides.

# » VARIATIONS

Arm Openings can be performed with numerous variations such as different lever lengths or positions that still benefit from the thoracic rotation.

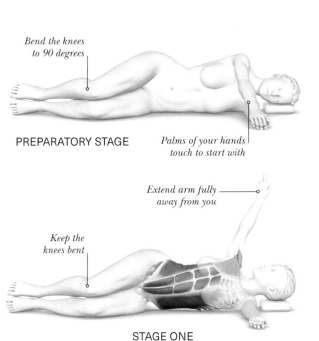

*Bend the knees to 90 degrees*

PREPARATORY STAGE

*Palms of your hands touch to start with*

*Extend arm fully away from you*

*Keep the knees bent*

STAGE ONE

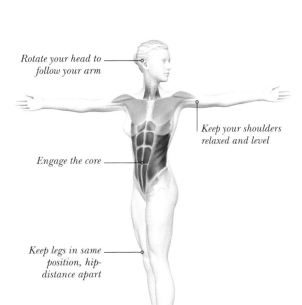

*Rotate your head to follow your arm*

*Keep your shoulders relaxed and level*

*Engage the core*

*Keep legs in same position, hip-distance apart*

STAGE ONE

## MODIFIED ARM OPENINGS

This modification reduces the long lever length of the arm and large circular motion of the shoulder. It is a good option for beginners and it can teach control of the trunk through thoracic rotation without flaring the ribcage.

### PREPARATORY STAGE
Lie in the preparatory position on your left side, resting your head on a block. Your legs and hips are flexed; your hips and shoulders are stacked on top of each other. Stretch your arms out in front of you.

### STAGE ONE
Exhale as you bend your right elbow and slide your top hand along your left arm to your chest and then out to your right side, allowing your spine and head to rotate to the left with you.

### STAGE TWO
Inhale as you rotate your head and spine back to the start, returning your arm to the start position. Repeat 3–6 times, then switch to the other side.

## STANDING ARM OPENINGS

This variation is more practical and can be added to the start or end of a workout, or during a lunch break. As your trunk is not fixed like it is when you are on the mat, your pelvis will rotate with you.

### PREPARATORY STAGE
Stand with your feet hip-distance apart and your spine and pelvis in neutral. Raise both arms up to shoulder height, with your shoulders relaxed and your palms facing inwards.

### STAGE ONE
Exhale as you open one arm outwards to the same side and round behind you as far as able, rotating your spine and head at the same time. Keep the front arm lengthened and still.

### STAGE TWO
Inhale as you return back to the start position. Repeat on the opposite side and continue alternating for 3–6 repetitions.

# THREAD THE NEEDLE

This is a simple, calming exercise to mobilize the spine into rotation and open up the chest and shoulders. It also provides shoulder stability while you work through the movement.

**Caution**

Rock your hips back slightly behind you as you thread the arm underneath and upwards to avoid overloading the static shoulder joint or straining your neck. It should all move smoothly and freely.

*The twisting element in **Thread the Needle** can aid digestion by gently massaging the digestive organs.*

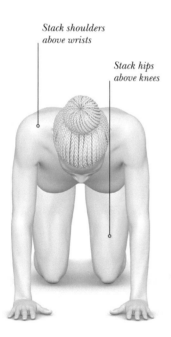

Stack shoulders above wrists

Stack hips above knees

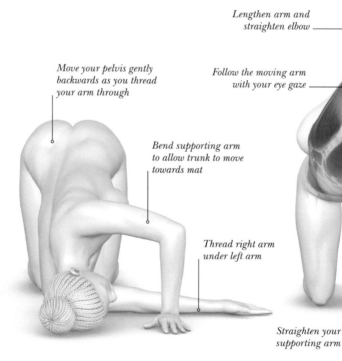

Move your pelvis gently backwards as you thread your arm through

Bend supporting arm to allow trunk to move towards mat

Thread right arm under left arm

Lengthen arm and straighten elbow

Follow the moving arm with your eye gaze

Straighten your supporting arm

**PREPARATORY STAGE**
Begin in four-point kneeling with your shoulders stacked above your wrists and your hips above your knees. Bring your spine and pelvis into neutral.

**STAGE ONE**
Exhale as you lift your right hand with palm facing upwards and thread it underneath your left arm, bringing your right shoulder and ear down towards the mat and rotating your head and trunk towards the left.

**STAGE TWO**
Inhale as you bring your right arm back towards the starting position and continue to raise it out to the right side and upwards towards the ceiling. Repeat 3–6 times, then switch sides.

# » VARIATIONS

Thread the Needle can be varied for additional stretches alongside thoracic rotation by changing either the upper body or lower body elements.

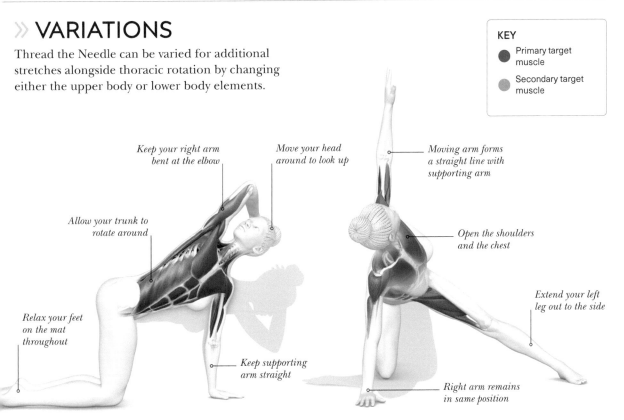

KEY
● Primary target muscle
● Secondary target muscle

*Keep your right arm bent at the elbow*

*Move your head around to look up*

*Allow your trunk to rotate around*

*Relax your feet on the mat throughout*

*Keep supporting arm straight*

*Moving arm forms a straight line with supporting arm*

*Open the shoulders and the chest*

*Extend your left leg out to the side*

*Right arm remains in same position*

PREPARATORY STAGE / STAGE ONE

PREPARATORY STAGE / STAGE ONE

## HAND BEHIND HEAD

Placing your hand behind your head reduces the arm lever length, which may be useful for tight or tender shoulders. This also allows greater focus on trunk rotation instead of leading with the arm. Keep the hips still when you perform this variation.

### PREPARATORY STAGE
Begin in four-point kneeling with your shoulders stacked above your wrists and your hips above the knees. Lift your your right hand and bring it to the side of your head.

### STAGE ONE
Inhale as you rotate from your waist and trunk to open your chest and shoulders towards your right side. Look to your right and up to the ceiling.

### STAGE TWO
Exhale to return to the start position of four-point kneeling, bringing your right arm down and returning your eye gaze to the floor. Repeat the sequence 3–6 times, then switch sides.

## THREAD THE NEEDLE
### IN ADDUCTOR STRETCH

This variation allows the same thoracic and upper body stretch while also stretching the inner thigh muscles of the leg. It is a strong, deep stretch for the whole body. Be careful of any adductor or pelvic pain conditions.

### PREPARATORY STAGE
Begin in four-point kneeling and extend your left leg out to the side. Exhale as you thread your left arm underneath the right arm, bringing your chest and left shoulder towards the mat.

### STAGE ONE
Inhale as you open the left arm outwards and up to the ceiling, rotating your trunk and allowing your chest and head to follow.

### STAGE TWO
Bring your left arm back down and thread it again under your right arm. Repeat the sequence 3–6 times then reset to four-point kneeling before repeating the same exercise on the other side.

# MERMAID

This side stretch exercise lengthens and opens the side of your body while mobilizing the thoracic spine, creating space in the ribcage to promote lateral breathing. It is a great exercise to transition smoothly between exercises in different positions.

KEY
● Primary target muscle
● Secondary target muscle

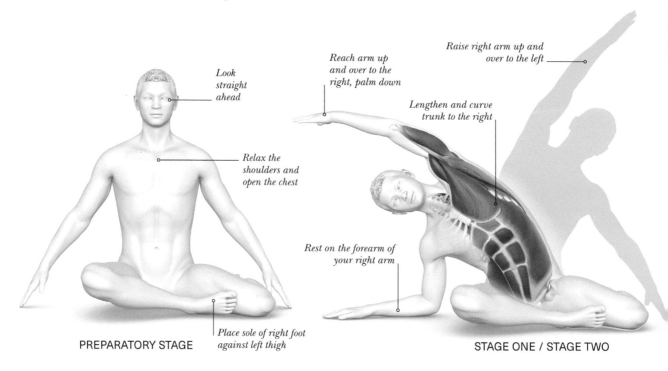

Look straight ahead

Relax the shoulders and open the chest

Place sole of right foot against left thigh

PREPARATORY STAGE

Reach arm up and over to the right, palm down

Raise right arm up and over to the left

Lengthen and curve trunk to the right

Rest on the forearm of your right arm

STAGE ONE / STAGE TWO

### PREPARATORY STAGE
Sit up tall with your head, neck, spine, and pelvis in neutral and your legs bent to the left side with both knees flexed. The sole of the right foot connects to the left thigh. Extend both arms by your sides with your fingertips lightly touching the mat.

### STAGE ONE
Inhale as you raise your left arm out to the side and overhead. Exhale as you reach the arm up and over to your right side, lengthening and curving your spine to the right. Your right arm slides along the mat until you rest on your forearm with your palm facing downwards.

### STAGE TWO
Inhale to return back to the upright sitting position. Exhale and raise your right arm up and over to your left side, allowing your spine to follow. Repeat 3–5 times each side, and then switch the legs around so that they are leaning to the right side and repeat the sequence.

*Use the Mermaid **exercise** **to warm** up or to stretch at the **end of a Pilates** routine.*

## ≫ VARIATIONS

Mermaid is safe for all participants and can be varied to add deeper stretches, different directions, and increase movements for maximum benefits. Combining some of these keeps your workout fun!

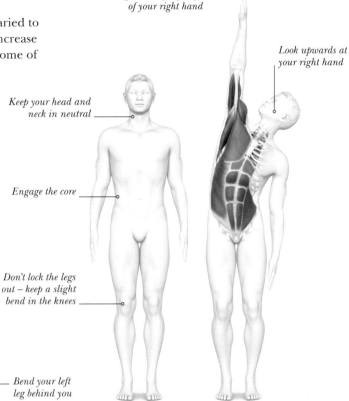

*Lengthen the fingertips of your right hand*

*Look upwards at your right hand*

*Keep your head and neck in neutral*

*Engage the core*

*Don't lock the legs out – keep a slight bend in the knees*

*Bring your left arm overhead*

*Reach forwards with left arm*

*Flex your spine forwards as you lean to the right*

*Bend your left leg behind you*

STAGE ONE / STAGE TWO

PREPARATORY STAGE / STAGE ONE

## MERMAID WITH A TWIST

This variation encourages spinal mobilization through every direction, with lateral flexion in the preparatory stage, flexion in stage 1, and extension in stage 2. It is a great all-round mobility exercise to restore movement and reduce spinal stiffness.

### PREPARATORY STAGE
From the Mermaid preparatory position, inhale as you raise your left arm out to the side and overhead. Exhale as you reach the arm up and over to your right side, lengthening and curving your spine to the right. Your right arm slides along the mat until you rest on your forearm, palm down.

### STAGE ONE
Inhale as you reach forwards with your left arm, flexing your spine forwards.

### STAGE TWO
Exhale as you rotate your left arm and chest up towards the ceiling. Inhale to return to upright sitting and relax your left arm by your side as per the preparatory position. Repeat 3–5 times, then switch sides.

## STANDING MERMAID

The Standing Mermaid allows greater spinal mobility as the pelvis is not fixed on the mat and the knee flexion can facilitate more movement. As one arm reaches upwards, opposition is encouraged with the opposite arm downwards to maximize the lateral stretch.

### PREPARATORY STAGE
Stand tall with both arms lengthened down by your sides and palms facing inwards.

### STAGE ONE
Inhale to prepare and exhale as you simultaneously reach your left arm down your left side, and lengthen your right arm upwards with palm facing away from you and bending your knees slightly. Turn your head to look up at your hand.

### STAGE TWO
Inhale to return to the starting position, then repeat on the opposite side, bringing the left arm upwards and the right arm downwards. Repeat 3–5 times, alternating sides each time.

177

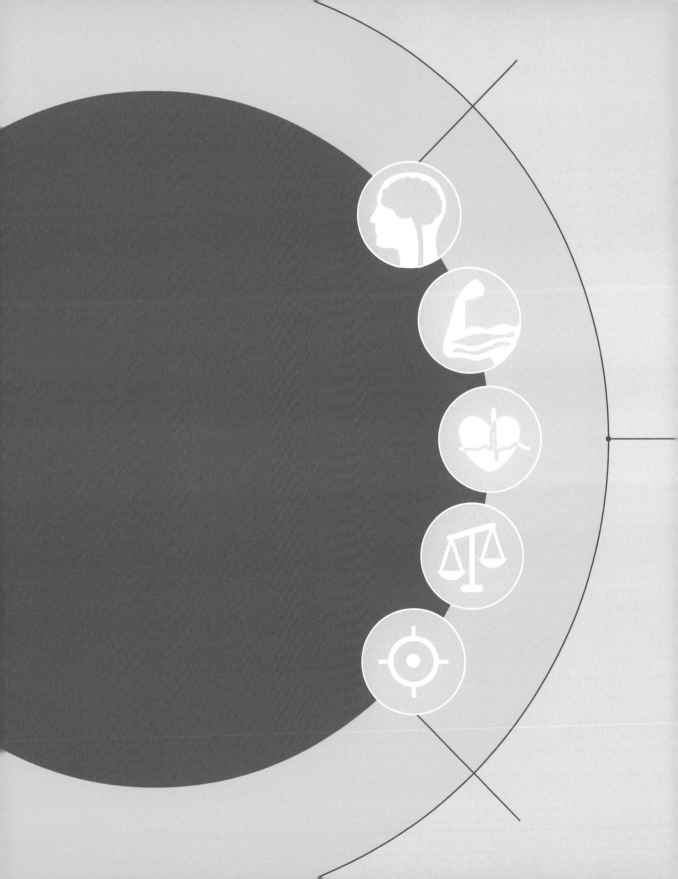

# PILATES
# TRAINING

**The benefits of Pilates should be experienced by everyone**. Regardless of fitness level, experience, ability, medical condition, or injury, Pilates can be adapted to be safe and effective while still utilizing the basic Pilates principles and ethos. Presented in this section are suggested workouts for numerous settings – whether you are a beginner, intermediate, or advanced, suffer back pain or arthritis, have a desk-bound job, are pregnant, or simply want to enhance a favourite sport, such as swimming or running. Working through this section will make it clear that Pilates is inclusive for everybody, but more importantly demonstrates the brilliance of the method in its ability to assist all kinds of requirements.

# GENERAL **FITNESS**

**Pilates exercises can be modified for any level of proficiency**, as you will have seen throughout this book with all the variation options. Here are key points to consider when starting or enhancing your Pilates journey, and advice on how to progress. Listen to your body, and stop or go down a level if you feel you need to.

## TYPES OF **PROGRAMME**

The general fitness Pilates programmes within this section are divided into beginner, intermediate, and advanced, and each programme offers several workouts and progressions.

### BEGINNER

Start with this programme if you are new to Pilates, have not participated in Pilates for a considerable time, or are recovering from an injury or medical condition. This programme focusses on the basics to allow you to learn the preparatory positions, correct engagement of the core muscles, and the fundamental movement patterns. These are crucial to lay a strong foundation from which to move and support the body at increasing difficulties.

If the core muscles cannot be engaged effectively at this level, or cannot cope with the low levels of load here, any progression of load will be difficult to achieve and may cause injury too. If initial weaknesses are observed, exercises can be modified for this, and noted for future exercises. The small equipment may be used to provide assistance, for example the addition of the soft ball between the knees to increase core activation further and stabilize an exercise. The slower pace also allows introduction to the Pilates principles and will solidify your practice as you progress through the levels.

### INTERMEDIATE

Workouts will introduce more exercises here to establish a broader skills base. Repetitions and circuits will be increased, and more variations of each exercise will be introduced to expand on strength and endurance. You can use small equipment more to challenge each exercise as it becomes comfortable, without needing to move on to the advanced exercises.

The Pilates principles may also be encouraged within other activities – for instance within strength training or aerobic exercise – to utilize the skills further and strengthen the mind-body connection throughout everyday life. Pilates may also be used as a warm up prior to these activities, or

**PROGRESSION CHART**
Each of the programmes can be completed as many times as you wish, both for enjoyment and to improve your Pilates skills. When you achieve the goals listed here, you may consider progressing to the next level. If the next level feels too challenging, pick a couple of the new exercises to try and return to the previous level for the rest of your session.

**BEGINNER**
- **Can control core** engagement and neutral position
- **Can integrate** movement and breathing
- **Can achieve** each exercise with ease

**INTERMEDIATE**
- **Less thinking** on technique
- **No body** compensations occurring
- **Have explored** adding small equipment and additional variations

**ADVANCED**
- **Continue** to perform exercises with skill
- **Full integration** of movement and breath
- **Excellent** transition between exercises

as an adjunct to the end of their session to integrate it into your schedule further.

You can increase the pace of the session to sequence several exercises together before a rest period. Rests will still be programmed, however, to ensure technique remains optimal.

## ADVANCED

These sessions still begin with some low level exercises to warm up, but the exercise progressions occur faster and there are more exercises included. There may also be more variations added on to each exercise, such as pulses and holds, to further challenge the body and build endurance within the same exercise before moving on.

Position changes are frequent to keep the body moving and increase heart rate, while continuing to maintain excellent technique. These also demand more technique awareness to reset the body's start position each time and progress to executing the advanced exercise at a high level. The advanced exercises require less description, as technique and knowledge are already installed from previous sessions. Rest periods may be minimal to keep the pace of the session and the intensity high, or there may be the introduction of active rest periods, where lower level exercises are performed instead of taking a complete rest.

*A regular* **Pilates** *practice is beneficial for both your* ***physical health*** *and your mental* wellbeing.

## Comparison table

A Pilates programme can be structured to reflect the level of the session. Here is an overview of the guidelines to creating the right balance within your programme. You can adapt these as required.

| VARIABLES | BEGINNERS | INTERMEDIATE | ADVANCED |
|---|---|---|---|
| NUMBER OF EXERCISES | 3–6 | 8–10 | 10 |
| SETS AND REPETITIONS | 1–2 circuits of 5–10 repetitions | 2–3 circuits of 8–10 repetitions | 3–4 circuits of 8–12 repetitions |
| REST BETWEEN EXERCISES | High if required | Moderate | Minimal |
| LOAD | Low | Medium | High |
| POSITION CHANGES | Minimal; 2–3 | Moderate; 3–4 | Many and frequent |
| CLASS PACE | Slow | Moderate | Varied with increased pace at times |

# **BEGINNER** WORKOUT PLANS

There are three beginners' programmes detailed here. When starting out, go through the
checklist, then the basic moves session. Repeat this several times to familiarize yourself,
then progress to the other sessions within Programme 1, completing 1 to 2 sessions a week.

## **Starting out checklist**

✔ Practise finding your neutral spine
and pelvis position in lying, side lying,
prone, and four-point kneeling.

✔ Set your legs in alignment, draw
your ribcage downwards, relax your
shoulders and arms, and lengthen
your neck with your head in neutral.

✔ Gently engage your core
approximately. 30 per cent by drawing
your lower abdominals inwards (not
forcing inwards or bracing outwards).

✔ Maintain this abdominal
contraction as you inhale and exhale
equally for 3–5 breaths.

✔ Carry these principles over to the
basic moves session

## **Basic moves**

**Repetitions:**
8 of each exercise
**Circuits: 1**

1. Pelvic Tilts p.47

2. Overhead Arm Circles p.47

3. Hip Twist (Legs on Mat) p.107

4. One Leg Stretch
(Beginner Level) p.62

5. Shoulder Bridge (Basic
Shoulder Bridge) p.86

6. Abdominal Curls p.48

## PROGRAMME 1

### **Spinal mobility and core**

**Repetitions:**
8–10 of each exercise
**Circuits:** 1–2

1. Pelvic Tilts p.47

2. Shoulder Bridge (Basic
Shoulder Bridge) p.86

3. Scissors (Single Leg Lifts) p.80

4. Hundred (Single Leg) p.54

5. Abdominal Curls p.48

6. Cobra p.170

## **Shoulders and hips**

**Repetitions:**
8–10 of each exercise
**Circuits:** 1–2

1. Shoulder Bridge (Basic Shoulder
Bridge) p.86

2. One Leg Circle (Legs Bent) p.98

3. Clam p.116

4. Leg Lift and Lower p.117

5. Side Bend (Half Side Bend) p.112

6. Swimming (Slower Option) p. 90

## **Full body 1**

**Repetitions:**
8–10 of each exercise
**Circuits:** 1–2

1. One Leg Stretch
(Band Support) p.63

2. Scissors (Single Leg Lifts) p.80

3. Oblique Curls p.49

4. Side Kick
(With Knees Flexed) p.102

5. Swan Dive
(Upper Body Only) p.72

6. Leg Pull Front (Hover) p.142

## **Full body 2**

**Repetitions:**
8–10 of each exercise
**Circuits:** 1–2

1. Hundred (Single Leg) p.54

2. Scissors (Single Leg Lifts) p.80

3. Hip Twist (Legs On Mat) p.107

4. Roll Up
(With Band Support) p.125

5. Swan Dive
(Upper Body Only) p.72

6. Swimming (Slower Option) p.90

## PROGRAMME 2

### Spinal mobility and core

**Repetitions:**
8–10 of each exercise
**Circuits:** 2–3

1. Hip Twist (Legs on Mat) p.107

2. Shoulder Bridge (Hip Abductions) p.86

3. Hundred (Single Leg) p.54

4. Scissors (Single Leg Lifts) p.80

5. Arm Openings p.172

6. Abdominal Curls p.48

### Shoulders and hips

**Repetitions:**
8–10 of each exercise
**Circuits:** 2–3

1. Overhead Arm Circles p.47

2. One Leg Stretch (With Band Support) p.63

3. One Leg Circle (With Band Support) p.99

4. Clam p.116

5. Push Up (Box Push Up) p.160

6. Side Bend (Half Side Bend) p.112

### Full body

**Repetitions:**
8–10 of each exercise
**Circuits:** 2–3

1. Roll Up (With Band Support) p.125

2. Oblique Curls p.49

3. Shoulder Bridge (Hip Abductions) p.86

4. Side Kick (With Knees Flexed) p.102

5. Swimming (Four Point Kneeling) p.91

6. Leg Pull Front (Hover) p.142

## PROGRAMME 3

### Spinal mobility and core

**Repetitions:**
8–10 of each exercise
**Circuits:** 2–3

1. Shoulder Bridge (Basic Shoulder Bridge) p.86

2. Hundred (Single Leg) p.54

3. Hip Twist (Legs on Mat) p.107

4. Abdominal Curls p.48

5. Spine Stretch (Modified Spine Stretch) p.165

6. Scissors (Single Leg Lifts) p.80

### Shoulders and hips

**Repetitions:**
8–10 of each exercise
**Circuits:** 2–3

1. Mermaid p.176

2. One Leg Circle (One Leg Extended) p.98

3. Clam p.116

4. Leg Lift and Lower p.117

5. Side Bend (Half Side Bend) p.112

6. Push Up (Box Push Up) p.160

### Full body

**Repetitions:**
8–10 of each exercise
**Circuits:** 2–3

1. Thread The Needle p.174

2. Abdominal Curls p.48

3. Oblique Curls  p.49

4. Swimming (Slower Option) p.90

5. Swimming (Four Point Kneeling) p.91

6. Spine Twist (Modified Spine Twist) p.169

# INTERMEDIATE WORKOUT PLANS

These programmes challenge you to branch out from the beginner exercises and are creative in their mixing of the exercises. Ensure you are able to perform the beginner programmes first and complete the warm up prior and cool down after each programme. Focus on your technique and breathing control in each exercise to master these next stages.

---

## Warm up

**Repetitions:**
6–8 of each exercise
**Circuits:** 1

1. Mermaid p.176

2. Overhead Arm Circles p.47

3. Pelvic Tilts p.47

4. Shoulder Bridge (Basic Shoulder Bridge) p.86

5. One Leg Stretch (Single Leg Option) p.62

6. Scissors (Single Leg Lifts) p.80

---

## Cool down

**Repetitions:**
6–8 of each exercise
**Circuits:** 1

1. Cat Cow p.46

2. Shell Stretch p.47

3. Hip Twist (Legs on Mat) p.107

4. Saw p.166

5. Thread the Needle p.174

6. Standing Arm Openings p.173

---

## Programme 1: Traditional sequence

**Repetitions:**
8–10 of each exercise
**Circuits:** 2–3

1. Hundred (Double Table Top) p.54

2. Roll Up (On a Mat) p.124

3. One Leg Stretch p.60

4. Rolling Back p.56

5. One Leg Stretch (Double Table Top) p.63

6. Scissors p.78

7. Shoulder Bridge (Leg Extensions) p.87

8. Side Kick (Both Legs Elevated) p.103

9. Swimming p.88

10. Leg Pull Back p.144

11. Spine Twist p.168

12. Breaststroke p.154

---

## Programme 2: Full body

**Repetitions:**
8–10 of each exercise
**Circuits:** 2–3

1. Oblique Curls p.49

2. Criss Cross p.155

3. Roll Up p.122

4. Roll Over p.126

5. Leg Pull Back (Single Leg Slides) p.147

6. Hip Twist p.104

7. Saw p.166

8. Double Leg Lift p.118

9. Side Kick in Kneeling p.108

10. Side Bend (Half Side Bend with Clam) p.112

11. Swimming p.88

12. Swan Dive (Swan Dive Preparation) p.73

### Programme 3:
### Upper body focus

**Repetitions:**
8–10 of each exercise
**Circuits:** 2–3

1. Cobra p.170

2. Breaststroke p.154

3. Swan Dive (Swan Dive Preparation) p.73

4. Side Bend (Half Side Bend With Elbow to Knee) p.113

5. Arm Openings p.172

6. Double Leg Stretch (With Abdominal Curl) p.67

7. Leg Pull Back (Leg Pull Back Lifts) p.146

8. Spine Stretch p.164

9. Swimming (Four Point Kneeling) p.91

10. Leg Pull Front (Hover) p.142

11. Push Up (Push Up on Knees) p.160

12. Shell Stretch p.47

### Programme 4:
### Lower body focus

**Repetitions:**
8–10 of each exercise
**Circuits:** 2–3

1. Shoulder Bridge (Leg Extensions) p.87

2. Hip Twist (Both Legs Move) p.107

3. One Leg Circle p.96

4. Scissors p.78

5. Bicycle p.82

6. Side Kick p.100

7. Double Leg Lift p.118

8. Swimming (Four Point Kneeling) p.91

9. Leg Pull Front p.140

10. Leg Pull Front (Leg Abductions) p.143

11. Thread the Needle in Adductor Stretch p.175

12. Neck Pull p.132

### Programme 5:
### Full body

**Repetitions:**
8–10 of each exercise
**Circuits:** 2–3

1. One Leg Stretch (Double Table Top) p.63

2. Double Leg Stretch (Single Leg Coordination) p.67

3. Hip Twist (Both Legs Move) p.107

4. Criss Cross p.155

5. Roll Up p.122

6. Shoulder Bridge p.84

7. Clam p.116

8. Side Kick (Both Legs Elevated) p.103

9. Breaststroke p.154

10. Leg Pull Front (Hover to High Plank) p.143

11. Push Up p.158

12. Seal p.92

# **ADVANCED** WORKOUT PLANS

Only attempt these advanced matwork programmes after you are completely comfortable with the intermediate programmes. Start with the warm up before each programme, and conclude with the cool down. Aim to perfect each exercise individually before trying them in the sequence of these programmes.

## Warm up

**Repetitions:**
6–8 of each exercise
**Circuits:** 1

1. Cat Cow p.46

2. Mermaid With a Twist p.177

3. Overhead Arm Circles p.47

4. Shoulder Bridge (Basic Shoulder Bridge) p.86

5. One Leg Stretch (Single Leg Option) p.62

6. Scissors (Reciprocal Legs) p.80

## Cool down

**Repetitions:**
6–8 of each exercise
**Circuits:** 1

1. Cobra p.170

2. Shell Stretch p.47

3. Thread the Needle In Adductor Stretch p.175

4. Hip Twist (Legs on Mat) p.107

5. Push Up (Push Up on Knees) p.160

6. Standing Mermaid p.177

## Programme 1: Traditional sequence

**Repetitions:**
8–12 of each exercise
**Circuits:** 2–4

1. Hundred (Double Table Top and Abdominal Curl) p.55

2. Roll Up p.122

3. One Leg Stretch p.60

4. One Leg Circle p.96

5. Double Leg Stretch p.64

6. Scissors (Reciprocal Legs Extended) p.81

7. Shoulder Bridge p.84

8. Spine Twist p.168

9. Swimming p.88

10. Leg Pull Front p.140

11. Side Bend p.110

12. Push Up p.158

## Programme 2: Full body

**Repetitions:**
8–12 of each exercise
**Circuits:** 2–4

1. Scissors (Reciprocal Legs) p.80

2. Double Leg Stretch (With Abdominal Curl) p.67

3. Criss Cross p.155

4. Spine Stretch p.164

5. Side Kick in Kneeling p.108

6. Side Bend p.110

7. Side Twist p.114

8. Push Up p.158

9. Cobra p.170

10. Double Leg Kick p.76

11. Swimming p.88

12. Leg Pull Front p.140

## Programme 3:
## Upper body focus

**Repetitions:**
8–12 of each exercise
**Circuits:** 2–4

1. Abdominal Curls p.48

2. Criss Cross p.155

3. Spine Stretch p.164

4. Leg Pull Back p.144

5. Arm Openings p.172

6. Swimming p.88

7. Breaststroke p.154

8. Shell Stretch p.47

9. Leg Pull Front (Hover to High Plank) p.143

10. Push Up p.158

11. Swan Dive p.70

12. Side Twist p.114


## Programme 4:
## Lower body focus

**Repetitions:**
8–12 of each exercise
**Circuits:** 2–4

1. Shoulder Bridge p.84

2. One Leg Circle p.96

3. Scissors (Reciprocal Legs Extended) p.81

4. Bicycle p.82

5. Clam p.116

6. Leg Lift and Lower p.117

7. Double Leg Kick p.76

8. Side Kick in Kneeling p.108

9. Control Balance p.156

10. Saw p.166

11. One Leg Kick p.74

12. Swimming p.88


## Programme 5:
## Full body

**Repetitions:**
8–12 of each exercise
**Circuits:** 2–4

1. Roll Up (On a Mat) p.124

2. Double Leg Stretch p.64

3. Teaser p.136

4. Jack Knife p.134

5. Corkscrew p.128

6. Boomerang p.148

7. Neck Pull p.132

8. Side Kick (On Elbows with Both Legs Elevated) p.103

9. Side Bend (Half Side Bend with Elbow to Knee) p.113

10. One Leg Kick p.74

11. Swimming p.88

12. Leg Pull Front (Leg Abductions) p.143

# PILATES FOR **RUNNING**

**Pilates exercises can reduce the rate of injury in runners**, research has shown. Pilates exercises can also be used as an effective warm up, cool down, and as part of a strengthening routine to complement your running programme.

## COMMON **RUNNING INJURIES**

Running-related injuries occur in up to 80 per cent of runners every year. The causes of injury are multifactorial, but the majority of these are preventable with the right interventions.

### WHY RUNNERS COMMONLY EXPERIENCE INJURIES

Running is one of the most common and accessible forms of exercise and forms the basis for many other sports. The high rate of over-use injuries relates to the constant, repetitive, and high impact nature of running. Injuries are primarily to the lower limb and 60 per cent are the result of training error. This is simply progressing distance, speed, or frequency of running too quickly. The running load then exceeds the body's ability to cope with the increased demand.

The runner's technique is also crucial to their performance and risk of injury. Those who rearfoot strike (land on their heel) are more likely to sustain an injury due to the increased load through their knees. If your hip muscles are lacking in strength, the hip may adduct or rotate inwards, followed by the knee and ankle (see image on the right). The force from striking the ground is then transferred up the leg incorrectly, overloading the muscles and joints.

### HOW PILATES CAN HELP

Neutral spine and pelvis, and good full body posture is the foundation of a Pilates practice. Pilates teaches correct engagement of the core for localized stabilization from which the limbs can move effectively with the additional muscle support. This supports the reciprocal arm and leg coordination required for running, as well as generating the core and oblique powerhouse to move from. Core endurance also supports long distance runners to prevent fatigue and continue good technique. Improve your core fitness with the suggested core workout plan (right).

Pilates can correct the biomechanics of the lower limb by improving hip and knee control as well as strengthening the lateral hip muscles. This prevents hip adduction, internal rotation, and improves leg alignment. Pilates exercises that focus on gluteal muscle strength in hip extension (see workout on the right) also enhance the mechanism that propels you forwards and generates the power required to run.

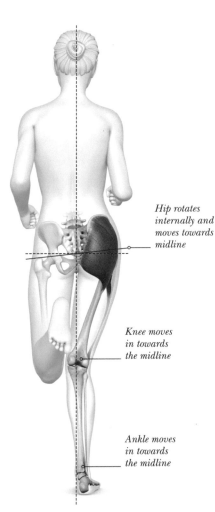

Hip rotates internally and moves towards midline

Knee moves in towards the midline

Ankle moves in towards the midline

**POOR RUNNING BIOMECHANICS**
Weak hip muscles in runners can cause both valgus collapse, when the knee moves inwards, and ankle pronation, when the ankle moves inwards.

# WARM UP

A running warm up should consist of active, dynamic movements to increase joint mobility of the spine, shoulders, hips, knees, and ankles, and reduce the muscle stiffness within these regions. It should also activate the key muscles of the gluteals, hip abductors, and core to stimulate them for readiness.

The warm up provided here is all matwork-based and can be done before starting your run. Spine Twist, Scissors, and Clam exercises may also be replicated in standing by performing the same movement in the upright position. This can enhance muscle activation in a more functional position and prepare the body and legs for the running movements.

## Warm up workout plan

**Repetitions:**
6–8 of each exercise
**Circuits:** 1

1. Thread the Needle p.174

2. Swimming (Four Point Kneeling) p.91

3. Shoulder Bridge (Basic Shoulder Bridge) p.86

4. Hip Twist (Single Leg) p.106

5. Spine Twist (Modified Spine Twist) p.169

6. Scissors (Reciprocal Legs) p.80

7. Clam p.116

8. Side Kick (With Knees Flexed) p.102

# COOL DOWN

During running, your muscles are constantly contracting and relaxing to withstand the repetitive load and reacting to ground reaction forces as you strike the ground. Post-run mobility and stretching exercises (see below) can relieve any muscle tightness that has accumulated.

Exercises performed for 5–30 seconds can reduce the muscle tendon stiffness and increase joint motion. If these exercises are accompanied by slower breathing patterns, you will also slow your heart rate back down, restoring a sense of relaxation and a psychological conclusion of the run. The combination of effective movement patterns and breathing control make Pilates ideal for cooling down after running.

## Core workout plan

**Repetitions:**
8–10 of each exercise
**Circuits:** 2–3

1. Hundred p.52

2. Scissors (Reciprocal Legs Extended) p.81

3. One Leg Stretch p.60

4. Double Leg Stretch p.64

5. Scissors p.78

6. Bicycle p.82

7. Criss Cross p.155

8. Leg Pull Front p.140

## Hip/glutes workout plan

**Repetitions:**
8–10 of each exercise
**Circuits:** 2–3

1. Shoulder Bridge p.84

2. One Leg Circle p.96

3. Hip Twist (Single Leg) p.106

4. Clam p.116

5. Leg Lift and Lower p.117

6. Side Bend (Half Side Bend with Clam) p.112

7. Side Kick p.100

8. Swimming (Four Point Kneeling) p.91

## Cool down workout plan

**Repetitions:**
4–6 of each exercise
**Circuits:** 1–2

1. Push Up p.158

2. Cobra p.170

3. Shell Stretch p.47

4. Spine Twist (Modified Spine Twist) p.169

5. Mermaid p.176

6. Saw p.166

7. Hip Twist (Legs on Mat) p.107

8. Thread the Needle In Adductor Stretch p.174

# PILATES FOR **SWIMMING**

**Swimming has the unique features** of exercising against water resistance while remaining afloat with no point of contact. Swimmers rely on their core as the support source, and their inbuilt strength through the entire kinetic chain to generate power for propulsion. Pilates complements swimming with its non-impact nature, movement from the core, and dissociation of the limbs from the trunk.

## SWIMMING **BIOMECHANICS**

The aim of swimming is to complete a specific distance in the fastest time possible. This is achieved by accelerating the body through the water in such a way that you minimize water resistance.

Swimmers need to maintain a body position that is as horizontal and streamlined as possible (mainly for front crawl), and keep a strong trunk position within all strokes. A strong core allows greater transfer of energy to the limbs, and the arms and legs must dissociate from the trunk to generate power for propulsion and to overcome the water drag.

Body symmetry allows equal power to be generated from each side and therefore will provide a more efficient stroke that covers greater distance faster. Swimmers do not usually develop symmetrically however, and where there is muscle imbalance they usually compensate by using other muscles more than normal to ensure the total force generated is the same.

Scapular stability is essential for the lengthening and lateral rotation of the shoulder blades during the swim stroke, in conjunction with cervical spine and thoracic mobility. Hip extension primarily drives the power from the lower half of the body with pelvic and lumbar stability. Finally, a regular breathing pattern that integrates with the stroke is essential to maintain the full stroke coordination.

### PILATES FOR SWIMMING PERFORMANCE

One of the key benefits of Pilates is its ability to isolate specific joints and strengthen the stabilizing muscles locally, while maintaining a connection through the core for trunk stability. This has been shown to positively influence front crawl performance, with significant

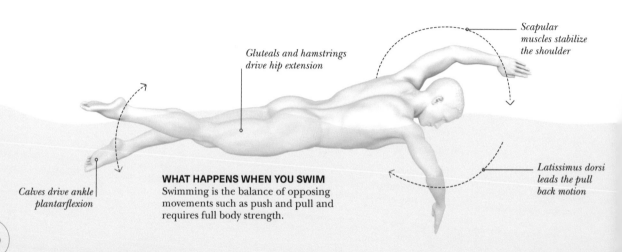

*Scapular muscles stabilize the shoulder*

*Gluteals and hamstrings drive hip extension*

*Latissimus dorsi leads the pull back motion*

*Calves drive ankle plantarflexion*

**WHAT HAPPENS WHEN YOU SWIM**
Swimming is the balance of opposing movements such as push and pull and requires full body strength.

improvements in overall swim speed and performance following a turn.

The latissimus dorsi is the largest muscle of the back and is responsible for overhead strokes and pulling the body through the water. Pilates exercises that focus on the posterior oblique sling can maximize the muscle's potential.

Swimming training and long-distance races require extensive core endurance for continued trunk support and transfer of force through the body. Pilates exercises that target the core also have highly relatable movements to swimming, for example Rolling Back and Roll Over actually involve the rolling motion involved in turns and strengthen the core for this specific purpose.

Pilates for swimming sessions should integrate the whole body to match the whole body effort of the sport. If there is a specific weakness, the programme can be tailored to target this region to restore full body symmetry. The exercises that isolate areas important for swimming are:

- **Shoulder/upper back exercises:** Breaststroke p.154; Swan Dive p.70; Push Up p.158; Side Bend p.110.

- **Hip exercises:** Shoulder Bridge p.84; Leg Lift and Lower p.117; One Leg Circle p.96; One Leg Kick p.74.

- **Core exercises:** Hundred p.52; Double Leg Stretch p.64; Criss Cross p.155; Oblique Curls p.49; Teaser p.136, Hip Twist p.104; Jack Knife p.134; Corkscrew p.128; Leg Pull Front p.140.

- **Core exercises for turns:** Rolling Back p.56; Roll Over p.126; Roll Up p.122.

# WORKOUTS

These workouts are designed to enhance your training by working you to a high level outside of the pool. Complete on a rest day or a few hours before pool training.

## Beginner

**Repetitions:**
8–10 of each exercise
**Circuits:** 2

1. Hundred (Double Table Top) p.54
2. One Leg Stretch (Double Table Top) p.63
3. Hip Twist (Legs on Mat) p.107
4. Leg Pull Back (Reverse Table Top) p.146
5. Side Bend (Half Side Bend) p.112
6. Swimming (Slower Option Head Down) p.90
7. Leg Pull Front (Hover to High Plank) p.143
8. Thread the Needle (Hand Behind Head) p.175

## Beginner to intermediate

**Repetitions:**
10 of each exercise
**Circuits:** 2–3

1. Rolling Back p.56
2. Double Leg Stretch (Single Leg Coordination) p.67
3. Oblique Curls p.49
4. Half Side Bend (With Elbow to Knee) p.113
5. Breaststroke p.154
6. Swimming p.88
7. Swimming (Four Point Kneeling) p.91
8. Push Up p.158

## Intermediate to advanced

**Repetitions:**
10–12 of each exercise
**Circuits:** 4

1. Hundred p.52
2. Double Leg Stretch p.64
3. Criss Cross p.155
4. Teaser p.136
5. Double Leg Lift p.118
6. Side Twist p.114
7. Leg Pull Front (complete up to 10 repetitions on each leg) p.140
8. Rocking p.152

# PILATES FOR
# STRENGTH TRAINING

**Strength training in the form of lifting weights** and Pilates are very different exercise types but their methods are not exclusive from one another. They are both forms of resistance training with the end goal of improving muscle strength, muscle endurance, and core strength.

## PILATES FOR **LIFTING**

Strength training exercises such as squat, deadlift, and bench press are primarily linear movements that focus on a specific muscle or muscle group, require a stiff spine, and follow a single movement pattern.

Strength training exercises involve moving an external weight, or the body's own weight, to provide resistance. These can either be compound (multiple muscle groups and joints) or isolated muscle group exercises. Both methods mostly involve movements in one plane of motion. This develops strength within the specific movement but any deviation from, or dysfunction within the movement pattern can lead to a reduction in overall performance.

While repetition of the exercise itself may build further strength in this movement, it will not address individual weaknesses. Movement impairments are often asymptomatic in experienced trainers and can cause injury. Pilates encourages a full body approach, with frequent positional changes. Posture, body awareness, and correct movement patterns are continuously enforced.

Here we look at the three main compound lifts and identify the role of Pilates within each.

### SQUAT

The squat is driven by the gluteus maximus and the hamstring muscles. Pelvic stability is achieved by the gluteus medius to prevent hip adduction. Poor squat performance is associated with hip weakness. Side-lying Pilates exercises such as Clam (p.116) and Leg Lift and Lower (p.117) can isolate gluteus medius and restore pelvic stability.

### DEADLIFT

The deadlift is often a culprit of lower back pain from poor technique or lifting excessive load without core stability. Learning how to activate and strengthen the core prior to lifting will protect the lumbar spine. Utilizing the deep musculature may also offload the global musculature, such as the erector spinae, which can compensate if core support is lacking. The combination of good core strength and gluteal strength will enhance the lower body drive.

### Mindfulness

Pilates exercises are cued with very accurate technique instructions. This is called internal focus, where you concentrate your mind on the movement the body region is executing. External focus is the awareness of the end result of the movement. When weight lifters adopted an internal focus method, research showed that muscle activity was greater, with enhanced movement patterns. Internal focus creates a stronger mind-body connection and improves body awareness, so Pilates could be used to correct movement impairments in weight lifting.

### BENCH PRESS

Thirty-six per cent of injuries in weight lifting relate to the shoulder joint and are due to a lack of shoulder stability. The further the weight is pressed away from the body, the more stability the shoulder requires. The activation of the deep shoulder and core muscle stabilizers through Pilates exercises can address this weakness and provide localized support to accommodate the high loads on the joint.

## HOW TO ADD PILATES TO YOUR STRENGTH TRAINING

- As a warm up to prepare the body for strength training.

- As a cool down to mobilize the body after repetitive muscle contractions.

- After a strength session to ensure full body muscle stimulation, even on specific body split days.

- To further work a body region, e.g. on back day, perform scapular stability Pilates exercises.

- As a full body strengthening session on separate days to maintain postural awareness and low level muscle activation.

### Warm up

**Repetitions:**
6–8 of each exercise
**Circuits:** 1–2

1. Cat Cow p.46

2. Thread the Needle in Adductor Stretch p.175

3. Hip Twist (Legs on Mat) p.107

4. Clam p.116

5. Shoulder Bridge (Hip Abductions) p.86

6. Push Up p.158

### Cool down

**Repetitions:**
6–8 of each exercise
**Circuits:** 1–2

1. Saw p.166

2. Spine Twist p.168

3. Hip Twist (Legs on Mat) p.107

4. Basic Shoulder Bridge (hold for up to 30 seconds and place a soft ball under the pelvis to rest on) p.86

5. Standing Arm Openings p.173

6. Standing Mermaid p.177

### Full body workout plan 1

**Repetitions:**
8–10 of each exercise
**Circuits:** 3–4

1. Hundred p.52

2. One Leg Stretch p.60

3. Shoulder Bridge p.84

4. Clam p.116

5. Leg Lift and Lower p.117

6. Side Bend (Half Side Bend with Clam) p.112

7. Double Leg Kick p.76

8. Push Up p.158

### Full body workout plan 2

**Repetitions:**
8–10 of each exercise
**Circuits:** 3–4

1. Hundred p.52

2. Hip Twist p.104

3. Double Leg Stretch p.64

4. Criss Cross p.155

5. Side Kick p.100

6. Clam p.116

7. Saw p.166

8. Leg Pull Front p.140

### Full body workout plan 3

**Repetitions:**
8–10 of each exercise
**Circuits:** 3–4

1. Abdominal Curls p.48

2. Hip Twist (Single Leg) p.106

3. Leg Lift and Lower p.117

4. Breaststroke p.154

5. Side Bend p.110

6. Teaser p.136

7. Shoulder Bridge (Hip Abductions) p.86

8. Leg Pull Back Lifts p.146

# PILATES FOR
# SEDENTARY WORKERS

**The digital revolution and growth of working from home** has created a more sedentary lifestyle than ever before. The accumulation of both prolonged and static positions can lead to adaptations in our posture which can manifest as pain, tightness, or disc problems. These can affect our daily activities, and even our mental health.

## 15%
OF LUMBAR MUSCLE STIFFNESS IS CAUSED BY PROLONGED SITTING.

## WHAT **HAPPENS**

Our bodies are designed to move and the positions that we adopt when we must sit for long periods at a desk are often not ideal. Pilates can strengthen and restore posture and mobility throughout the body.

We can find ourselves sitting in the same positions for too long for the body to maintain and over time muscles that are over working start to fatigue or reach fatigue earlier. This can lead to slouching and adapting to more "comfortable" positions which, in the long term, can start to strain other muscles that are not designed to absorb additional loads. This leads to symptoms such as muscular aches, pains, and disorders, and further unhealthy posture adaptations: a vicious cycle is formed.

Pilates exercises can introduce mobility to open the chest, shoulders, and hips to ease muscle tightness, as well as strengthen the shoulder blade region, core, and gluteal muscles. Prolonged sitting weakens the gluteal muscles as they are inactive when sitting – muscles require regular engagement to maintain their strength and efficiency. The gluteal

muscles are the primary muscles involved in initiating hip movements in basic actions such as walking and running, so gluteal weakness can also lead to pain in the hips.

A good Pilates routine can improve muscle activation, strength, and endurance so that your body can maintain the correct posture and minimize these discomforts. Exercise also boosts our energy levels and, combined with the mind-body connection Pilates creates, can positively influence our mood. Introducing a short Pilates routine to your week, or even performing a few exercises at your desk, can provide so many physical and mental benefits and also improve your desk posture.

**WHAT IT CAUSES**
Postural syndrome (see right) can tighten the chest, hips, and front of the body, and lengthen the back of the body, causing weakness in the upper back, spine, and gluteal muscles.

## PILATES BENEFITS

Pilates training breaks the vicious cycle of sedentary work body issues:

**Introduces mobility**
**Breaks the static posture**
**Strengthens postural muscles**
**Restores alignment**
**Boosts energy**
**Improves mood**

## DESK TIPS

Set yourself up for success from the moment you sit down at your desk.

● **Sit back in your chair** so that your spine is supported and lengthened against the chair.

● **Place a rolled-up towel** or lumbar roll in the small of your back to support your natural spinal curves.

● **Place both feet flat on the floor** with equal weight distributed between them.

● **Ensure your pelvis is neutral** and you have equal weight bearing through each sitting bone.

● **Align your ribs** over your pelvis.

● **Rest your elbows on your desk** with a 90-degree bend at the elbows and your wrists in neutral.

● **Lift your chest and keep** your collar bones wide, with your shoulders relaxed.

● **Take a movement break** every 30 minutes,. away from your desk, and reset.

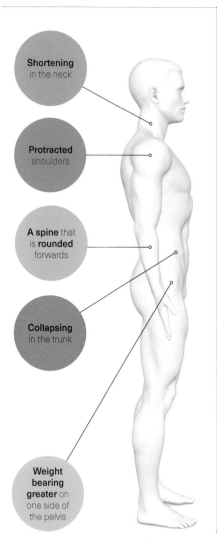

**Shortening** in the neck

**Protracted** shoulders

**A spine** that is **rounded** forwards

**Collapsing** in the trunk

**Weight bearing greater** on one side of the pelvis

# AT YOUR DESK EXERCISE PLAN

Pilates can have a positive impact on our posture. It can improve head and pelvis alignment, hip angle, spinal vertical alignment, thoracic kyphosis, and lumbar lordosis. See page 31 for explanations of these postural dysfunctions.

Use this simple exercise plan to break up your sitting position throughout the day. Aim to complete the programme twice per day. Complete 6–8 repetitions of each exercise. You can follow the routine once if you are short for time. Complete 2–3 circuits of the exercises if you have more time available, or if you feel your posture could benefit from a longer session.

*It's easy to forget to move and stretch when* **concentrating** *on work.*

### Desk job routine

This simple routine of six exercises will provide a break from your sedentary desk work. Try to complete at least one circuit.

**Repetitions:**
6–8 of each exercise
**Circuits:** Complete 1–3

**1.** Pelvic Tilts (perform on a chair) p.47

**2.** Roll Up (On a Chair) p.124

**3.** Scissors (Single Leg Lifts: perform on a chair) p.80

**4.** Arm Openings (Standing Arm Openings) p.173

**5.** Shoulder Bridge (Hip Abductions) p.86

**5.** Mermaid (stage 1) p.176

**6.** Dumb Waiter p.46

# MATWORK **EXERCISE PLAN**

This matwork exercise plan has been designed to improve your trunk stability and endurance in your sitting posture. It also incorporates posterior chain-based exercises, which target the muscles that run down the back of your body from your neck to your ankles.

These exercises will help to reduce the tightness in forward flexion and strengthen the back of the body to help lift your body upright. Each session finishes with a mobility-based exercise to keep your spine moving well and minimize stiffness from static sitting. Make sure you warm up before each workout.

Start with the Beginner Programme, and complete the workouts in order. Repeat the three beginner-level workouts each week until you can complete all three workouts with ease. You can then progress to the Intermediate Programme, then finally move on to the Advanced Programme.

Each programme has a suggested number of repetitions and circuits to complete, but if you don't have time to complete the full workout, you can just select a few exercises from the programme. You could also complete the exercises by duration – the boxes to the right suggest how to implement this to your workout. The break between exercises and recovery between sets is very important to prevent muscle fatigue.

## Beginner programme

Each exercise length is 30 seconds, with a 15-second break between exercises, and 30–60 seconds of recovery between each set.

## Intermediate programme

Each exercise length is 45 seconds, with a 15-second break between exercises, and 30–45 seconds of recovery between each set.

## Advanced programme

Each exercise length is 60 seconds, with no break between exercises, and 30–45 seconds of recovery between each set.

---

## Beginner workout 1

**Repetitions:**
8–10 of each exercise
**Circuits:** 1

1. Dumb Waiter p.46

2. Hundred (Single Leg) p.54

3. Scissors (Single Leg Lifts) p.80

4. One Leg Stretch (Beginner Level) p.62

5. Shoulder Bridge (Basic Shoulder Bridge) p.86

6. Swimming (Slower Option: Head Down) p.90

7. Spine Twist (Modified Spine Twist) p.169

8. Arm Openings (Standing Arm Openings) p.173

## Beginner workout 2

**Repetitions:**
8–10 of each exercise
**Circuits:** 1

1. Dumb Waiter p.46

2. Hundred (Single Leg) p.54

3. Scissors (Single Leg Lifts) p.80

4. Hip Twist (Legs on Mat) p.107

5. Clam p.116

6. Double Leg Kick p.76

7. Swan Dive (Upper Body Only) p.72

8. Mermaid (Standing Mermaid p.177

## Beginner workout 3

**Repetitions:**
8–10 of each exercise
**Circuits:** 1

1. Roll Up (On a Chair) p.124

2. Hundred (Single Leg) p.54

3. Scissors (Single Leg Lifts) p.80

4. Shoulder Bridge (Basic Shoulder Bridge) p.86

5. Swimming (Slower Option: Head Down) p.90

6. Leg Pull Back (Reverse Table Top) p.146

7. Swan Dive (Upper Body Only) p.72

8. Cobra p.170

## Intermediate workout 1

**Repetitions:**
8–10 of each exercise
**Circuits:** 2

1. Roll Up (On a Mat) p.124

2. Hundred (Double Table Top) p.54

3. Scissors (Reciprocal Legs) p.80

4. One Leg Stretch (Double Table Top) p.63

5. Shoulder Bridge (Hip Abductions) p.86

6. Swimming (Four Point Kneeling) p.91

7. Breaststroke p.154

8. Arm Openings p.172

## Intermediate workout 2

**Repetitions:**
8–10 of each exercise
**Circuits:** 2

1. Double Leg Stretch (Preparation) p.66

2. Hundred (Double Table Top) p.54

3. Scissors (Reciprocal Legs) p.80

4. One Leg Stretch (Double Table Top) p.63

5. Clam p.116

6. Double Leg Kick p.76

7. Breaststroke p.154

8. Mermaid (Standing Mermaid) p.177

## Intermediate workout 3

**Repetitions:**
8–10 of each exercise
**Circuits:** 2

1. Roll Up (On a Mat) p.124

2. Hundred (Double Table Top) p.54

3. Scissors (Reciprocal Legs) p.80

4. Shoulder Bridge (Knee Raises) p.87

5. Swimming (Four Point Kneeling) p.91

6. Leg Pull Back (Leg Pull Back Lifts) p.146

7. Swan Dive (Upper Body and Arms) p.72

8. Cobra p.170

## Advanced workout 1

**Repetitions:**
8–10 of each exercise
**Circuits:** 2–3

1. Double Leg Stretch (Single Leg Coordination) p.67

2. Hundred (Double Table Top) p.54

3. Scissors (Reciprocal Legs Extended) p.81

4. One Leg Stretch (Double Table Top) p.63

5. Shoulder Bridge (Knee Raises) p.87

6. Swimming p.88

7. Breaststroke p.154

8. Spine Twist p.168

## Advanced workout 2

**Repetitions:**
8–10 of each exercise
**Circuits:** 2–3

1. Double Leg Stretch (Single Leg Coordination) p.66

2. Hundred (Double Table Top and Abdominal Curl) p.55

3. Scissors (Reciprocal Legs Extended) p.80

4. One Leg Stretch p.60

5. Side Kick p.100

6. Double Leg Kick p.76

7. Breaststroke p.154

8. Thread the Needle p.174

## Advanced: Workout 3

**Repetitions:**
8–10 of each exercise
**Circuits:** 2–3

1. Double Leg Stretch p.64

2. Hundred (Double Table Top and Abdominal Curl) p.55

3. Scissors (Reciprocal Legs Extended) p.81

4. Shoulder Bridge (Leg Extensions) p.87

5. Swimming p.88

6. Leg Pull Back (Single Leg Slides) p.147

7. Swan Dive (Swan Dive Preparation) p.73

8. Cobra p.170

# PILATES FOR
# WOMEN'S HEALTH

**Pregnancy, the postnatal period, and the menopause** are all life events with profound physical, hormonal, and psychological effects on the body. These key stages each require specific modifications to accommodate and treat the changes that they impose. Pilates is an excellent method for each stage due to its non-impact nature, focus on the core and pelvic floor, and ease of adaptability.

## PREGNANCY

From conception, changes occur within the body, and pregnancy affects the majority of our body systems. Regular exercise is recommended for a healthy pregnancy to support both mother and baby.

As the baby grows the centre of gravity moves forwards without the base of support, and can cause postural adjustments such as an increased lumbar lordosis (see p.31). This results in weakening of the abdominals anteriorly, and the gluteals posteriorly. The hormone relaxin causes ligament laxity from as early as eight weeks and may lead to pelvic instability or increased joint mobility. The additional weight gain can further overload the pelvis and joints.

### HOW PILATES CAN HELP

Pilates is a safe exercise method in pregnancy and research supports its role in the reduction of lumbar and pelvic pain. It can achieve this by improving core stability and strength and supporting the spine to correct postural dysfunctions. There is a direct link between lower back pain and pelvic floor and breathing dysfunction, and Pilates exercises address each of these issues at the foundation of the technique.

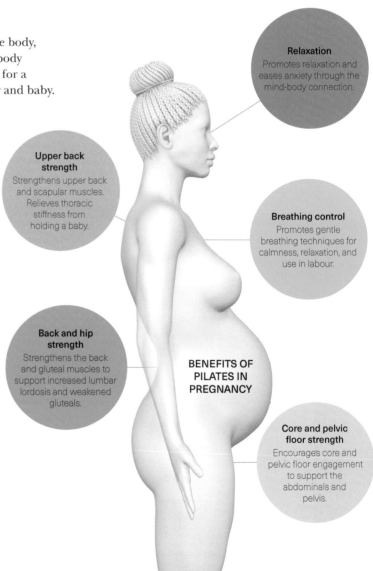

**Relaxation**
Promotes relaxation and eases anxiety through the mind-body connection.

**Upper back strength**
Strengthens upper back and scapular muscles. Relieves thoracic stiffness from holding a baby.

**Breathing control**
Promotes gentle breathing techniques for calmness, relaxation, and use in labour.

**Back and hip strength**
Strengthens the back and gluteal muscles to support increased lumbar lordosis and weakened gluteals.

**BENEFITS OF PILATES IN PREGNANCY**

**Core and pelvic floor strength**
Encourages core and pelvic floor engagement to support the abdominals and pelvis.

## PRECAUTIONS TO NOTE FOR PILATES IN PREGNANCY

| | |
|---|---|
| Low blood pressure | Avoid multiple/quick position changes, including Roll Down. |
| Ligament laxity | Avoid stretching joints too far. |
| Supine position | Avoid from 16 weeks, or perform no longer than 2 minutes. |
| Abdominal loading | Avoid double table top exercises and those with abdominal curl movements from 16 weeks. |
| Prone position | Use four point kneeling instead. |
| Inversions | Avoid inverted positions, such as Jack Knife (see p.134) |

## Tips for pelvic girdle pain

Pelvic girdle pain is classed as any pain within the pelvis and buttock region. To avoid further discomfort:
• Use a pillow/ball between your knees.
• Avoid opening the legs greater than hip-distance apart.
• Avoid rotating the hips inwards or outwards.
• Avoid Shoulder Bridge and squat positions.
• Try isometric-based exercises: push against resistance without moving.

## Tips for lower back pain

Lower back pain can occur in any trimester but is often more prevalent in the later stages as the baby's weight increases and posture changes further.
• Ensure the back is always supported.
• Use mobility-based exercises such as Pelvic Tilts and Cat Cow.
• Exercise in side lying to take the load off the back.
• Ensure good core and pelvic floor muscle activation.

## Pelvic floor exercises

• Commence as soon as possible, and complete three times per day throughout pregnancy and thereafter.
• Use the optimal cue of closing your back passage through to your front and then lifting upwards approximately 30 per cent.
• Perform two different styles: fast contractions for 10 repetitions, and slow contractions for 10 repetitions with 10 second holds.

## Workout plan for first trimester

**Repetitions:**
10–12 of each exercise
**Circuits:** 2–3

1. Shoulder Bridge (Hip Abductions) p.86

2. Scissors (Reciprocal Legs) p.80

3. Abdominal Curls p.48

4. Clam p.116

5. Arm Openings p.172

6. Swimming (Slower Option) p.90

7. Swan Dive (Upper Body Only) p.72

## Workout plan for second trimester

**Repetitions:**
10–12 of each exercise
**Circuits:** 2–3

1. Cat Cow p.46

2. Scissors (Single Leg Lifts: use pillows to incline upper body) p.80

3. One Leg Stretch (Single Leg Option: use pillows to incline upper body) p.62

4. Hip Twist (Legs on Mat) p.107

5. Leg Lift and Lower p.117

6. Side Kick (With Knees Flexed) p.102

7. Thread the Needle p.174

## Workout plan for third trimester

**Repetitions:**
8–10 of each exercise
**Circuits:** 2–3
Listen to your body, reduce or slow down as required.

1. Dumb Waiter p.46

2. Hundred (Single Leg: sitting on a chair) p.54

3. Scissors (Single Leg Lifts: sitting on a chair) p.80

4. Side Kick (With Knees Flexed) p.102

5. Swimming (Four Point Kneeling) p.91

6. Standing Arm Openings p.173

# THE **POSTPARTUM PERIOD**

This refers to the stage after birth. Among the emotional adjustments women face at this time, physical symptoms may also present, along with with postural changes caused by attending to a baby. Pilates can address these needs straight away or in the future.

## DIASTASIS

Diastasis rectus abdominis is the natural separation of the abdominal muscles vertically. It occurs in 100 per cent of women by their third trimester due to the stretching of the linea alba, the connective tissue that joins the rectus abdominis. About 50 per cent of diastasis cases will resolve naturally postpartum within eight weeks, but in some, this can cause an abdominal weakness which remains. These muscles are responsible for trunk and pelvic floor support, as well as coughing, sneezing, laughing, and toileting, and a weakness can impair these functions.

Pilates exercises teach correct engagement of the abdominal muscles and these exercises are one of the best ways to cause muscle adaptation and resolve the symptoms of diastasis.

A Pilates programme for diastasis should begin with isolated core and pelvic floor exercises, progress to oblique and rectus abdominis exercises, and finally mimic everyday tasks in functional movements.

Exercises to avoid with a diastasis until core is improved include those for the obliques, raising both legs up simultaneously, and full sit ups.

## PELVIC FLOOR DYSFUNCTION

Pelvic floor dysfunction can occur as the pressure increases within the pelvis and bears downwards during pregnancy, as well as the result of vaginal delivery trauma, high birth weight, and multiple births. Up to 75 per cent of postpartum women will experience pelvic floor dysfunction; problems occur with both vaginal and Caesarean section births. This includes a wide range of conditions such as urinary or faecal incontinence, pelvic organ prolapse, and painful sex. It is also related to lower back pain and diastasis and can impact mental health.

About 25–40 per cent of women are not aware of their pelvic floor muscles and how to exercise them. Training these muscles can reduce the risk of urinary incontinence by 50 per cent when performed during pregnancy and 35 per cent when performed postnatally.

It is important to integrate this activation into exercises such as squats, lunges, and deadlifts to train the muscles within normal activities. Relax the muscles fully after each exercise. Complete your exercises three times per day for 3–6 months.

**NORMAL VERSUS DIASTASIS**
The normal abdomen shows the intact rectus abdominis and linea alba. The diastasis recti abdomen shows the widened abdominals and stretching of the linea alba.

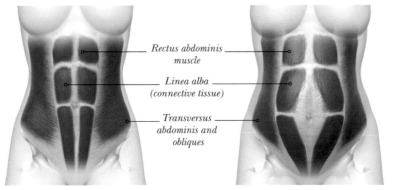

Rectus abdominis muscle

Linea alba (connective tissue)

Transversus abdominis and obliques

**NORMAL ABDOMEN**          **DIASTASIS RECTI ABDOMEN**

### Precautions to note for postpartum Pilates

- No Pilates exercise should cause you pain of any kind postpartum. If there is an increase in pain, postpartum bleeding, incontinence, or a heavy dragging sensation in your vagina, seek further advice.

- Avoid overloading the abdominals with sit ups, full planks, or lifting or lowering down both legs.

- Avoid bearing down into the pelvic floor. This may be exaggerated with Abdominal Curl movements.

- Be aware of fatigue and energy levels and don't overexert yourself.

## Workout plan
## 6–12 weeks after birth

**Repetitions:**
5–10 of each exercise
**Circuits:** 1–3

1. Hundred (Single Leg) p.54

2. One Leg Stretch
   (Beginner Level) p.62

3. Scissors (Single Leg Lifts) p.80

4. Shoulder Bridge (Basic Shoulder
   Bridge) p.86

5. Hip Twist (Legs on Mat) p.107

6. Cat Cow p.46

7. Dumb Waiter p.46

## Workout plan
## 12–18 weeks after birth

**Repetitions:**
8–10 of each exercise
**Circuits:** 2–3

1. Hundred
   (Double Table Top) p.54

2. Shoulder Bridge
   (Knee Raises) p.87

3. Abdominal Curls p.48

4. One Leg Stretch
   (Double Table Top) p. 63

5. Clam p.116

6. Side Bend (Half Side Bend) p.112

7. Swimming
   (Four Point Kneeling) p.91

## Workout plan
## 18–24 weeks after birth

**Repetitions:**
10–12 of each exercise
**Circuits:** 3–4

1. Shoulder Bridge p.84

2. One Leg Stretch p.60

3. Double Leg Stretch
   (Single Leg Coordination) p. 67

4. Side Kick p.100

5. Breaststroke p.154

6. Leg Pull Front
   (Hover to High Plank) p.143

7. Spine Twist p.168

# MENOPAUSE

Menopause is the natural end of the menstrual cycle and occurs 12
months after the last menstrual period. Research shows that Pilates
significantly improves strength, function, and quality of life in
menopausal women.

Menopausal symptoms occur due to
the depletion of the sex hormone
oestrogen and cessation of ovarian
function. It occurs between the ages
of 45 and 55, however premature
menopause can affect those in their
twenties. It can cause profound
changes that see up to 90 per cent
of women seeking help. Strength
training exercises are recommended
to relieve symptoms that can lead to
osteoporosis, a reduction in muscle
mass and strength, pelvic floor
muscle atrophy, balance problems,
depression, and anxiety.

### HOW PILATES CAN HELP
Pilates can help menopausal
symptoms by improving lumbar and
muscle strength and bone integrity
in as little as 8–12 weeks with 2–3
classes per week. Menopause
accelerates bone loss from one
year prior to and up to five years
post-menopause, so continued
participation is crucial to support
the skeletal system long term.
Exercises should focus on core and
pelvic floor connection, and the use
of the soft ball between the knees
can strengthen this connection.

## General training plan
## to help in menopause

**Repetitions:**
8–10 of each exercise
**Circuits:** 2–3

1. Hundred (Double Table Top
   and Abdominal Curl) p. 55

2. One Leg Stretch p.60

3. One Leg Circle p.96

4. Clam p.116

5. Leg Pull Front p.140

6. Push Up pp.158, 160, 161

7. Mermaid p.176

# PILATES FOR **BACK PAIN**

**Lower back pain is the number one cause of disability worldwide**, and Pilates is renowned for treating this type of pain. Amongst other benefits, Pilates strengthens the core and provides stability to the spine – both crucial for avoiding back pain. Those who suffer with the condition can be reassured by the widespread evidence available that backs up these benefits.

*Back* pain *has a* **high** *recurrence rate that can be* reduced *with localized* **spinal stability** *exercises.*

## LOWER BACK PAIN

Back pain causes are predominantly non-specific, as the source of pain is unknown. Classification is based on location and an understanding of mechanical back pain.

Research suggests that up to 80 per cent of adults will suffer from lower back pain. The incidence is higher in working-age groups with poorer environmental, social, and economic factors, psychological conditions, or previous back pain history. Our backs are the centre of our bodies and therefore regularly succumb to mechanical stress.

### MECHANICAL BACK PAIN
Acute episodes of back pain can resolve within weeks. Of those with back pain, 2–3 per cent will go on to develop chronic back pain. The bigger problem is that 60–85 per cent of cases recur, mostly within a year of the first episode.

This high rate may be explained by Panjabi's Stability Model (see p.34), which suggests that a loss of control within the spine segments may be responsible for the pain mechanisms as a result of muscle weakness or injury to the intervertebral discs and nerves.

The local spine stabilizing muscles, multifidus and transversus abdominis, both control spinal motion at the segmental level and are associated with back pain. Changes in the multifidus, such as the muscle fibre composition, cross-sectional area, and fatiguability can occur as early as 24 hours after an acute episode of back pain.

Chronic back pain shows a delayed activation of the transversus abdominis when the arms or legs perform a movement. In healthy situations, the central nervous system would prepare for movements in advance – such as reaching outwards from the body – and initiate the required muscle contractions.

Fear of pain exacerbates back pain, highlighting the psychological link to physiological changes, and can explain recurring pain. The alteration in motor control causes a restriction to spinal movement, as the global muscles engage to compensate for the lack of local muscle stability. Long term this reduces the stimulation and need for local muscle support and back pain will increase in frequency because the spine has continued deterioration of support.

## HOW PILATES CAN HELP

Research shows that eight weeks of a regular Pilates programme can lead to improvements in the motor control of the spinal stabilizing muscles. Pilates teaches local activation of the core muscles, which includes the multifidus and transversus abdominis. This co-contraction increases local spine engagement and the feedforward mechanism the nervous system uses in anticipation of movement to improve motor control.

A Pilates programme for back pain also demonstrated positive outcomes with pain, disability, mobility, strength, and muscle endurance. Endurance of both local and global muscles is improved, leading to less effort being required to create muscle activation.

Spinal mobility is integral to Pilates, and when the spine stiffens from global muscle activation, Pilates can restore this movement and, in turn, restore overall function.

## TIPS FOR EVERY DAY

Small changes on a daily basis can keep your back healthy and reduce injury risk.

- **Stand up** and walk about every 30–60 minutes.
- **Correct seating** posture to an optimal position (see p.195).
- **Keep loads close** to the body when lifting.
- **Avoid excessive twisting** or over-reaching.
- **Stretch** to keep joints mobile.
- **Perform basic core** engagement.

# WORKOUTS FOR BACK PAIN

If you are new to Pilates or symptoms are increased, start with the beginner programme. As symptoms ease and strength develops, progress through to the beginner/intermediate and intermediate/advanced programmes.

## Beginner

**Repetitions:**
5–8 of each exercise
**Circuits:** 1

1. Pelvic Tilts p.47

2. Overhead Arm Circles p.47

3. One Leg Stretch (Beginner Level) p.62

4. Scissors (Single Leg Lifts) p.80

5. Clam p.116

6. Shoulder Bridge (Basic Shoulder Bridge) p.86

7. Cat Cow p.46

8. Shell Stretch p.47

## Beginner to intermediate

**Repetitions:**
8–10 of each exercise
**Circuits:** 1–2

1. Hundred (Single Leg) p.54

2. One Leg Stretch (Single Leg Option) p.62

3. Scissors (Reciprocal Legs) p.80

4. Clam p.116

5. Leg Lift and Lower p.117

6. Hip Twist p.104

7. Mermaid p.176

8. Spine Twist p.168

## Intermediate to advanced

**Repetitions:**
10 of each exercise
**Circuits:** 2

1. Hundred (Double Table Top and Abdominal Curl) p.55

2. Scissors (Reciprocal Legs) p.80

3. Abdominal Curls p.48

4. One Leg Stretch (Single Leg Option) p.62

5. Hip Twist (Legs on Mat) p.107

6. Shoulder Bridge (Basic Shoulder Bridge) p.86

7. Swimming (Four Point Kneeling) p.91

8. Mermaid p.176

# PILATES FOR **NECK PAIN** AND **HEADACHES**

**Neck pain is a common and disabling condition** characterized by pain and a restriction in neck range of motion. It is associated with poor posture and feelings of anxiety and depression. Headaches can also result from this poor neck posture.

## NECK PAIN

Up to 70 per cent of adults will experience neck pain within their lifetime, with a recurrence of 75 per cent within five years. These statistics require a better understanding of the causes of neck pain.

Acute neck pain can resolve within days or weeks, but in approximately 10 per cent of cases, symptoms can become chronic and prevail for years. Acute pain is often the result of a trauma such as a whiplash or sporting injury. Chronic neck pain is generally related to postural dysfunctions, and the consequential muscle imbalances and stresses placed upon surrounding structures. This is more prevalent with the increasing use of technology and screen time that demands prolonged sitting postures, often with head tilted looking down.

### POSTURE THAT CAN CONTRIBUTE TO NECK PAIN
Neck pain is often diagnosed when the sufferer has a forward head posture. This head position can then lead to a posture called upper crossed syndrome – a system of muscle imbalances. Weak deep neck flexors cause the head to protrude forwards, while the tightness in levator scapulae

increases the cervical lordosis (inward curve of the neck). Tightness in the upper trapezius and weakness in the middle and lower trapezius and serratus anterior cause elevation, protraction, and abduction of the scapulae and can lead to a thoracic kyphosis posture (outward curve of the spine). Tightness in the pectorals further exacerbates shoulder protraction. This can reduce shoulder joint stability and, as a result, muscles such as the levator scapulae and upper trapezius then increase further in activity to attempt to stabilize the shoulder joint.

Prolonged time in functional positions, such as sitting at a desk, warrants minimal stimulation from gravity, such that neck stabilizing muscles weaken and atrophy over time. This causes mobility muscles to increase their activity to assist with stability of the neck and their over-contractions lead to muscle tightness and a restricted range of neck movement. Forward head

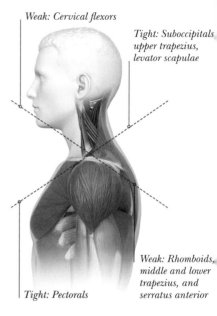

*Weak: Cervical flexors*

*Tight: Suboccipitals upper trapezius, levator scapulae*

*Weak: Rhomboids, middle and lower trapezius, and serratus anterior*

*Tight: Pectorals*

**UPPER CROSSED SYNDROME**
There are two diagonal lines that represent the muscle imbalance, with one line showing muscle weakness and the other muscle tightness.

posture in standing is further linked to a lack of core abdominal muscle control and thoracic kyphosis. These postural changes and muscle imbalances occur before symptoms become apparent, and it is only when the function becomes impaired that pain onsets and people identify their problem.

By this stage there may be a lot of work to undo to rehabilitate the neck back to normal function.

## PAIN AND RESPIRATION

Neck pain can be associated with changes in breathing mechanics. During respiration the cervical and thoracic spine must be stabilized to allow efficient ribcage movement and diaphragm function. Sitting and standing increase respiratory muscle activity. If the increase is excessive, for example due to neck postural changes, the upper ribcage will become elevated by neck muscles and the upper trapezius, which can impact diaphragm function, and exacerbate muscle overactivity.

# CERVICOGENIC **HEADACHES**

Differing from migraines, such headaches are caused by dysfunction in the upper neck and associated postural changes that can occur with neck pain. Symptoms can move to the head and/or face.

Cervicogenic headaches occur when there is a dysfunction in the upper three cervical vertebrae. This is due to the upper cervical region having an extensive supply of receptors that detect changes in posture, as well as the nerves that supply this region and surrounding structures such as the joints, intervertebral discs, ligaments, and muscles relaying pain signals to the central nervous system. Any neck pathology or muscle fatigue and lack of stability can increase sensitivity of the area further.

These headaches account for 1–4 per cent of all headaches, and are more common in people aged between 30 and 44 years. They affect males and females equally and are worsened by neck movement and postural positions.

# HOW **PILATES** CAN **HELP**

Practising Pilates can have a positive impact on neck pain and headaches as a consequence of correcting muscle imbalances, restoring mobility, and improving general posture.

Exercises such as the Swan Dive variations (p.72) can improve deep neck flexor strength. Breaststroke (p.154) and Swimming (p.88) can strengthen the scapular muscles to resolve forward head posture. The full body approach of Pilates includes strengthening for the core and postural improvements; studies showed that performing Pilates three times a week for 12 weeks resulted in benefits for pain, strength, function, and quality of life in neck pain sufferers.

Pilates breathing can also aid muscle imbalances by utilizing diaphragmatic/lateral breathing (see p.36) and offloading the upper trapezius/levator scapulae muscles that over work during neck pain.

# WORKOUTS

These workouts are specifically for neck pain and/or headaches and are suitable for all levels.

## Workout 1

**Repetitions:**
6–8 of each exercise
**Circuits:** 1–2

1. Overhead Arm Circles p.47

2. Hundred (Single Leg) p.54

3. Scissors (Single Leg Lifts) p.80

4. Arm Openings p.172

5. Swan Dive (Upper Body Only) p.72

6. Breaststroke p.154

7. Dumb Waiter p.46

## Workout 2

**Repetitions:**
6–8 of each exercise
**Circuits:** 1–2

1. Spine Twist (Modified Spine Twist) p.169

2. Hundred (Single Leg) p.54

3. Overhead Arm Circles p.47

4. One Leg Stretch (Beginner Level) p.62

5. Clam p.116

6. Swimming (Slower Option: Head Down) p.90

7. Shell Stretch p.47

# PILATES FOR **SCOLIOSIS**

**Scoliosis is a lateral curvature of the spine.** The word is derived from ancient Greek where it means "bent" or "crooked". Pilates is an effective treatment method for scoliosis and can have an impact on the curve and the pain associated with it.

## HOW TO **TREAT THE CURVES**

A normal spine runs from the head to the pelvis in a straight line; its standard curves are the anterior (front) and posterior (back) curves. By contrast, a scoliotic spine has lateral curves to one or both sides and is diagnosed if the curvature is more than 10 degrees. A C-shaped spine has one curve that will cause shortening of the spine and body on one side, and elongation on the opposite side. An S-shaped spine is more common and has two curves within the spine.

Exercise can correct mild to moderate curve deformities if the curvature is no more than 35 degrees. You need to identify the curve and its direction to create the correct exercise plan.

The elongated region of the trunk (convex curve) requires strengthening exercises to increase muscle support. The shortened side (concave curve) requires lengthening via stretching and

mobility-based exercises. Treating an S-shaped curve is more complex. You can attempt to treat the upper and lower curves, but may also find a combination of exercises works best.

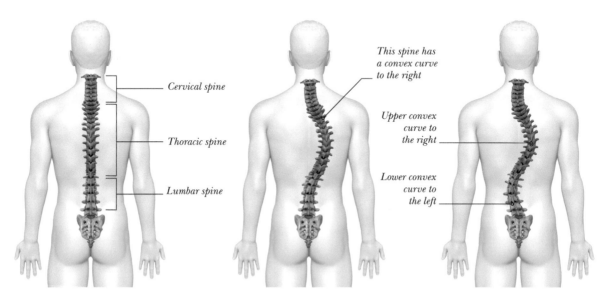

Cervical spine

Thoracic spine

Lumbar spine

*This spine has a convex curve to the right*

*Upper convex curve to the right*

*Lower convex curve to the left*

**NORMAL SPINE**
The spine runs vertically from the occiput at the skull to the pelvis, with no lateral deviation.

**C-SHAPED SPINE**
This spine has a convex curve to the right and a concave curve to the left. It should be strengthened on the right side and stretched on the left side.

**S-SHAPED SPINE**
The top curve should be strengthened on the right and stretched on the left; the bottom curve strengthened on the left and stretched on the right.

# HOW **PILATES** CAN **HELP**

Scoliosis affects up to 12 per cent of the population worldwide and 80 per cent of cases are idiopathic (from an unknown cause). The condition is progressive and affects spinal alignment and trunk mobility, impacting body image, mental health, and quality of life. The body's asymmetry and muscle imbalance can also cause pain.

Pilates exercises can slow the progression of scoliosis and reduce the curvature of the spine by up to 32 per cent. Reducing the spine deformity is the primary outcome to the Pilates treatment programme. This involves a combination of core stability exercises which stabilize the spine, and a series of exercises that lengthen the compressed side and strengthen the elongated side. This will restore muscle balance and improve overall posture. Collectively, improvements in these aspects have been found to reduce pain levels.

Corrections of posture have a positive effect on body image and, together with reduced pain and increased function, can greatly improve the quality of life of someone who has scoliosis.

### KEEP SCOLIOSIS AT EASE

Try these simple tips daily to keep your spine symptoms minimal and prevent a build up of pain.

- Avoid sinking into your curve.

- Sit upright and supported, using cushions where necessary to balance your body.

- Move often and change position frequently, more often than you think you should.

- Complete stretching exercises regularly throughout the day, with a longer stretch session twice a week.

- Feel positive that you are managing your condition and that there are many different exercise options to relieve your symptoms.

### Role of Pilates breathing

The spine curvature alters the trunk alignment and can compress the chest and thoracic cavity. This can restrict lung capacity and movement and impact breathing. Lateral breathing techniques (see p.36) elongate the trunk and expand the ribcage to stretch the affected muscles. They also encourage relaxation, which may aid painful or anxious episodes.

---

### Stretching for scoliosis

**Repetitions:** 5–8 of each exercise or hold for a single 10 seconds.

1. Mermaid p.176

2. Cat Cow p.46

3. Shell Stretch p.47

4. Thread the Needle p.174

5. Arm Openings p.172

6. Hip Twist (Legs on Mat) p.107

### Strengthening for scoliosis Session 1: Beginner

**Repetitions:** 5–10 of each exercise
**Circuits:** 1–2

1. One Leg Stretch (Beginner Level) p.62

2. Shoulder Bridge (Basic Shoulder Bridge) p.86

3. Side Bend (Half Side Bend) p.112

4. Leg Lift and Lower p.117

5. Cobra (only to a comfortable height) p.170

6. Leg Pull Front (Hover) p.142

### Strengthening for scoliosis Session 2: Intermediate

**Repetitions:** 6–10 of each exercise
**Circuits:** 2–3

1. One Leg Stretch (Single Leg Option) p.62

2. One Leg Circle (One Leg Extended) p.98

3. Side Bend (With Elbow to Knee) p.113

4. Side Kick p.100

5. Swimming (Four Point Kneeling) p.91

6. Leg Pull Front (Hover to High Plank) p.143

# PILATES FOR
# HYPERMOBILITY

**Hypermobility is a connective tissue disorder** where joints have a range of movement beyond normal limits. It can present with pain in multiple joints for no reason and needs specific strengthening and control exercises to relieve symptoms.

## ABOUT **HYPERMOBILITY**

The presentation of joint hypermobility can manifest over a wide spectrum. There are specific determinants and symptoms of the condition, or it may pose no symptoms at all.

Hypermobility affects up to 13 per cent of people, however this is likely much higher due to its under-diagnosis. The varied and vague presentation with no particular cause can delay diagnosis.

### FACTORS INVOLVED
Hypermobility occurs as the result of faulty or weak collagen, the connective tissue which is the "glue" that holds your entire body together. The resulting lack of support reduces joint proprioception (the body's ability to sense movement) and overall body awareness.

This dysfunction in the collagen makeup is genetically inherited, is three times more likely to occur in females than males, and is greater in African and Asian ethnicity. Children and teenagers have a higher incidence and the condition eases with age as joint mobility and muscle tension stiffens.

### HYPERMOBILITY SYMPTOMS
The repetitive joint trauma can lower the pain threshold and produce both acute and chronic pain. Joint laxity (looseness) can cause dislocations in worst cases and create fear of movement.

The laxity within the tendons renders them less effective at transmitting forces to generate strength, therefore skeletal muscle mass and strength can be reduced. This also applies to the abdominal muscles and the pelvic floor, and increases the risk of musculoskeletal injury and incontinence.

### Range of hypermobility symptoms
The range and severity of hypermobility symptoms is multifactorial and different for each person. The prescription of Pilates should be tailored to their presentation.

| Asymptomatic | Localized joint/region hypermobility | Multi-joint hypermobility | Chronic multi-joint hypermobility |
|---|---|---|---|
| • No symptoms<br>• Fully functional | • Single joint pain<br>• Laxity | • Widespread pain<br>• Laxity<br>• Hyperalgesia<br>• Musculoskeletal injuries | • Ongoing pain for more than three months<br>• Anxiety<br>• Depression<br>• Chronic fatigue |

# HOW **PILATES** CAN **HELP**

Exercise programmes for hypermobility focus mostly on muscle stability and control. Generic strength programmes often do not account for the lack of muscle power and endurance in this population.

For example, slow-twitch muscle fibres that support joints locally atrophy (degenerate) much faster than other muscle fibres and require high repetitions to produce change within the muscle. These participants cannot withstand high repetitions initially and require a graded approach with local stabilizing exercises. This is how Pilates programmes function.

In Pilates, a "chain" refers to a series of joints that link body sections. Closed-chain exercises, such as the Push Up, stimulate the functional demand while protecting the joints. These can then be progressed to open-chain exercises, such as One Leg Circle, for additional strength benefits. An eight-week programme was shown to significantly improve lower limb strength and knee alignment, as well as reducing pain and improving quality of life in hypermobile participants.

Hypermobility Pilates programmes should begin with basic muscle isometric activation and include muscle activation and control, trunk and spine control, and full body strength exercises.

## Muscle activation and stability

**Repetitions:**
6–10 of each exercise
**Circuits:** 1

1. One Leg Stretch (With Band Support) p.63

2. Shoulder Bridge (Hip Abductions) p.86

3. Hip Twist (Single Leg: with band around knees) p.106

4. One Leg Circle (With Band Support) p.99

5. Hover (place a band around your wrists and/or knees) p.142

6. Swimming (Four Point Kneeling) p.91

7. Side Bend (Half Side Bend) p.112

## Trunk and spine control

**Repetitions:**
6–10 of each exercise
**Circuits:** 1

1. Spine Twist p.168

2. Thread the Needle (Hand Behind Head) p.175

3. Mermaid (sit on a resistance band and pull it over to the side) p.176

4. Roll Up (With Band Support) p.125

5. Abdominal Curl p.48

6. Spine Stretch p.164

7. Arm Openings (Standing Arm Openings: using a band) p.173

## Strengthening workout 1

**Repetitions:**
8–10 of each exercise
**Circuits:** 2–3

1. Hundred (Single Leg) p.54

2. Clam (with resistance band tied around knees) p.116

3. One Leg Stretch (With Band Support) p.63

4. Hip Twist (Single Leg: with band around knees) p.106

5. Shoulder Bridge (Hip Abductions) p.86

6. Abdominal Curl p.48

7. Side Bend (Half Side Bend) p.112

## Strengthening workout 2

**Repetitions:**
8–10 of each exercise
**Circuits:** 2–3

1. Dumb waiter (hold a resistance band between the hands) p.46

2. Hundred (Single Leg) p.54

3. One Leg Stretch (With Band Support) p.63

4. Shoulder Bridge (With Hip Abductions) pg 86

5. Abdominal Curl p.48

6. Spine Stretch p.164

7. Swimming (Four Point Kneeling) p.91

# PILATES FOR
# OSTEOPOROSIS

**Osteoporosis is a systemic skeletal disease** that occurs when bone mineral density decreases. This weakens the structure and strength of bones and increases the risk of fractures. Resistance training can slow bone loss and build strength to support the skeletal system.

> *Pilates can* **significantly** *reduce* pain *caused by* **osteoporosis;** *a regular practice is encouraged to* maximize *benefits.*

## WHAT CAUSES OSTEOPOROSIS?

Bone loss is often not diagnosed until the first fracture, or subsequent fractures occur, making osteoporosis a silent disease. More fractures increase mortality and intervention is essential.

Osteoporosis is estimated to affect more than 200 million people worldwide and has an annual fracture frequency of 8.9 million. The most common fracture sites are the hips and spine, and women are four times more likely to develop osteoporosis compared to men. This is mainly due to the depletion of oestrogen – an essential sex hormone for bone health – during the menopause, and can lead to a 2–3 per cent loss in bone density within the first five years. Forty per cent of women over the age of 50 will sustain a fracture because of osteoporosis. This, coupled with lighter, thinner bones in females, as well as lower muscle mass, make women more susceptible.

### BONE LOSS AND FRACTURE

From the age of 30 years the rate of bone remodelling starts to decline. It is now highly recommended to capitalize on bone density from an early age, with regular high intensity resistance training. Loading the muscles and bones through external resistance increases the force production of the muscles and they stress the bones via their attachments. This stimulates osteoblast activity (the bone-forming cells) and causes bone remodelling to occur, further strengthening the bones.

High intensity resistance training is also recommended as the exercise choice to treat osteoporosis to minimize bone loss and maintain or improve bone strength. This can be a fracture risk in osteoporotic individuals and the level of impact should be carefully prescribed based on a person's fitness level, fracture history, and severity of osteoporosis.

Research also suggests that osteoporosis is associated with low back extensor and lower limb muscle weakness. Deficits within these muscles should be trained first prior to progressing to an exercise programme.

## Guidelines for exercise for osteoporosis

The osteoporosis guidelines recommend three different types of exercise as treatment for the condition: strength training for both bone and muscle strength, balance exercises to reduce falls and risk of fractures, and postural exercises to improve back strength and improve spinal pain. Pilates is recommended within all three categories, making it an important treatment choice for those with osteoporosis, or those at increased risk of falls and fractures.

### GENERAL EXERCISE

Exercises should be gradually progressed and tailored to each individual and their abilities. Forward flexion-based movements should be avoided and replaced with hip hinge movements to protect the spine. Those with vertebral fractures or multiple fractures elsewhere should perform low impact rather than moderate impact exercise.

### STRENGTH

For bone strength, perform weight bearing and impact exercises on most days with an average of 50 impacts per day. Try running, jogging, dancing, racquet sports, and Nordic walking. The level of impact is reduced for those less able or with fractures.

For muscle strength, perform resistance exercises 2–3 days per week building up to 3 sets of 8–12 repetitions. Try weight lifting, gardening, DIY, and stair-climbing.

### BALANCE

To improve balance, perform exercises including Pilates, yoga, tai chi, or dance 2–3 days per week.

### POSTURE

Incorporate postural exercises to improve upright posture 2–3 days per week. Perform back strengthening exercises, including Pilates, swimming, and yoga daily.

# HOW **PILATES** CAN HELP

Pilates exercises strengthen muscles, which exert force on the bone and stimulate bone growth. They also focus on posture and can be adapted to weight bearing positions for further bone stress.

Pilates can be modified to reduce fracture risk in osteoporosis by avoiding flexion, spinal side flexion, hip adduction, and internal rotation. Pilates is a recommended exercise form in all three sections (strength, balance, and posture) of the osteoporosis treatment guidelines. These matwork programmes are a starting point and you should bring the exercises into standing practice for additional benefits.

## Beginner

**Repetitions:**
10 of each exercise
**Circuits:** 1–2

1. Hundred (Single Leg) p.54

2. One Leg Stretch (Beginner Level) p.62

3. Shoulder Bridge (Basic Shoulder Bridge, via hip thrust, not spinal articulation) p.86

4. Clam p.116

5. Swan Dive (Upper Body Only) p.72

6. Swimming (Slower Option, Head Down) p.90

7. Leg Pull Front (Hover) p.142

## Beginner to intermediate

**Repetitions:**
10–12 of each exercise
**Circuits:** 2–3

1. Hundred (Single Leg) p.54

2. One Leg Stretch (With Band Support) p.63

3. Shoulder Bridge (Hip Abductions) p.86

4. Clam (tie a band around the knees) p.116

5. Leg Lift and Lower p.117

6. Swimming (Four Point Kneeling) p.91

7. Swan Dive (Upper Body and Arms) p.72

## Intermediate to advanced

**Repetitions:**
10–12 of each exercise
**Circuits:** 3

1. One Leg Stretch (Double Table Top) p.63

2. Double Leg Stretch (Single Leg Coordination) p.67

3. Shoulder Bridge (Hip Abductions, via hip thrust, not spinal articulation) p.86

4. Side Kick p.100

5. Leg Pull Front (Hover to High Plank) p.143

6. Push Up (without the roll down) p.158

7. Breaststroke p.154

# PILATES FOR **ARTHRITIS**

**Arthritis is a disease of the joints** characterized by pain, swelling, and stiffness. There are many different types of arthritis, and symptoms can fluctuate with a range from minimal to severe.

## SYMPTOMS OF ARTHRITIS

Arthralgia refers to pain within a joint, but each arthritis has a different presentation and pathology. Here we will consider osteoarthritis and rheumatoid arthritis, two of the more common conditions.

Osteoarthritis (see also p.24) is caused by the deterioration of the joint's smooth cartilage – its gradual wearing down can expose the joint surface and cause friction and pain between the bones. It often affects a single joint initially, with its primary symptoms being joint pain and reduced range of joint motion. Additional soft tissues such as muscle, tendon, and ligament are all also weakened and can impact proprioception (the body's ability to sense movement).

Osteoarthritis prevails more with advancing age and women are more affected – 47 per cent of females compared to 40 per cent of males are expected to suffer from osteoarthritis at some stage. Obesity, as well as low body weight (due to a reduction in calcium intake for bone health), joint trauma, and reduced quadriceps strength are all risk factors.

The goal of osteoarthritis treatment is to reduce pain and improve function. Research has shown that regular Pilates exercises for eight weeks can significantly improve pain and physical function,

with additional benefits to posture, core stability, and muscle endurance.

Rheumatoid arthritis is a chronic autoimmune disease, where your immune system attacks the synovial membrane and secretes inflammatory substances that destroy the joint structure. It often targets multiple joints and can be symmetrical within the body. The main symptoms are joint pain and inflammation and it also displays symptoms such as fatigue and depression, with these being five times more prevalent than in a healthy population.

Genetic factors are a main cause of rheumatoid arthritis, alongside environmental factors, where the immune system responds to a stress by triggering the inflammatory cascade.

Pharmacological management is the main treatment option for rheumatoid arthritis, along with a gentle range of motion and strengthening exercises. Eight weeks of Pilates exercises three times per week has been shown to improve quality of life in sufferers.

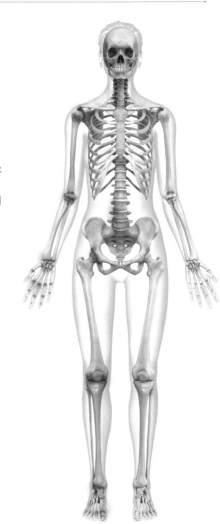

**WHERE ARTHRITIS PRESENTS**
The left side of this model shows common joints affected by arthritis. Osteoarthritis can affect single or multiple joints, while rheumatoid arthritis mostly affects several joints.

# HOW **PILATES** CAN HELP

The use of Pilates as a treatment for arthritic conditions provides a huge range of benefits, both physically and psychologically.

It has been shown to be equal or superior to other exercise forms due to the choice of exercises available, and ease of modifying them to the symptoms as well as these other parameters:

- **Increases muscle strength.** Additional muscle strength can protect the joints and reduce force transfer to the painful joint. This can also improve the joint mechanics and minimize deviation due to pain and the condition.

- **Gentle on joints.** Painful and inflamed joints can reduce physical activity levels in those with arthritis. Pilates can offload the joints by being non weight bearing while still offering muscle strengthening benefits to protect the joints.

- **Improves posture and core stability.** These can both improve balance and alignment to protect the joints.

- **Improves flexibility.** Pilates encourages whole body mobility, and stretching is included in various exercises.

- **Improves wellbeing.** Pilates can reduce depression and fatigue in arthritis patients.

## Mild symptoms

**Repetitions:** 8–10 of each exercise
**Circuits:** 2

1. Hundred (Single Leg) p.54
2. One Leg Stretch (Single Leg Option) p.62
3. Double Leg Stretch p.64
4. Shoulder Bridge (Basic Shoulder Bridge) p.86
5. One Leg Circle (Legs Bent) p.98
6. Side Kick (With Knees Flexed) p.102
7. Swimming (Slower Option, Head Down) p.90
8. Mermaid p.176

## Mild to moderate

**Repetitions:** 8–10 of each exercise
**Circuits:** 2

1. Hundred (Single Leg) p.54
2. One Leg Stretch (With Band Support) p.63
3. Scissors (Single Leg Lifts) p.80
4. Hip Twist (Legs on Mat) p.107
5. Clam p.116
6. Shoulder Bridge (Basic Shoulder Bridge) p.86
7. Cat Cow p.46
8. Arm Openings p.172

## Moderate to severe

**Repetitions:** 6–8 of each exercise
**Circuits:** 1–2

1. Pelvic Tilts p.47
2. Hundred (Single Leg) p.54
3. Overhead Arm Circles p.47
4. One Leg Stretch (Beginner Level) p.62
5. Arm Openings p.172
6. Hip Twist (Legs on Mat) p.106
7. Shell Stretch p.47
8. Lateral Breathing p.37

## Chair-based pilates

With no need to get on the floor, chair-based Pilates is easier on the joints.

**Repetitions:** 6–8 of each exercise
**Circuits:** 1–2

1. Pelvic Tilts p.47
2. Dumb Waiter p.46
3. Roll Up (On a Chair) p.124
4. Overhead Arm Circles p.47
5. Modified Spine Twist p.169
6. Mermaid p.176
7. Arm Openings (Standing Arm Openings) p.173

# INDEX

# BIBLIOGRAPHY

**8–9: History and Principles of Pilates**
J. Robbins and L. V. H. Robbins, *Pilates' Return to Life Through Contrology*, Revised Edition for the 21st Century, 2012.

**10–11: Advances in Research**
N. Bogduk et al., "Anatomy and biomechanics of the psoas major", *Clinical Biomechanics*, 7 (1992).
A. Keifer et al., "Synergy of the human spine in neutral postures", *European Spine Journal*, 7 (1998).
G. T. Allison et al., "Transversus abdominis and core stability: has the pendulum swung?", *British Journal of Sports Medicine*, 42 (2008).
J. Robbins and L. V. H. Robbins, *Pilates' Return to Life Through Contrology*, Revised Edition for the 21st Century, 2012.

**14–15: Muscular Anatomy**
Haff G. G. and N. T. Triplett, *Essentials of Strength Training and Conditioning*, Fourth Edition, Human Kinetics, 2016.

**16–17: Understanding Local and Global Muscles**
Haff G. G. and N.T. Triplett, *Essentials of Strength Training and Conditioning*, Fourth Edition, Human Kinetics, 2016.
P. W. Hodges and G. L. Moseley. "Pain and motor control of the lumbopelvic region: effect and possible mechanisms", *Journal of Electromyography and Kinesiology*, 13 (2003).
G. T. Allison et al., "Feedforward responses of transversus abdominis are directionally specific and act symmetrically: implications for core stability theories", *Journal of Orthopaedic Sports Physical Therapy*, 38 (2008).
P. W. Hodges and C. A. Richardson. "Contraction of the abdominal muscles associated with movement of the lower limb", *Physical Therapy*, 77 (1997).

**18–19: Understanding Muscle Slings**
Brown S. and McGill S. M., "Transmission of muscularly generated force and stiffness between layers of the rat abdominal wall", *Spine*, 15; 34, (2009), E70-5. doi: 10.1097/BRS.0b013e31818bd6b1.
A .L. Pool-Goudzwaard et al., "Insufficient lumbopelvic stability: a clinical, anatomical and biomechanical approach to 'a-specific' low back pain", *Manual Therapy*, 3 (1998).
T. L. W. Myers, D. Maizels, P. Wilson, and G. Chambers, *Anatomy Trains: Myofascial Meridians for Manual and Movement Therapists*, Second Edition. Edinburgh: *Elsevier Health Sciences*, 2008.
A. Vleeming et al., "The posterior layer of the thoraco-mubar fascia", *Spine*, 20 (1995).

**20–21: How Muscles Work**
Haff G. G. and N. T. Triplett, *Essentials of Strength Training and Conditioning*, Fourth Edition, Human Kinetics, 2016.

**22-23: Skeletal System**
K. L. Moore and A. M. R. Agur, *Essential Clinical Anatomy*, Second Edition. Lippincott Williams & Wilkins, 2002.

**24–25: Bone Strength and Joints**
K. L. Moore and A. M. R. Agur, *Essential Clinical Anatomy*, Second Edition. Lippincott Williams & Wilkins, 2002.
N. Saleem et al., "Effect of Pilates-based exercises on symptomatic knee osteoarthritis: A Randomized Controlled Trial", *Journal of Pakistan Medical Association*, 72 (2022).

**26–27: Core Muscles**
R. R. Sapsford et al., "Co-activation of the abdominal and pelvic floor muscles during voluntary exercises", *Neurology and Urodynamics*, 20 (2000).
K. L. Moore and A. M .R. Agur, *Essential Clinical Anatomy*, Second Edition. Lippincott Williams & Wilkins, 2002.
J. Borghuis et al., "The importance of sensory-motor control in providing core stability: implications for measurement and training". *Sports Medicine*, 38 (2008).

**28–29: Neutral Spine Anatomy**
Middleditch A. and Oliver J., *Functional Anatomy of the Spine*, Second Edition, pp.1–3., Elsevier Butterworth Heinemann, 2005.
N. Bogduk et al. "Anatomy and biomechanics of the psoas major", Clinical Biomechanics, 7 (1992).
R. R. Sapsford et al., "Co-activation of the abdominal and pelvic floor muscles during voluntary exercises", *Neurology and Urodynamics*, 20 (2001).
H. Schmidt et al., "How do we stand? Variations during repeated standing phases of asymptomatic subjects and low back pain patients", *Journal of Biomechanics*, 70 (2018).
C.E. Gooyers et al., "Characterizing the combined effects of force, repetition and posture on injury pathways and micro-structural damage in isolated functional spinal units from sub-acute -failure magnitudes of cyclic compressive loading", *Clinical Biomechanics*, 30 (2015).

**30–31: Understanding Posture**
Kendall F. P. et al., *Muscle Testing and Function*, 4th Edition. Williams and Wilkins, Baltimore, p.71.
F. Carini et al., "Posture and Posturology, anatomical and physiological profiles: overview and current state of art" *Acta Biomed*, 88 (2017).
A. Middleditch and J. Oliver, *Functional Anatomy of the Spine*, 2nd Edition. Elsevier Butterworth Heinemann, 2005 (p.328).
Y. Kwon et al., "The effect of sitting posture on the loads at cervico-thoracic and lumbosacral joints", *Technology and Health Care,* 26 (2018).
A. R. Kett et al., "The effect of sitting posture and postural activity on low back muscle stiffness", *Biomechanics*, 1, pp.214–224, (2021).

**32–33: The Nature of Mechanical Pain**
S. Raja et al., "The revised International Association for the study of pain definition of pain: concept, challenges and compromises", *Pain*, 161 (2020).
R. B. Fillingim, "Sex, gender, and pain", *Current Review of Pain*, 4 (2000).
K. Talbot et al., "The sensory and affective components of pain: are they differentially modifiable dimensions or inseparable aspects of a unitary experience? A systematic review", *British Journal of Anaesthesia*, 123 (2019).
J. A. Hides et al., "Evidence of lumbar multifidus muscle wasting ipsilateral to symptoms in patients with acute/subacute low back pain", *Spine*, 19 (1994).

**34–35: Pilates and Pain Relief**
J. A. Hides et al., "Evidence of lumbar multifidus muscle wasting ipsilateral to symptoms in patients with acute/subacute low back pain", *Spine*, 20 (1994).
M. M. Panjabi, "The stabilizing system of the spine Part I, Function, Dysfunction, Adaptation, and Enhancement", *Journal of Spinal Disorders*, 5 (1992).
M. M. Panjabi. "The Stabilizing System of the Spine, Part II, Neutral Zone and Instability Hypothesis", 5 (1992).
D. C. Cherkin et al., "Effect of mindfulness-based stress reduction vs cognitive behavioral therapy or usual care on back pain and functional limitations in adults with chronic low back pain", *Journal of American Medical Association*, 315 (2016).

P. O'Sullivan, "Lumbar segmental instability: A clinical perspective and specific stability exercise management", *Journal of Manual Therapy*, 1 (2000).

### 36–37: Breathing Techniques
G.T. Allison et al., "Transversus abdominis and core stability: has the pendulum swung?", *British Journal of Sports Medicine*, 42 (2008).
Lung strength: S Prakash et al., "Athletes, yogis and individuals with sedentary lifestyles; do their lung functions differ?" *Indian Journal of Physiology and Pharmacology*, 51 (2007).
J. Robbins and L. V. H. Robbins, *Pilates' Return to Life Through Contrology*, Revised Edition for the 21st Century, 2012.

### 38–39: Gut Health
J. Robbins and L. V. H. Robbins, *Pilates' Return to Life Through Contrology*, Revised Edition for the 21st Century, 2012.
A. Dalton et al, "Exercise influence on the microbiome-gut-brain axis", Gut Microbes, 10 (2019).

### 40–41: Pilates and Mindfulness for Stress and Anxiety
K. M. Fleming et al. "The effects of pilates on mental health outcomes: a meta-analysis of controlled trials", *Complementary Therapies in Medicine*, 37 (2018).
J. J. Steventon et al., "Hippocampal blood flow is increased after 20 minutes of moderate-intensity exercise", *Cerebral Cortex*, 21 (2020).
S. G. Patil et al., "Effect of yoga on short term heart rate variability measure as a stress index in subjunior cyclists: a pilot study", *Indian Journal of Physiology and Pharmacology*, 57 (2013).
S. Brand et al. "Influence of mindfulness practice on cortisol and sleep in long-term and short-term mediators", *Neuropsychobiology*, 65 (2012).
L. Andrés-Rodríguez et al., "Immune-inflammatory pathways and clinical changes in fibromyalgia patients treated with mindfulness-based stress reduction (MBSR): A randomized, controlled trial: Brain Behavior and Immunity", 80 (2019).
P. H. Ponte Márquez et al., "Benefits of mindfulness meditation in reducing blood pressure and stress in patients with arterial hypertension", *Journal of Human Hypertension*, 33 (2019).
J. Rocha et al., "Acute effect of a single session of Pilates on blood pressure and cardiac autonomic control in middle-aged adults with hypertension", *The Journal of Strength and Conditioning Research*, 34 (2019).

### 48–49: Abdominal Curls / Oblique Curls
R. Agur, *Essential Clinical Anatomy*, Second Edition. Lippincott Williams & Wilkins, 2002.
M. Sinaki and B.A. Mikkelsen, "Postmenopausal spinal osteoporosis: flexion versus extension exercises", *Archives of Physical Medicine and Rehabilitation*, 65 (1984).

**For the selection of traditional exercises as featured on pp.52, 56, 60, 64, 68, 70, 74, 76, 78, 82, 84, 88, 92, 100, 104, 106, 108, 110, 115, 123, 126, 128, 130, 132, 135, 136, 140, 144, 148, 152, 156, 158, 164, 166, 168, 170:**
J. Robbins and L. V. H. Robbins, *Pilates' Return to Life Through Contrology*, Revised Edition for the 21st Century, 2012.

### 68–69: Rocker with Open Legs
M. F. Mottola et al., "Is supine exercise associated with adverse maternal and fetal outcomes? A systematic review", *British Journal of Sports Medicine*, 53 (2019).

### 84–85: Shoulder Bridge
M. F. Mottola et al., "Is supine exercise associated with adverse maternal and fetal outcomes? A systematic review", *British Journal of Sports Medicine*, 53 (2019).

M. Sinaki and B.A. Mikkelsen, "Postmenopausal spinal osteoporosis: flexion versus extension exercises", *Archives of Physical Medicine and Rehabilitation*, 65 (1984).

### 188–189: Pilates for Running
A. Laws et al., "The effect of clinical Pilates on functional movement in recreational runners", *International Journal of Sports Medicine*, 38 (2017).
A. Hreljac, "Impact and overuse injuries in running", American College of Sports Medicine. DOI: 10.1249/01.MSS.0000126803.66636.DD, 845–849 (2004).
R. W. Willy et al., "Gluteal muscle activation during running in females with and without patellofemoral pain syndrome", *Clinical Biomechanics*, 26 (2011).
Aleisha F.K., "Exploring the role of the lateral gluteal muscles in running: implications for training", *Strength and Conditioning Journal*, 42 (2020).
K.J. Homan et al., "The influence of hip strength on gluteal activity and lower extremity kinematics", *Journal of Electromyography and Kinesiology*, 23 (2013).
J. L. N. Alexander et al., "Infographic running myth: static stretching reduces injury risk in runners", *British Journal of Sports Medicine*, 54 (2020).

### 190–191: Pilates for Swimming
J. Karpinski et al., "The effects of a 6-week core exercises on swimming performance of national level swimmers", *PLOS ONE*, 15(8): e0227394. https://doi.org/10.1371/journal.pone.0227394.
F. Wanivenhaus et al., "Epidemiology of injuries and prevention strategies in competitive swimmers", *Sports Health*, 4 (2012).
J. Evershed et al., "Musculoskeletal screening to detect asymmetry in swimming", *Physical Therapy in Sport*, 15 (2013).
D. Salo et al., "Complete Conditioning for Swimming", *Human Kinetics*, 2008; pp.87–110; 197–225.
Karpiński J. and Gołaś A., *Pływacki atlas ćwiczeń na lądzie*, Zając A, Karpiński R, editors, Kraków: AKNET-Press; (2018).

### 192–193: Pilates for Strength Training
J. Vance et al., "EMG as a function of the performer's focus of attention", *Journal of Motor Behavior*, 36 (2004).
M. J. Kolber et al., "The influence of hip muscle impairments on squat performance", *Strength and Conditioning Journal*, 39 (2017).
M. A. Alabbad et al., "Incidence and prevalence of weight lifting injuries: An update", *Saudi Journal of Sports Medicine*, 16 (2016).

### 194-195: Pilates for Sedentary Workers
Kett et al., "The effect of sitting posture and postural activity on low back muscle stiffness", *Biomechanics*, 1, 214–224, (2021).
F. Hanna et al., "The relationship between sedentary behaviour, back pain, and psychosocial correlates among University employees", Front Public Health, 7 (2019).

### 198–199: Pilates for Women's Health
M. H. Davenport et al., "Exercise for the prevention and treatment of low back, pelvic girdle and lumbopelvic pain during pregnancy: a systematic review and meta-analysis", *British Journal of Sports Medicine*, 53, (2019)
J. Keeler et al. "Diastasis recti abdominis", *Journal of Womens' Health Physical Therapy*, 36 (2012).
T.M. Spitznagle et al., "Prevalence of diastasi recti abdominis in a urogynecological patient population", *International Urogynecology Journal and Pelvic Floor Dysfunction*, 18 (2007).
D. G. Lee, "Stability, continence and breathing: the roles of fascia following pregnancy delivery", *Journal of Bodywork Movement Therapy*, 12 (2008).
D. G. Lee, "New perspectives from the integrated systems model for treating women with pelvic girdle pain, urinary incontinence, pelvic organ prolapse and/or diastasis rectus abdominis", *Journal of Association of Chartered Physiotherapists in Womens Health*, 114 (2014).

T. Goom et al., "Return to running postnatal – guidelines for medical, health and fitness professionals managing this population", https://absolute.physio/wp-content/uploads/2019/09/returning-to-running-postnatal-guidelines.pdf. (2019).

K. Crotty et al., "Investigation of optimal cues to instruction for pelvic floor muscle contraction: a pilot study using 2D ultrasound imaging in pre-menopausal, nulliparous, continent women", *Neurology andl Urodynamics*, 30 (2011).

J. Borghuis et al., "The importance of sensory-motor control in providing core stability: implications for measurement and training", *Sports Medicine*, 38 (2008).

M. F. Mottola et al., "Is supine exercise associated with adverse maternal and fetal outcomes? A systematic review", *British Journal of Sports Medicine*, 53 (2019).

H. Lee et al., "Effects of 8-week Pilates Exercise program on menopausal symptoms and lumbar strength and flexibility in postmenopausal women", *Journal of Exercise Rehabiltation*, 12 (2016).

M. Bergamin et al., "Effects of a Pilates Exercise program on muscle strength, postural control and body composition: results from a pilot study in a group of post-menopausal women", *National Library of Medicine*, (2015).

N. Santoro, "Perimenopause: From research to practice", *Journal of Women's Health*, 25 (2016).

M. R. Apkarian, "Blood pressure characteristics and responses during resistance exercise", *Strength and Conditioning Journal,* 43 (2021).

N. Santoro, "Menopausal symptoms and their management", *Journal of Endocrinology and Metabolism Clinics of North America*, 44 (2015).

G. A. Greendale et al., "Bone mineral density loss in relation to the final menstrual period in a multiethnic cohort: results from the study of women's health across the nation (SWAN)", *The Journal of Bone and Mineral Research*, 27 (2012).

## 202–203: Pilates for Back Pain
J. Hartvigsen et al., "What low back pain is and why we need to pay attention", *The Lancet*, 391 (2018).

J. A. Hides et al., "Long-term effects of specific stabilizing exercises for first-episode low back pain", *Spine*, 26 (2001).

P.W. Hodges and G.L. Moseley, "Pain and motor control of the lumbopelvic region: effect and possible mechanisms", *Journal of Electromyography and Kinesiology*, 13 (2003).

G. L. Moseley et al., "Attention demand, anxiety and acute pain cause differential effects on postural activation of the abdominal muscles in humans", *Society for Neuroscience Abstracts*, 2001.

P. M. Machado et al., "Effectiveness of the Pilates Method for individual with nonspecific low back pain: clinical and electromyographic aspects", *Motriz Rio Claro*, 23 (2017).

## 204–205: Pilates for Neck Pain and Headaches
R. Fejer et al., "The prevalence of neck pain in the world population: a systematic critical review of the literature", *European Spine Journal*, 15 (2006).

L. J. Carroll et al., "Course and prognostic factors for neck pain in the general population: results of the Bone and Joint Decade 2000–2010 Task Force on Neck Pain and Its Associated Disorders", *Journal of Manipulative Physiological Therapeutics*, 39 (2009).

A. Middleditch and J. Oliver, *Functional Anatomy of the Spine*, 2nd Edition. Elsevier Butterworth Heinemann, 2005 (p.328).

Lee et al., "Clinical effectiveness of a Pilates treatment for forward head posture", *Journal of Physical Therapy Science*, 28 (2016).

A. Binder, "Neck Pain", *BMJ Clinical Evidence*,1103 (2008).

A. Legrand et al., "Respiratory effects of the scalene and sternomastoid muscles in humans", *Journal of Applied Physiology*, 94 (2003).

Cemin N. F. et al., "Effects of the Pilates Method on neck pain: a systematic review", *Fisioterapia et Movimento,* 30 (2017).

## 206–207: Pilates for Scoliosis
W. J. Brooks et al., "Reversal of childhood idiopathic scoliosis in an adult, without surgery: a case report and literature review", *Scoliosis*, 15 (2009).

T. Kotwicki et al., "Methodology of evaluation of morphology of the spine and the trunk in idiopathic scoliosis and other spinal deformities – 6th SOSORT consensus paper", *Scoliosis*, 4 (2009).

Y. Gou et al., "The effect of Pilates Exercise training for scoliosis on improving spinal deformity and quality of life", *Medicine*, 13 (2020).

S. Rrecaj-Malaj et al., "Outcome of 24 weeks of combined Schroth and pilates exercises on Cobb angle, angle of trunk rotation, chest expansion, flexibility and quality of life in adolescents with scoliosis", *Medical Science Monitor Basic Research*, 26 (2020).

S. Otman et al., "The efficacy of Schroths 2-dimensional exercise therapy in the treatment of adolescent idiopathic scoliosis in Turkey", *Saudi Medical Journal*, 26 (2005).

W. R. Weiss et al., "Incidence of curvature progression in idiopathic scoliosis patients treated with scoliosis in-patient rehabilitation (SIR): an age-and sex-matched controlled study", *Pediatric Rehabilitation*, 6 (2003).

## 208–209: Pilates for Hypermobility
J. V. Simmonds et al., "Hypermobility and hypermobility syndrome", *Manual Therapy*, 12 (2007).

M.R. Simpson, "Benign joint hypermobility syndrome evaluation, diagnosis, and management", *Journal of Osteopathic Medicine*, 106 (2006).

B. Kumar et al., "Joint hypermobility syndrome: recognizing a commonly overlooked cause of chronic pain", *The American Journal of Medicine*, 130 (2017).

A. Hakim et al., "Joint hypermobility", *Best Practice and Research Clinical Rheumatology*, 17 (2003).

A. J. Hakim et al., "The genetic epidemiology of joint hypermobility: a population study of female twins", *Arthritis and Rheumatology*, 50 (2004).

L. C. Decoster et al., "Prevalence and features of joint hypermobility among adolescent athletes", *Archives of Pediatric Adolescent Medicine*, 151 (1997).

## 210–211: Pilates for Osteoporosis
S. Epstein, "Update of Current Therapeutic Options For The Treatment of Postmenopausal Osteoporosis", *Clinical Therapeutics*, 28 (2006).

J. E. South-Paul, "Osteoporosis: Part II. Nonpharmacologic and pharmacologic treatment", *American Family Physician*, 63 (2001).

E. J. Chaconas et al., "Exercise interventions for the individual with osteoporosis", *Strength and Conditioning Journal*, 35 (2013).

K. Brooke-Wavell et al., "Strong, steady and straight: UK consensus on physical activity and exercise for osteoporosis", *British Journal of Sports Medicine*, doi:10.1136/bjsports-2021-104634 (2022).

## 212–213: Pilates for Arthritis
J. Braga et al., "Biological causes of depression in systemic lupus erythematosus", *Acta Reumatol Port*, 39 (2014).

R. S. Hegarty et al., "Feel the fatigue and be active anyway: physical activity on high-fatigue days protects adults with arthritis from decrements in same-day positive mood", *Arthritis Care and Research*, 67 (2015).

S. B. Yentür et al., "Comparison of the Effectiveness of Pilates Exercises, aerobic exercises, and pilates with aerobic exercises in patients with rheumatoid arthritis", *Irish Journal of Medical Science*, 190 (2021).

N. Saleem et al., "Effect of Pilates based exercises on symptomatic knee osteoarthritis: a randomized controlled trial", *Journal of Pakistan Medical Association*, 71 (2022).

# ABOUT THE AUTHOR

**Tracy Ward** is a Pilates teacher, Pilates course presenter, physiotherapist, and writer.

She holds a first class honours degree in Biomedical Science, a masters degree with merit in Physiotherapy, and a diploma in Orthopaedic Medicine. She also completed postgraduate study in the McKenzie Institute in Medical Diagnosis and Therapy. Tracy is an APPI Pilates Teacher and a certified Pilates Women's Health practitioner, is qualified in kids' and teens' Pilates, and is also a therapeutic yoga teacher.

Tracy joined the Australian Physiotherapy and Pilates Institute (APPI) Health Group Pilates teaching team in 2016. As part of the team she was able to to expand her teaching skills and share her knowledge with others. She films for their industry-leading Pilates TV and is part of their course creation faculty.

In 2020, Tracy published her first ebook, *The Postnatal Pilates Guide*, an evidence-based guide to returning to fitness safely after having a baby, with a six-week plan to restore your core, optimize your strength, and generally feel good postpartum.

The Anytime Studio is Tracy's on-demand Pilates membership platform. It hosts a variety of classes and specialized six-week programmes with educational resources.

Tracy is passionate about Pilates, movement, rehabilitation, and using the evidence as a basis for her practice, both within Pilates and in her clinical work as a physiotherapist. She runs her award-winning Pilates business – Freshly Centered, in Aberdeen, Scotland – and works as a senior musculoskeletal physiotherapist within a private hospital. She also writes regularly for various sports medicine publications and has a popular YouTube channel.

Visit **www.freshlycentered.com** and follow Tracy on Instagram, Youtube, and Facebook at @freshlycentered.

## ACKNOWLEDGEMENTS

**Author's acknowledgements**

The biggest thank you to the entire team at DK, but especially to Alastair for so openly believing in me and inviting me on this journey; Susan and Amy for endlessly guiding me, editing, and designing this book to its beautiful finish; and Arran for my wonderful illustrations.

Thank you to Glenn, Elisa, and the rest of the APPI team. Joining APPI has re-directed my career, you provide a continuous inspiration, and your constant encouragement and opportunities is so refreshing. I'm forever grateful to be a part of your team.

I'll be forever grateful to Jennifer Darlington, Anya Hayes, and Sara Rohan, whose exceptional input helped me begin this project, and to Sarah Chambers for assisting with references.

Thank you to my children Aiden and Anya, for sleeping when it mattered and showing me that anything really is possible. Love you forever and a day. To my partner Mark, for accepting when I have yet another idea, holding the fort, and continually encouraging me to keep going. To my ever-supportive mum and my late dad, I hope I've made you proud.

Finally, to all of my Pilates clients and students. Without you, none of this would be possible. Thank you for your continued support, but most importantly, your loyalty shows that you value the benefits of Pilates just as much as I do.

**Publisher's acknowledgements**

Dorling Kindersley would like to thank Marie Lorimer for indexing and Kathy Steer for proofreading.

**Picture credits**

The publisher would like to thank the following for their kind permission to reproduce their photographs:
(Key: a-above; b-below/bottom; c-centre; f-far; l-left; r-right; t-top)

14 Science Photo Library: Professors P.M. Motta, P.M. Andrews, K.R. Porter & J. Vial (clb). 23 Science Photo Library: Biophoto Associates (cla)

All other images © **Dorling Kindersley**

For further information see: **www.dkimages.com**

DK | Penguin Random House

**Project Art Editor** Amy Child
**Project Editor** Susan McKeever
**Senior Editor** Alastair Laing
**Senior Designer** Barbara Zuniga
**Jacket Designer** Amy Cox
**Jacket Coordinator** Jasmin Lennie
**Senior Production Editor** Tony Phipps
**Senior Production Controller** Luca Bazzoli
**Managing Editor** Ruth O'Rourke
**Design Manager** Marianne Markham
**Senior Acquisitions Editor** Zara Anvari
**Art Director** Maxine Pedliham
**Publishing Director** Katie Cowan

**Illustrations** Arran Lewis

First published in Great Britain in 2022
by Dorling Kindersley Limited
DK, One Embassy Gardens, 8 Viaduct Gardens, London, SW11 7BW

The authorised representative in the EEA is Dorling Kindersley
Verlag GmbH. Arnulfstr. 124, 80636 Munich, Germany

Text copyright © Tracy Ward 2022
Copyright © 2022
Dorling Kindersley Limited
A Penguin Random House Company
10 9 8 7 6 5 4
012–332615–Dec/2022

A CIP catalogue record for this book
is available from the British Library.
ISBN: 978-0-2415-8057-8

Printed and bound in China

**For the curious**
**www.dk.com**

This book was made with Forest Stewardship Council
™ certified paper – one small step in DK's commitment
to a sustainable future. For more information go to
www.dk.com/our-green-pledge.